THE SQUIRREL
MONKEY

THE SQUIRREL
MONKEY

EDITED BY

Leonard A. Rosenblum

Department of Psychiatry
Primate Behavior Laboratory
State University of New York
Downstate Medical Center
Brooklyn, New York

Robert W. Cooper

Primate Research Colony
Institute for Comparative Biology
Zoological Society of San Diego
San Diego, California

ACADEMIC PRESS
NEW YORK   LONDON   1968

Frontispiece courtesy of the San Diego Zoo

ACADEMIC PRESS, INC.
111 Fifth Avenue, New York, New York 10003

United Kingdom Edition published by
ACADEMIC PRESS, INC. (LONDON) LTD.
Berkeley Square House, London W.1

LIBRARY OF CONGRESS CATALOG CARD NUMBER: 68-23478

PRINTED IN THE UNITED STATES OF AMERICA

List of Contributors

Numbers in parentheses indicate the pages on which the authors' contributions begin.

DIETRICH E. BEISCHER (347), *Chemical Sciences Division, Naval Aerospace Medical Institute, Pensacola, Florida*

ROBERT W. COOPER (1, 193), *Primate Research Colony, Institute for Comparative Biology, Zoological Society of San Diego, San Diego, California*

FRANK V. DuMOND (87), *Monkey Jungle, Miami, Florida*

FREDERICK L. DUNN (31), *The George Williams Hooper Foundation, Department of Epidemiology and International Health, San Francisco Medical Center, University of California, San Francisco, California*

JOHN L. FUSILER (171), *Louisiana State University School of Medicine, New Orleans, Louisiana*

CHARLES M. GOSS (171), *Department of Anatomy, George Washington University School of Medicine, Washington, D. C.*

HARLEY M. HANSON (365), *Neuropsychopharmacology, Merck Institute for Therapeutic Research, West Point, Pennsylvania*

C. MAX LANG (393), *Animal Resource Facility, College of Medicine, The Pennsylvania State University, Hershey, Pennsylvania*

JAMES O. LONG (193), *Primate Research Colony, Institute for Comparative Biology, Zoological Society of San Diego, San Diego, California*

ALBERT E. NEW (417), *United States Air Force, Veterinary Services, Naval Aerospace Medical Institute, Pensacola, Florida*

LAWRENCE R. PINNEO (319), *Biobehavioral Sciences Department, Stanford Research Institute, Menlo Park, California*

LEE T. POPEJOY II (171), *Louisiana State University, School of Medicine, New Orleans, Louisiana**

LEONARD A. ROSENBLUM (147, 207), *Department of Psychiatry, Primate Behavior Laboratory, State University of New York, Downstate Medical Center, Brooklyn, New York*

*Present address: Dickerson Drive, Jasper, Texas

DUANE M. RUMBAUGH (255), *Department of Psychology, San Diego State College, and Institute for Comparative Biology, Zoological Society of San Diego, San Diego, California*

TOM SMITH (171), *Louisiana State University School of Medicine, New Orleans, Louisiana*

RICHARD W. THORINGTON, JR. (69), *Primatology Department, New England Regional Primate Research Center, Harvard Medical School, Southborough, Massachusetts*

PETER WINTER (235), *Max-Planck-Institut für Psychiatrie, Abteilung für Verhallensforschung, Munich, Germany*

Preface

During the past decade, a great burgeoning of research interest in the biological sciences has taken place. Outpacing even this general growth has been an enormous increase in research on nonhuman primates. Evidence of this growth is reflected in the fact that during the past eight years two international journals of primatology have appeared, and to enhance further the communication process among primatologists throughout the world, the International Primatological Society was founded in 1964.

One result of this growth has been a recognition of the need to study all primate forms to prepare a foundation for the development of a proper perspective of the order Primates. Studies of the chimpanzee and rhesus monkey, long the major foci of primate research, have now been extended to representatives of virtually all primate families and, indeed, to members of most major genera.

Among the primates which recently have become major foci of research interest, none has exceeded the common South American squirrel monkey, *Saimiri sciureus*, in terms of widespread acceptance and use. Their status near the middle of the primate evolutionary scale makes relatively complex behavioral tasks well within their repertoire and places their physiological functioning on a level at which significant comparative work may be carried out. Their relative cost, which for purchase and upkeep generally runs considerably less than that for the more commonly used macaques, makes them attractive from a budgetary standpoint. In addition, their small size (600 – 1100 gm at adulthood) and ease of handling and maintenance once acclimated to a captive environment, permits minimal animal care staffing and maximal utilization of laboratory space. It is not surprising then that the squirrel monkey has become such a popular choice for so many biomedical studies.

The rapid growth of research interest in this relatively unstudied species has not been without problems, however. Seasonality of supply, seriously confused taxonomy, lack of normative biometric values, clinical problems relating to parasitic, metabolic, and infectious disease, and nutritional and reproductive difficulties have all been obstacles to the full development of this species as a subject for biomedical research.

In response to the growing need for information about squirrel monkeys, the editors undertook the organization of the First Round Table Conference on Squirrel Monkey Reproduction in the spring of 1965. This conference, hosted at the Bowman Gray School of Medicine, was attended by some 25 investigators from the United States and Europe. It quickly became evident that significant quantities of valuable data regarding the basic biological characteristics of *Saimiri* and its care, treatment, and use in research had recently been acquired; this information, however, either was scattered widely in the literature of many fields or had not been published in any form.

In light of the growing number of squirrel monkeys being established each year in many laboratories quite diverse in interest, there appeared the need to pool existing knowledge in concise form. The present volume, the first of its kind on any single primate, attempts to meet this need. In many cases, the information included either has not been published previously or has appeared in a widely dispersed literature. The topics have been selected to cover thoroughly areas of research in which *Saimiri* has been utilized. This material ranges widely from taxonomy and behavioral studies through husbandry and clinical management of the species, to investigations in aerospace medicine and in a number of basic biological sciences. Since the problems encountered in the squirrel monkey, though sometimes taking a particular form, are not unique in principle, the authors have attempted to provide an appropriate phylogenetic context for their material. It is hoped as a result that this compendium may serve as a valuable source of information during various phases of work on other subjects of primatological and comparative biological investigation as well.

Finally, we must not overlook the fact that the squirrel monkey is the most popular primate taken as a pet. Responsible pet owners are anxious to care properly for these animals and to maintain them as the lively, responsive creatures they can be. We trust that they, together with the veterinarians faced with the problem of treating squirrel monkeys that have been victims of neglect, ignorance, or clinical disease, will find this compilation to be a significant aid in their efforts.

The editors would like to thank their many colleagues for encouragement and assistance in compiling this volume. To each of the authors we express our gratitude for their considerable efforts, sustained enthusiasm, and patience with the demands placed upon them. Our particular thanks go to Duane Rumbaugh who, from the initiation of the project to its completion, was a constant source of sound judgment and assistance. In the preparation of this treatise, the efforts of L. A. Rosenblum were aided by support of U.S.P.H.S. Research Career Development Award (level II; MH-K3-23685) and those of R. W. Cooper by Contract PH-43-63-56 within the Special Virus Leukemia Program of the National Cancer Institute, National Institutes of Health, Public Health Service.

                                                    LEONARD A. ROSENBLUM
August, 1968   ROBERT W. COOPER

Contents

1 Squirrel Monkey Taxonomy and Supply
Robert W. Cooper

2 The Parasites of *Saimiri*: in the Context of Platyrrhine Parasitism
Frederick L. Dunn

3 Observations of Squirrel Monkeys in a Colombian Forest
Richard W. Thorington, Jr.

4 The Squirrel Monkey in a Seminatural Environment
Frank V. DuMond

5 Some Aspects of Female Reproductive Physiology in the Squirrel Monkey

Leonard A. Rosenblum

6 Observations on the Relationship between Embryological Development, Time of Conception, and Gestation

Charles M. Goss, Lee T. Popejoy II, John L. Fusiler, and Tom M. Smith

7 Physical Growth and Dental Eruption in Captive—Bred Squirrel Monkeys, *Saimiri sciureus* (Letica, Colombia)

James O. Long, and Robert W. Cooper

8 Mother—Infant Relations and Early Behavioral Development in the Squirrel Monkey

Leonard A. Rosenblum

CHAPTER 1 _____

Squirrel Monkey Taxonomy and Supply

Robert W. Cooper

I. Introduction

The popularity of squirrel monkeys as pets in recent years has been a major factor in the development of *Saimiri* as an important laboratory animal. The ready availability of such an attractive small simian on the pet market made it inevitable that scientists would eventually find means to utilize this promising fellow primate. In retrospect, it is surprising that the research popularity of squirrel monkeys has been only a comparatively recent development.

Heinrich Klüver of the Division of Biological Sciences at the University of Chicago actually pioneered the laboratory colonization and experimental use of *Saimiri*. He initially introduced them into his laboratory about 1930 and in his classic volume, *Behavior Mechanisms in Monkeys*, reported the first formal behavioral experiments with squirrel monkeys (1933, pp. 178-181 and 186-190). Between 1940 and 1945, Klüver's *Saimiri* colony produced nine births, the first ever reported in captivity (Klüver and Brunschwig, 1947). It was not until 1949, 19 years after Klüver's original introduction, that a second laboratory *Saimiri* colony was established, by Charles Goss in the Anatomy Department of Louisiana State University School of Medicine (see Chapter 6). It was only as recently as 1958 that squirrel monkeys were first actually utilized in organized biomedical research (see Beischer, Chapter 12).

As the research use of *Saimiri* and, to a lesser extent, other New World primates increased during the early 1960's, many investigators and laboratory animal medical specialists became quite concerned with the poor or

1

inconsistent quality of primates that were supplied by many dealers. The animals received in the laboratory were often heavily parasitized, in a poor state of nutrition, and badly stressed, and as a result high morbidity and mortality were frequently experienced. Also distressing was the lack of information that primate suppliers seemed to have concerning the exact sources of their animals and the management conditions under which they were maintained in South American dealers' compounds.

In an effort to gain a clearer picture of the New World primate supply situation, I was sent on an investigative survey in mid-1963 by the National Cancer Institute (contract PH 43-63-56). For one month I observed the entire primate supply process from the facilities of the major primate suppliers in Florida to the main South American collection areas (Barranquilla, Colombia; Leticia, Colombia; and Iquitos, Peru). In late 1964, Alvin F. Moreland, Director of the Health Center Animal Department at the University of Florida, Gainesville, and I undertook a second survey that encompased all of the primate supply areas and major dealers in Brazil as well as in Iquitos, Peru and Leticia, Colombia. Much of the information and insight gained during these studies is utilized in the following discussion of taxonomy and supply. In addition, I wish to acknowledge information shared by Charles C. Middleton stemming from his primate field research experiences in Leticia, Colombia during the summers of 1964 and 1965 (see Middleton and Rosal, 1967). I am also deeply indebted to the many primate dealers both in South America and in Florida for their cooperation and particularly to Mike Tsalickis of Leticia, Colombia for his invaluable guidance and investigative assistance.

II. Taxonomy

The failure of otherwise competent investigators to concern themselves with the taxonomy and zoogeography of their experimental subjects is the most glaring fault attendant to the rapidly increasing use of nonhuman primates of many species in biomedical and behavioral research. Even scientists who are meticulous in detailing the materials and methods used in their studies are likely to describe primate subjects by a common name or perhaps with a generic and specific designation given them by an animal dealer. This practice is no more acceptable or excusable than it would be to identify all specific strains of *Mus musculus* used in research only as "laboratory mice." The gravity of the present situation is underscored by the distressing insensitivity existing even in regional, national, and international primate research programs to the importance of systematic investigation (see Hershkovitz, 1965).

Unfortunately, the solution to this problem, though imperative to the continued advancement of primatology, does not seem imminent. The few investigators who do recognize the importance of carefully defining the provenance of wild-caught primates as the first step in making a proper taxonomic identification, find that most primate suppliers either do not know or are reluctant to reveal the exact geographic sources of their animals (see Schrier, 1964a). Furthermore, even when provenance can be established, much of the primate taxonomic literature is in a state of confusion, such that it is often impossible to determine correct scientific nomenclature (see Schrier, 1964b). Since only a scant handful of competent systematic research specialists are engaged in primate studies and there is little inducement for others to enter the field, progress in this area will be painfully slow. Therefore, it is essential that investigators take steps to preserve the identity of primates used in experimental studies today in order that re-examination can be made in the light of any future taxonomic revisions (see Holdenried, 1964).

All of the points mentioned above with regard to primates in general apply equally well to squirrel monkeys. There are a number of taxonomic and nomenclatural problems specific to this popular primate, beginning with a disagreement among various authors as to whether the binominal designation *Saimiri sciurea* (see Sanderson, 1957; Hill, 1960) or *Saimiri sciureus* (see Elliot, 1912; Cabrera, 1957) is correct. In response to an opinion by the editors of the *Laboratory Primate Newsletter* (Schrier and Schrier, 1963) that the correct name was *Saimiri sciurea*, Dr. David H. Johnson, Curator of the Division of Mammals of the United States National Museum responded with an authoritative reply which the *Newsletter* (Schrier, 1963) quoted in part as follows:

"According to the rules of nomenclature ... (*Saimiri sciurea*) ... is incorrect. The specific name *sciureus* is a Latin adjective meaning squirrel-like, based on *sciurus*, the Latin noun for squirrel. Being an adjective the name is modified in form to agree with the gender of the genus with which it is associated. As first used by Linnaeus in the 10th edition of the Systema Naturae (1758) it was a species of the feminine genus *Simia*, hence had the form *Simia sciurea*. As used currently under the masculine genus *Saimiri*, it takes the form *Saimiri sciureus*."

From the *International Code of Zoological Nomenclature* (London, Int. Trust for Zool. Nomenclature, 1961) the *Newsletter* reported the following confirmatory rule. "In names of the species-group, the ending must be changed, if necessary, to conform with the gender of the generic name with which the species-group name is at any time combined" (Article 34b, p. 37). The definite masculine origin of the word "saimiri" is noted by Cabrera (1957, p. 171) along with the nomenclatural rule that for purposes of agreement generic names taken from barbaric languages and which do not have Latin endings should be considered masculine. With this evidence in hand there should be no further question that, according to the rules of zoological nomenclature, the scientific binominal *Saimiri sciureus* is correct.

Unfortunately the basic problem with regard to squirrel monkeys cannot be solved by nomenclatural rules. Although the fact is not appreciated by the vast majority of research users of *Saimiri*, there is no modern taxonomic revision for squirrel monkeys. It has been noted that although a great body of squirrel monkey literature has accumulated and is rapidly growing, without a workable taxonomy we are hard put to organize, interpret, and evaluate this data on *Saimiri sciureus* (Hershkovitz, 1966).

Squirrel monkeys are native to areas of every Central and South American country within the latitudinal boundaries of 10° N. and 15° S., namely Costa Rica, Panama, Colombia, Ecuador, Peru, Bolivia, Venezuela, Guyana, Surinam, French Guiana, and Brazil. There is by no means agreement on the number of species and subspecies of *Saimiri* that exist within this extensive zoogeographic range. In his *Review of the Primates*, Elliot (1912) recognized seven species and one subspecies of *Saimiri* based largely upon differences in color of the head, arms, and "upper parts." With reference to *Saimiri* populations in Costa Rica and Panama, he introduced the concept that differences in head coloration within a specific *Saimiri* population may be age related, i.e., darker with age, possibly confusing the observer who is unaware of "the great diversity of head coloring that exists at different periods of the animal's existence." Elliot also noted that the ranges of the various *Saimiri* "species" were imprecisely defined due to inadequate collecting and that previous writers may have inadvertently combined some "species" and united their separate ranges.

A later author, Lima (1945), in his volume, *Mammals of Amazonia*, reduced the number of Amazonian "species" of squirrel monkeys to 4 (from Elliot's 6) but described a total of 12 subspecies. He acknowledged that "Some of these species are based exclusively on the coloring of the fur, but, in view of the slight individual variation, many authors, including several modern ones, consider the species valid and well characterized. Others disagree, grouping several species into a single species, and in spite of Elliot's opinion it would seem that a comparative study of large series would result in the conversion of some species into mere subspecies."

The most recent primate monographer, Hill (1960), adopted Lima's *Saimiri* taxonomy in its entirety with the addition of one Amazonian subspecies plus the inclusion of a Central American species (2 subspecies) not covered in *Mammals of Amazonia* for a total of 5 species and 15 subspecies. The shaky foundations of *Saimiri* taxonomy are also noted by Hill in his statements that "Unfortunately the exact ranges of the different forms have not been clearly defined, though it is clear that the common *S. sciurea* (sic) is more widely represented than the others. The range even of this, however, is not precisely delineated, largely due to confusion with other forms . . . Four, possibly five distinct species of *Saimiri* may be recognized at the present time, some of them with minor local colour variations. It is possible that some of the species may, with further knowledge, be reduced to the rank of subspecies."

Considering the equivocation of most authors and the obvious fact that a complete taxonomic revision of the genus *Saimiri* is needed, the most logical position for the present seems to be that suggested by Cabrera (1957). He states (in translation):

The numerous 'species' which have been described for this genus should be reduced to two at most: *sciureus*, from South America, and *orstedi*, from Central America, and it is probable that the second is just a subspecies of the first. Authors have given excessive importance to purely individual differences and as a result have frequently arbitrarily applied different names to specimens from the same area and vice versa. For example, any specimens with slightly large molars have been called *S. macrodon* and those with a redder back than is common are called *S. ustus*, regardless of where they come from; Allen (Bull. Americ. Mus. Nat. Hist., 35, 1916: 586) considered a specimen from Calama, above the river Madeiro to be *S. Cassaquiarensis* (sic) and another specimen from the same place was called *S. ustus*, without keeping in mind the proximity of Humayta, the type locality of *S. madeirae* Thomas, which would mean the coexistence of three closely related forms in the same place; Lonnberg, not only gave different names to specimens from the same locality but upon observing that some were as referrable to one nominal form as another, got out of difficulty by considering them to be interspecific hybrids.

Our opinion on the taxonomic position of the forms described until now is only provisional until such time as a conscientious revision permits clarification of the systematics of the genus.

Recent support for Cabrera's position has been forthcoming from Fooden (1966) who in his report identifying the type specimen of *Simia apedia* Linnaeus, 1758, as *Simia sciurea* (=*Saimiri sciureus*) may be interpreted to favor regarding squirrel monkeys as conspecific. In addition, Philip Hershkovitz, Research Curator in the Mammal Division of the Field Museum of Natural History and a foremost primate taxonomist, has completed a good deal of research on the genus *Saimiri* and in a 1966 personal communication noted that "so far as my material permits me to judge, there is but one species of *Saimiri*."

In the absence of an authoritative or workable *Saimiri* taxonomy, how then should researchers identify squirrel monkeys used in their studies? The most logical proposal and one supported by the editors of this volume is that suggested by Hershkovitz (1966), namely, "that investigators using squirrel monkeys employ the binominal *Saimiri sciureus*. Provenance, if

FIG. 1b

FIG. 1c

FIG. 1d

FIG. 1e

FIG. 1a. Saimiri sciureus (Leticia, Colombia), adult pair.

FIGS. 1b−1e (Opposite). b, Adult male, front view of head; *c,* adult male, side view of head; *d,* adult female, front view of head; *e,* adult female, side view of head. (Photographs courtesy of the San Diego Zoo.)

7

FIG. 2b

FIG. 2c

FIG. 2d

FIG. 2e

FIG. 3b

FIG. 3c

FIG. 3d

FIG. 3e

FIG. 2a. Saimiri sciureus (Leticia, Colombia), adult pair.

FIGS. 2b—2e (Opposite). b, Adult male, front view of head; *c*, adult male, side view of head; *d*, adult female, front view of head; *e*, adult female, side view of head. (Photographs courtesy of the San Diego Zoo.)

9

FIG. 3a. Saimiri sciureus (Leticia, Colombia), adult pair.

FIGS. 3b –3e (Opposite). b, Adult male, front view of head; *c*, adult male, side view of head; *d*, adult female, front view of head; *e*, adult female, side view of head. (Photographs courtesy of the San Diego Zoo.)

known, and a good photograph of the entire animal with closeups of front
and side of head should be included in the paper. The author would do well
to give sex, age, weight and, if possible, some standard external measurements. If the author believes two or more kinds of squirrel monkeys entered into his experiment, he should describe the distinguishing characters."

Figures 1a−e, 2a−e, and 3a−e are photographic poses of the type recommended for the identification of squirrel monkeys used in research. The
particular specimens shown are adult pairs typical of the squirrel monkeys
exported from Leticia, Colombia (Figs. 1a−e); Iquitos, Peru (Figs. 2a−e);
and Georgetown, Guyana (Figs. 3a−e). It is an unfortunate fact that precise collection localities are seldom if ever known for commercially available *Saimiri*. Therefore, as an alternative to the exact provenance, we recommend that the town or city in which squirrel monkeys are sold by trappers to dealers for exportation be designated in parentheses following the
correct taxonomic designation, e.g., *Saimiri sciureus* (Iquitos, Peru).

Several standard body measurements taken from the same adult *Saimiri*
specimens pictured in Fig. 1−3 are listed in Table I. It may be significant
that one pair has considerably shorter ears than the others while another
pair is much the longest in body, tail, and foot lengths and a third pair is the

TABLE I
BODY MEASUREMENTS OF THREE PAIRS OF ADULT SQUIRREL MONKEYS
FROM DIFFERENT LOCALITIES

Locality and sex	Overall length (cm)	Tail length (cm)	Head-body[a] length (cm)	Foot length (cm)	Ear length (cm)	Body weight (gm)
Saimiri sciureus (Leticia, Colombia)						
Male	68.1	39.4	28.7	8.6	2.3	1134
Female	61.8	34.6	27.2	8.0	2.1	750
Saimiri sciureus (Iquitos, Peru)						
Male	61.2[b]	32.9[b]	28.3	7.9	2.7	950
Female	62.2	35.9	26.3	7.8	2.6	491
Saimiri sciureus (Georgetown, Guyana)						
Male	77.0	46.1	30.9	9.2	2.6	581[c]
Female	69.0	40.0	29.0	8.8	2.5	756

[a] Obtained by subtracting tail length from overall length.
[b] Portion of tail missing.
[c] Extremely thin due to recent illness.

lowest in body weight. Short of the unlikely possibility that these physical features will all prove to be highly variable within any given natural population of squirrel monkeys, such standard body measurements may have considerable potential as characters of possible taxonomic value.

III. Supply

More than 90% of all the South American fauna exported to the United States is shipped by air to Florida from the Carribean port of Barranquilla, Colombia and the western Amazon ports of Iquitos, Peru and Leticia, Colombia. Although not well documented, the development of this trade has occurred largely over the past 25 years and has both stimulated and benefitted from the growth of commercial air freight transportation between these collecting areas and the United States. The principal market for South American animals is provided by the exotic pet and exhibit animal industry which utilizes a great variety of tropical fish, birds, mammals, and reptiles.

Primates (marmosets and monkeys) constitute the major portion of the mammals involved in this trade both in terms of numbers imported and invoice value. The primate admission figures maintained by the United States Quarantine Station in Miami are probably a good index of the total annual volume of New World primate trade (Table II) since the vast majority of New World primates shipped to the United States enter through the port of Miami and relatively few Old World primates enter there. [A comparison of these Miami figures with the total numbers of primates imported into the United States from all sources (Conway, 1966) suggests that New World primates now constitute more than 30% of the total primate market.]

TABLE II

PRIMATES ADMITTED THROUGH
UNITED STATES QUARANTINE STATION AT MIAMI

Fiscal Year	Without restriction	Provisionally	Excluded	Total admitted
1960	15,480	—	—	—
1961	15,433	11,439	465	26,872
1962	18,816	6,300	519	25,116
1963	27,772	9,386	454	37,158
1964	35,877	8,500	278	44,377
1965	32,863	8,637	258	41,500
1966	35,958	9,561	638	45,519
1967	46,577	5,924	187	52,501

Squirrel monkeys are exported to this country on a sustained basis only from Iquitos, Peru and Leticia, Colombia. At least four major and five or six minor dealers in Iquitos presently furnish about 90% of the total commercial *Saimiri* supply, while one major dealership in Leticia provides most of the remaining 10%. The squirrel monkeys that are shipped from Iquitos (Figs. 2a−e) are easily distinguishable from those supplied from Leticia (Figs. 1a−e) on the basis of several points of coloration, ear length, and body weight (Table I). The weight range of adult Iquitos squirrel monkeys tends to be less for both males (800−1000 gm) and females (450−650 gm) than for similar Leticia males (1000−1200 gm) and females (650−850 gm).

Considering the wide zoogeographic range from which *Saimiri* could potentially be collected for shipment to the United States, it is in a sense extremely fortunate that only two major sources have been developed. The vast majority of the more than several hundred recent publications on research in which squirrel monkeys have been involved *do not* indicate the source or give any description of the *Saimiri* utilized. However, as only one major dealer in the United States supplies *Saimiri* exclusively from Leticia, Colombia (Tarpon Zoo, Tarpon Springs, Florida) while all other dealers (see Sundborg, 1966, p. 49) supply animals from Iquitos, Peru, it is usually possible to determine the origin of experimental *Saimiri* simply by determining from whom they were purchased or by their appearance and the average body weights of adult specimens.

A publication by MacLean (1964) reports an experimentally induced behavioral difference between male *Saimiri* from these two geographic sources. Unfortunately, MacLean's suggestion as to the origin of his specimens was mistaken and his descriptive names for the two "varieties" stemming from the shape of the "circumocular patch" of white above the eyes, i.e., "Gothic arch" = *S. sciureus* (Leticia, Colombia); "Roman arch" = *S. sciureus* (Iquitos, Peru), have met with some opposition. With regard to Gothic and Roman "eyebrows," Hershkovitz (1966) states:

"The characters are widely distributed individual variables. They are fully intergrading and both types may be present in the same troop. There may be a greater frequency of one over the other type in some populations and either type may have a limited and qualified value of less than subspecific grade."

I would not dispute Hershkovitz' opinion concerning the value of this character in distinguishing among squirrel monkey populations in general because even a glance at the examples of *S. sciureus* (Leticia, Colombia) in Figs. 1b and 1d and those of *S. sciureus* (Georgetown, Guyana) in Figs. 3b and 3d suggests that no distinction can be made between these likely subspecies on the basis of "eyebrow" shape. However, from personal experience which has involved observation of hundreds of living squirrel monkeys in dealers' compounds in both Leticia, Colombia, and Iquitos, Peru, as well as many *Saimiri* from both of these sources in laboratories and dealers' compounds in the United States, I believe the Gothic and Roman eyebrow characters described by MacLean to be an entirely consistent difference between animals from these two limited geographic sources.

It is of interest that the British and European sources of squirrel monkeys have until quite recently been largely different from those of the United States. This fact was emphasized at a 1965 round-table conference on reproduction in *Saimiri* organized by the editors of this volume and hosted by the Bowman Gray School of Medicine, Winston-Salem, North Carolina. At that meeting, following a discussion of squirrel monkey taxonomy led by Dr. W.C. Osman Hill, typical specimens of *S. sciureus* (Iquitos, Peru) and *S. sciureus* (Leticia, Colombia) were displayed (see Hill, 1965). Dr. Hill, who had not long before come from Great Britain to join the staff of the Yerkes Regional Primate Research Center, remarked that he had never seen either type previously. The so-called "common" squirrel monkey with which Britains and some Europeans are most familiar has come largely from the Guianas (Fig. 3).

During our 1964 survey in Brazil Dr. Moreland and I found that a dealer in Reciffe regularly shipped to Europe modest numbers of squirrel monkeys from the Island of Marajo at the mouth of the Amazon River, while several dealers in Rio de Janeiro and Sao Paulo claimed to export to Europe occasional shipments of *Saimiri* from the Central and Eastern Amazon Basin. Air transportation costs and the relative availability of squirrel monkeys generally determine the markets to which *Saimiri* are shipped. The extremely favorable air freight rates that exist between Iquitos, Peru and Miami, Florida (23 cents per pound in 1964) effectively exclude most other *Saimiri* from this highly competitive market. As a result, European dealers today often import squirrel monkeys from suppliers in Florida at a lower cost than is possible from their more traditional sources in Brazil and the Guianas.

The quantities of *Saimiri* and other primates (excluding very small numbers of *Alouatta* and *Callimico*) shipped each month from Iquitos, Peru to the United States from 1962 to 1964 are presented in Table III. These figures were compiled by the Regional Forestry Division office in Iquitos based upon commercial invoice figures supplied for all outgoing animal shipments. It seems likely that these records are fairly accurate as shipments were frequently spot-checked and the modest (6%) export tax was calculated on total invoice value rather than on animal numbers. Squirrel monkeys constituted about three-quarters of the primates shipped to the United States from Iquitos during the period for which figures are presented.

If we assume that this ratio has not decreased, it is probable, based upon recent increased total primate admissions at Miami (Table II), that the pre-

TABLE III

SHIPMENTS OF PRIMATES FROM IQUITOS, PERU TO THE UNITED STATES,
1962–1964

Year and month	Saimiri	Saguinus	Cebus	Lagothrix	Cebuella	Ateles	Aotus	Callicebus	Pithecia	Cacajao
1962										
Jan.	843	42	59	161	48	20	12	5	4	1
Feb.	1,118	58	73	88	147	28	11	6	1	1
Mar.	2,525	12	202	210	102	58	22	16	9	6
Apr.	1,196	61	190	102	–	38	40	11	7	7
May	607	74	229	207	34	60	36	3	4	2
June	259	86	186	125	175	33	22	2	4	6
July	826	185	115	59	86	16	12	3	6	6
Aug.	3,706	751	160	125	12	27	24	6	7	3
Sept.	2,812	255	126	61	33	16	17	1	–	5
Oct.	1,625	66	114	98	95	19	14	2	1	4
Nov.	367	74	80	46	35	12	5	1	2	1
Dec.	704	50	66	107	134	22	14	–	4	1
	16,588	1,714	1,600	1,389	901	349	229	56	49	43
					Total 22,918					
1963										
Jan.	1,932	131	72	99	57	34	15	1	3	3
Feb.	951	111	93	122	10	30	11	2	–	5
Mar.	4,389	135	266	260	24	84	53	19	13	4

Apr.	3,542	78	245	179	4	47	59	20	6	6
May	2,331	156	289	167	13	66	51	12	10	9
June	418	132	133	106	—	42	10	—	9	1
July	2,097	443	172	124	84	39	46	12	9	1
Aug.	3,102	479	129	78	66	30	10	5	7	—
Sept.	2,762	196	209	93	18	31	18	—	4	2
Oct.	2,432	169	172	88	133	26	16	3	2	—
Nov.	1,748	169	89	86	98	35	12	—	—	—
Dec.	2,368	191	109	95	81	26	18	1	3	3
	28,072	2,390	1,978	1,497	588	490	319	75	66	34

Total 35,509

1964										
Jan.	2,691	181	142	124	29	50	16	2	2	3
Feb.	827	87	157	142	72	59	10	7	4	2
Mar.	435	42	190	163	94	55	13	4	—	2
Apr.	2,213	119	362	296	75	84	35	8	44	—
May	3,017	117	258	257	34	79	53	6	7	20
June	2,614	217	286	206	60	59	55	15	—	18
July	3,055	247	242	173	46	58	21	—	16	—
Aug.	2,429	92	162	121	35	26	14	2	1	9
Sept.	1,584	114	184	115	39	28	14	1	4	3
Oct.	3,398	247	247	157	100	58	49	3	6	3
	22,263	1,463	2,230	1,754	584	556	280	48	84	60

Total 29,322 (January – October)

sent volume of *Saimiri* shipments from Iquitos is well in excess of 30,000 animals per year.

Figures supplied by the Tarpon Zoo collecting compound for primate purchases (excluding very small numbers of *Alouatta*) at Leticia, Colombia from 1962 to 1967 are contained in Table IV. The annual volume of *Saimiri* purchases has ranged from about 3200 to 3700 animals since 1964; until recently this number also accounted for approximately 75% of the primates handled in Leticia. Since late 1966 a 5-fold increase in the collection of white-lipped marmosets, *Saguinus nigricollis*, to meet a sudden demand for their use in human hepatitis research has caused a reduction in the percentage of total primate volume represented by *Saimiri* but has not affected the actual number purchased.

The sizeable increase in commercial collection of white-lipped marmosets in the Leticia area in response to a research demand for this species illustrates the fact that the proportionate numbers of various primate species collected in a given area do not necessarily reflect the existence of similar proportions in the natural population. Factors such as market demand, ease of capture, ease of handling, and hardiness in captivity undoubtedly affect the number of any given species that is collected. For example, few dealers will purchase saki monkeys, *Pithecia*, or howler monkeys, *Alouatta*, because they seldom live long in captivity. Adults of large species such as woolly monkeys, *Lagothrix*, and spider monkeys, *Ateles*, are hunted for food throughout the protein-starved Amazon Basin and only infants and juveniles regularly reach the market.

The primary collection area for the squirrel monkeys that are purchased by dealers in Iquitos is generally reported to be over 100 miles upstream (3 days by canoe) on the Ucayali River beyond a village called Requena. In November 1964 several major dealers also reported that as much as 5% of the *Saimiri* brought to Iquitos came from the Marañon River region and that animals from this locality were easily distinguishable from the more common Ucayali River squirrel monkeys. During a 1-week period, however, none of the dealers was able to produce a representative Marañon River specimen from among more than 1000 *Saimiri* in Iquitos compounds. None of the Iquitos dealers questioned had visited *Saimiri* collection areas or apparently had first-hand knowledge of monkey trapping. Along with other species, squirrel monkeys are purchased in Iquitos from up-river animal trappers either at the dealer's compounds or at the waterfront market place. A few of the most ambitious trappers are said to supply as many as 100 *Saimiri* a month but, as trapping is seldom a fulltime pursuit, most sales to dealers are considerably smaller.

The animal dealers in Iquitos vary considerably in business volume and commitment to the industry (some deal also in tropical fish). Historically

TABLE IV

PRIMATE PURCHASES BY THE TARPON ZOO DEALERSHIP IN LETICIA, COLOMBIA
1962–1967

Year and month	Saimiri	Saguinus	Cebus	Lagothrix	Cebuella	Ateles	Aotus	Callicebus	Pithecia	Cacajao
1962										
Jan.	16	3	3	3	2	1	–	1	–	–
Feb.	22	4	3	2	2	3	–	1	–	–
Mar.	68	11	11	26	14	2	3	4	2	–
Apr.	136	6	17	20	11	2	4	3	3	1
May	163	5	27	35	9	8	2	3	4	1
June	196	8	16	18	15	1	2	–	2	–
July	73	8	11	9	6	2	5	1	–	–
Aug.	539	21	8	4	10	1	2	–	2	–
Sept.	597	15	12	4	7	–	–	7	2	–
Oct.	314	9	14	5	7	3	2	–	–	1
Nov.	15	5	13	7	7	–	–	–	–	–
Dec.	–	5	2	4	8	1	1	–	–	–
	2139	100	137	137	98	24	21	20	15	3
					Total 2694					
1963										
Jan.	–	–	–	–	2	–	–	–	–	–
Feb.	13	–	1	5	2	1	–	2	–	–
Mar.	2	8	4	1	1	1	1	–	–	–
Apr.	27	8	11	25	3	4	3	1	–	2
May	193	15	15	23	13	5	3	3	3	1
June	288	14	13	32	15	8	5	3	4	–
July	124	29	15	9	16	1	4	1	1	–
Aug.	471	40	13	19	7	30	4	–	2	1

TABLE IV (Continued)

PRIMATE PURCHASES BY THE TARPON ZOO DEALERSHIP IN LETICIA, COLOMBIA

1962–1967

Year and month	Saimiri	Saguinus	Cebus	Lagothrix	Cebuella	Ateles	Aotus	Callicebus	Pithecia	Cacajao
Sept.	266	8	16	9	8	—	3	—	1	—
Oct.	145	8	7	5	7	1	3	—	—	1
Nov.	29	—	6	1	5	—	—	—	—	—
Dec.	81	8	10	9	9	—	—	—	—	5
	1639	138	111	138	88	51	26	10	11	
					Total 2217					
1964										
Jan.	11	3	5	2	3	—	—	—	2	—
Feb.	30	18	3	13	8	—	—	1	3	—
Mar.	9	5	9	7	7	4	2	4	1	—
Apr.	124	12	6	8	6	—	—	1	3	—
May	321	36	21	53	9	4	5	4	10	—
June	299	45	16	21	6	—	2	1	3	—
July	630	28	15	6	11	—	4	—	—	2
Aug.	580	62	13	12	19	—	1	—	1	1
Sept.	256	14	11	4	6	3	—	—	2	—
Oct.	605	17	9	—	17	3	5	—	2	—
Nov.	94	4	—	—	2	—	—	—	—	—
Dec.	229	23	9	5	12	1	—	—	—	3
	3188	267	117	131	106	15	19	11	27	
					Total 3884					
1965										
Jan.	74	10	—	2	8	—	—	—	—	—
Feb.	133	3	63	22	8	8	1	7	1	—
Mar.	—	1	—	—	—	—	—	1	—	—

Apr.	52	4	7	12	29	1	1	4	3	—
May	76	14	4	—	2	—	1	14	1	—
	335	32	74	36	47	9	3	12	5	—

Total 553 (January–May)

1966										
Jan.	99	14	6	2	1	—	—	2	5	—
Feb.	35	9	2	1	1	1	3	3	—	—
Mar.	11	11	4	2	1	—	—	6	1	1
Apr.	40	13	2	—	1	—	2	—	1	—
May	78	14	4	2	3	1	5	4	4	1
June	210	26	13	19	6	2	4	—	3	—
July	454	35	15	17	4	—	9	—	2	—
Aug.	873	76	9	—	1	—	2	—	2	—
Sept.	600	42	15	1	2	—	2	2	2	—
Oct.	606	240	7	—	11	1	—	—	1	—
Nov.	250	281	7	1	1	—	—	2	2	—
Dec.	409	216	5	—	25	—	3	2	—	—
	3665	977	89	45	57	5	30	22	23	2

Total 4915

1967										
Jan.	155	262	7	1	11	—	—	1	—	—
Feb.	110	55	11	—	14	2	1	1	—	—
Mar.	58	137	2	—	24	1	2	2	—	—
Apr.	216	117	10	4	26	1	3	1	3	—
May	297	106	19	9	15	1	15	2	1	—
June	120	193	8	—	17	1	4	—	—	—
July	142	129	15	—	8	1	3	—	—	1
Aug.	804	304	26	4	11	2	9	—	1	1
Sept.	566	139	27	—	6	1	2	1	2	—
	2468	1442	125	19	132	9	39	56	8	2

Total 4254 (January–September)

FIG. 4. The well-designed animal compound of Jaime Vidal in Iquitos, Peru (November, 1964).

only three or four major dealers have exported animals in sizeable numbers on a sustained basis; perhaps relatedly, each has had a seemingly firm financial relationship with a major pet industry supplier in the Miami area. A number of minor dealers have supplied modest numbers of animals on a continuous but often irregular basis to small suppliers both in Florida and elsewhere in the United States. In addition there are several potentially large dealers who have been sporadically in and out of the business due largely to the financial hazards of this extremely competitive, high volume, low margin industry. As might be expected, the dealers compounds in Iquitos vary considerably in size and construction but most are protected from rain, well ventilated, and (if not overcrowded) adequate for housing squirrel monkeys and other primates for short periods prior to exportation. In November, 1964 the newest and most impressive facility then in use was that of Jaime Vidal (Figs. 4 and 5), the Iquitos agent for The Pet Farm in Miami. At that time Vidal was the largest buyer of *Saimiri* in Iquitos with an average monthly volume which he reported exceeded 1200 animals.

The squirrel monkeys that are purchased in Leticia, Colombia generally come from within 10—30 miles of Leticia and largely from the north bank of the Amazon in nearby Brazil. The source of these *Saimiri* is the basis for the possibly confusing (since Leticia is in Colombia) vernacular use of the term "Brazilian," as opposed to "Pervian," in designating squirrel monkeys exported from Leticia from those supplied from Iquitos. The trappers in the Leticia area are little different from those who market their animals in Iquitos except that their cultural heritage and language is more notably

22

FIG. 5. Squirrel monkeys awaiting shipment at the Jaime Vidal compound in Iquitos, Peru (November, 1964).

Portuguese than Spanish. The Tarpon Zoo dealership was established in Leticia about 15 years ago by co-owner Mike Tsalickis who has made his home there since that time. Although on occasion minor dealers have set up small compounds in Leticia, none had achieved permanence by 1964. This latter fact may be related to the considerably higher animal transportation costs that exist from Leticia to Miami as compared to those from Iquitos to Miami. The Tarpon Zoo animal compound (Figs. 6 and 7) has sizeable walk-in cages, sloped concrete floors (covered with wood shavings), a high roof, and a sunny, well-ventilated interior. It has served as a model for several more recently constructed facilities elsewhere, including the Vidal compound in Iquitos. In 1964 a field laboratory was constructed in Leticia at the Tarpon Zoo compound for a specific primate research program and it has since been available for use by other investigators (Middleton and Rosal, 1967).

In both Leticia and Iquitos there is some seasonal variation in squirrel monkey supply (Tables III and IV) said to be related to the rainfall cycle. The major rainy season in the Western Amazon Basin (with considerable geographic and interseasonal variation) extends from about February through May. This period is marked by a gradual but pronounced rise of the Amazon River system to overflowing of its banks in many areas. The major dry season, during which the level of the Amazon may fall in excess of 20 ft, usually occurs from June through September. A secondary rainy season may occur from October to November followed by a secondary dry season lasting through January. Many explanations of the relationship be-

23

FIG. 6. The Tarpon Zoo animal compound (left wing) and carpentry shop (right wing) co-owned and managed by Mike Tsalickis in Leticia, Colombia. (June, 1963).

tween annual rainfall cycle and the fluctuations in *Saimiri* trapping have been offered. One of the more plausible reports is that natural food supply fluctuates with the rainfall cycle and becomes relatively scarce during the major dry season. At this time cultivated bananas (a crop introduced to South America and thus not found in the bush) are said to be very effective bait for luring *Saimiri* into boxtraps and funnel traps of several types. It has also been suggested that, for the culturally mixed people of low socio-economic status who live in the bush, seasonal work patterns permit active trapping only during slack periods in their primary activities of farming and/or fishing. It also seems possible that dealers may condition the activities of trappers to a certain extent by showing reluctance to purchase squirrel monkeys during periods of low pet market demand. Although the exact causes of seasonal supply patterns and particularly the variation in these patterns from year to year are not clear, the case of the recent dramatic increase in *Saguinus* supply from Leticia (Table IV) suggests that established supply patterns are not inflexible.

An unfortunate truism with regard to the health of imported New World primates is that their physical condition is inversely proportional to the length of time they are held in trappers' and dealers' compounds in South America. This is due largely to the fact that the major and usually exclusive diet of captive monkeys prior to exportation is banana. A very starchy fruit, banana is essentially without protein content and as such is unable to provide the essential amino acids necessary for normal metabolic functioning. The average mortality rate in South America for squirrel monkeys that are not held longer than about 3 weeks from the time of capture to exportation is seldom more than 10%. However, mortality increases sharply if banana-fed *Saimiri* are held in dealers' compounds much longer than this period. Such lengthy holding sometimes occurs in Iquitos when suppliers in Miami become overstocked with squirrel monkeys or in Leticia when air-freight transportation difficulties are encountered. Dealers have occasionally lost hundreds of *Saimiri* because of such circumstances or have released weak and unsalable animals to prevent their deaths. Some South American deal-ers have occasionally imported commercial monkey food but the cost of providing this or other protein in the diet fed in the compounds is appar-ently prohibitive. As can be seen, the length of the holding period in South America is one of the most important factors in determining the "quality" of unconditioned squirrel monkeys that are received in the laboratory.

The strictly seasonal reproductive cycle of *Saimiri* (see Chapters 4 and 5) also has a certain affect upon the quality of animals trapped at various times during the year. Adult males are considerably heavier during the breeding season peak (usually July and August in the Iquitos and Leticia areas) than they are during other parts of the year (see DuMond and Hutchinson, 1967). Adult females are captured in increasingly advanced stages of pregnancy from September through December; unfortunately, squirrel monkeys captured during pregnancy almost invariably abort or produce stillborn infants. The birth season of *Saimiri* in Iquitos and Leticia usually begins in mid-December and extends well into February. Infants

FIG. 7. The Tarpon Zoo animal compound in Leticia, Colombia. Shipping crates are stacked above animal cages on the left (June, 1963).

FIG. 8. "Indoor-outdoor" *Saimiri* holding facilities at the Tarpon Zoo in Tarpon Springs, Florida (December, 1964).

from 3 to 5 months old when weaning is possible are very popular pet trade items and usually become available on the market in April.

Importation of squirrel monkeys from South America is subject to a number of United States Government regulations. Most significant are Public Health Service regulations intended to protect against the importation of enzootic yellow fever. Primates imported from "yellow fever areas" must arrive at the port of entry in mosquito-proof shipping crates and are supposed to have been maintained in mosquito-proof quarters for at least 9 days immediately before arrival. Animals not meeting these requirements are "conditionally admitted" until such a quarantine period has been completed. Monkeys that show signs of disease or symptoms of emaciation are required to be examined for evidence of communicable disease by a veterinarian selected by and at the expense of the importer.

Animals dead on arrival are "excluded" and cause any live specimens in the same shipping crate to be "provisionally admitted" until a necropsy of representative dead specimens reveals an absence of communicable disease. Since strict enforcement of these regulations began in about 1961, no yellow fever infection has been confirmed in any New World monkeys arriving in the United States, nor have other significant communicable disease hazards been detected. However, due to the inconvenience and expense caused importers by monkeys that arrive sick or dead, the major effect of the yellow fever regulations has been to assure relatively humane shipping conditions for *Saimiri* and other primates. The Miami primate admission figures found in Table III show that, in spite of an increasing volume of primates being imported, the numbers of animals "provisionally admitted" or "excluded" have actually decreased.

The care that squirrel monkeys and other primates in general receive after they reach dealers' compounds in Florida has improved considerably over the past few years. Most dealers now feed commercial monkey food

FIG. 9. Front view of *Saimiri* "indoor-holding" area at the Tarpon Zoo; rear door opens to a wire enclosed "outdoor" cage area (December, 1964).

and add electrolytes to the water given newly arrived animals. Several facilities have outdoor or indoor-outdoor holding pens to provide the exposure to direct sunlight that is so important to New World primates. The competitive nature of the pet industry precludes thorough acclimatization of squirrel monkeys by dealers due to the increased costs involved. However, some dealers have responded to the research demand for acclimatized and quality-selected (including age, weight, and sex) *Saimiri* and now utilize facilities that are particularly suitable for the longer holding periods (usually 4—6 weeks) which are required. In one such facility (shown in Figs. 8 and 9), both water-soaked commercial monkey chow and high-protein baby cereal in milk are provided during the conditioning period of squirrel monkeys intended for research. The cost of such special handling added to the price of the animal is of necessity in total three or four times that of newly imported *Saimiri*. However, the cost of accomplishing such acclimatization in research laboratories compares so unfavorably with the fee usually charged by dealers supplying research quality animals that many research users of squirrel monkeys now purchase only fully acclimatized and selected specimens.

A review of the vast numbers of *Saimiri* shipped from still limited areas of South America each year in conjunction with the indications that have begun to surface regarding the progressive changes occurring in the natural habitat of these animals (Heltne, 1967a,b) leads the student of *Saimiri* to two conclusions: first, the basic needs for *Saimiri* in research and pet markets readily can be met, perhaps even on an expanded scale for several years to come; and second, if totally unchecked, this level of exploitation surely cannot continue indefinitely. Clearly, the key question, which as yet defies an easy pronouncement (see Fletcher, 1967), is when the exhaustion of this irreplaceable resource might occur. Despite the growth in research use of *Saimiri*, two-thirds or more of the imported stock enters the pet market, [of roughly 35,000 sold in the United States each year, a recent *Laboratory Primate Newsletter* census (Schrier, 1964c) indicated less than 3000 in laboratories]. Without attempting to diminish the current and increasing importance of implementing conservation in the use of *Saimiri* for research, it is likely that at present at least, imposition of measures designed to minimize unnecessary wastage in the pet market—through education and more exacting laws regarding treatment, shipment, sale, and responsibility for ultimate disposition by the pet dealers and owners—will provide the most substantial safeguards against rapid depletion of the species. One cannot help but agree with Heltne (1967a) that, "History shows that precisely the resources and species thought to be unexhaustible are those in greatest danger of misuse and extinction" (p. 134), nor can one deny the certain applicability of this principle to *Saimiri*.

REFERENCES

Cabrera, A. (1957). "Catalago de los mamiferos de America del Sur," Vol 1. Museo Argentino de Cienias Naturales, Buenos Aires.

Conway, W. G. (1966). The availability and long-term supply of primates for medical research: A report on the conference held in New York. *Intern. Zoo Yearbook* **6**, 284-288.

DuMond, F. V. and Hutchinson, T. C. (1967). Squirrel monkey reproduction: the "fatted" male phenomenon and seasonal spermatogenesis. *Science* **158**, 1467-1470.

Elliot, D. G. (1912). "A Review of the Primates," Mon. 1, Vol. 1, pp. 306-317. Am. Museum Nat. Hist., New York.

Fletcher, A. M. (1967). Letters: Amazonian wildlife and forests. *Science* **157**, 991-992.

Fooden, J. (1966). Identification of the type specimen of *Simia apedia* Linnaeus, 1758. *Mammalia* **30**, No. 3, 507-508.

Heltne, P. G. (1967a). Letters: Animals from the Amazon Basin. *Science* **157**, 134.

Heltne, P. G. (1967b). Letters: Latin America: Call for conservation. *Science* **158**, 717.

Hershkovitz, P. (1965). Primate research and systematics. *Science* **147**, 1156-1157.

Hershkovitz, P. (1966). Personal communication.

Hill, W. C. O. (1960). "Primates. Comparative Anatomy and Taxonomy," Vol. IV, Part A, pp. 250-322, Edinburgh Univ. Press, Edinburgh.

Hill, W. C. O. (1965). Tentative identification of laboratory squirrel monkeys (*Saimiri*). *Lab. Primate Newsletter* **4**, **No 3**, 1-4.

Holdenried, R. (1964). Comments on the identification of monkeys. *Lab. Primate Newsletter* **3**, No. 2, 6-7.

Klüver, H. (1933). "Behavior Mechanisms in Monkeys." Univ. of Chicago Press, Chicago, Illinois.

Klüver, H., and Brunschwig, A. (1947). Oral carcinoma in a monkey colony. *Cancer Res.* **7**, 627-633.

Lima, E. da C. (1945). "Mammals of Amazonia i." General. Introduction and Primates, Oficina Grafica Maua Ltda., Rio de Janeiro, Brazil.

MacLean, P. D. (1964). Mirror display in the squirrel monkey, *Saimiri sciureus. Science* **146**, 950-952.

Middleton, C. C., and Rosal, J. E. (1967). Nonhuman primate field research in South America: Experiences at a field laboratory. *Lab. Primate Newsletter* **6**, No. 2, 1-7.

Sanderson, I. T. (1957). "The Monkey Kingdom." Doubleday, New York.

Schrier, A. M. (1963). Editor's notes. *Lab. Primate Newsletter* **2**, No. 3, iii.

Schrier, A. M. (1964a). Editor's notes. *Lab. Primate Newsletter* **3**, No. 1, iii.

Schrier, A. M. (1964b). On the identification of naming of "cynomolgus" and other monkeys: Editor's comments and letters to the editor. *Lab. Primate Newsletter* **3**, No. 2, 4-5.

Schrier, A. M. (1964c). Census of laboratory primates. *Lab. Primate Newsletter* **3**, No. 2, 8-9.

Schrier, A. M., and Schrier, J. E. (1963). Editor's notes. *Lab. Primate Newsletter* **2**, No. 1, iii.

Sundborg, M. B. (1966). Laboratory Animals: part II, Animals for Research; A directory of sources of laboratory animals, tissues and fluids, equipment, and materials. *Natl. Acad. Sci. —Natl. Res. Council, Publ.* **1413**.

CHAPTER **2**

The Parasites of *Saimiri:* in the Context of Platyrrhine Parasitism

Frederick L. Dunn

I. Introduction

A discussion of parasitism in squirrel monkeys cannot at this time range far into the realms of hypothesis and generalization for our knowledge in this field is indeed fragmentary. This chapter is therefore devoted largely to a review of present knowledge rather than to inference and speculation. We had hoped to be able to restrict our scope to the genus *Saimiri*, with a minimum of reference to parasites of other monkeys and marmosets, but as the work proceeded it became apparent that an overall review of neotropical primate parasitism would be needed to provide a background for discussion of each group of parasites. The resulting review is comprehensive but not definitive. A full and definitive review of this subject, even in the present state of knowledge, would constitute a substantial monograph.

There are three limitations that the reader should bear in mind: (1) In order to keep the length of the chapter within reasonable bounds, full bibliographical citation is not provided for each and every parasite. At least one reference is provided, however, which will lead the reader to the major publications (and to illustrations) for a particular group or species of parasite. For the same reason, scientific names are written without authorship and date, but the references should make it possible to track down any species rapidly. (2) Although every effort has been made to cover all published instances of natural, spontaneous, or experimental parasitism in the platyrrhine primates, records for one or more parasitic agents may have been overlooked, and any amendments to these listings would be welcome. (3) In most instances only the generic name or the common name of the primate host is given. This is to emphasize that this chapter is primarily a review of *Saimiri* parasitism; to reflect the fact that classification of the platyrrhines, particularly at the specific level, is in a state of great flux and confusion; and finally to stress the fact that host specificity of parasites is rarely so great (with a few exceptions such as the pinworms) that specific distinctions are meaningful, either among hosts or their parasites, when a host—parasite record is examined for its phylogenetic or ecological implications.

The parasites under review comprise all of those organisms living in or on platyrrhine hosts in some form of parasitic association. If we take the broadest view of parasitism these organisms include viruses and rickettsiae, bacterial and mycotic organisms, arthropods, protozoa, and helminths. Parasites infesting the external surfaces and orifices are termed ectoparasites; those infecting the inner body of the host are known as endoparasites. Many parasitic associations are commensal: the parasite benefits from the relationship while the host neither benefits nor suffers. Among the many parasites of New World primates the best examples of commensalism are probably found among the intestinal protozoa. Other parasites profit from their associations but also seem to benefit their hosts. These mutualist associations are well known in nature, but mutualism has not been sufficiently investigated in the primates. The best candidates for mutualists may be some of the intestinal bacteria usually regarded as commensals, but these microorganisms have scarcely been studied in the platyrrhines. A third category of parasitism is that in which the parasite benefits but the host is harmed—either directly or indirectly—through competition for essential nutrients. In this type of association the parasite is always to some degree pathogenic, but the host may accommodate itself to the pathogenic effects of parasitism in such a way that the presence of the organism is neither crippling nor "clinically apparent." Certain parasites, commensal or at least grossly nonpathogenic in their normal hosts, may cause disease when they find their way into abnormal hosts as a result of experimentation or unusual transmission conditions (as in the zoo or laboratory). Other parasites may become grossly pathogenic, even in their normal hosts, when disturbances of host physiology or unusual conditions of transmission permit large numbers of parasites to accumulate in the host — either through introduction from outside (in the case of those sexually reproducing organisms that cannot multiply in the host) or by multiplication in or on the host.

It is important that the reader be acquainted with our working position on the taxonomy of the primates mentioned in this review. With respect to the squirrel monkeys we accept and welcome the concept that there is but a single species, *Saimiri sciureus* (see Chapter 1), but in the absence of an authoritative, definitive review of *Saimiri* taxonomy we must still cope with the specific names that have appeared in the literature (see Hill, 1960). Host — parasite records exist for *Saimiri* collected in Panama and Costa Rica, Colombia, Peru, the Guianas, and Brazil. Fortunately only three specific names for squirrel monkeys appear in this literature (disregarding use of the generic name *Chrysothrix* and certain spelling differences): *S. oerstedi* (for Panamanian and Costa Rican animals), *S. boliviensis* (for black-headed forms from eastern Peru), and *S. sciureus* (for all other forms from all other localities). *Saimiri usta* and *S. madeirae* have not to my knowledge appeared as host names. In the account that follows, the names *S. sciureus, S. oerstedi,* and *S. boliviensis* will be recorded as they have appeared in parasitological writings, together with localities whenever possible. If the reader favors the concept of a single species, *S. sciureus,* he need only translate *S. oerstedi,* when it appears, to mean *S. sciureus* of Panama and Costa Rica, and *S. boliviensis* to mean black-headed forms of *S. sciureus* of eastern Peru.

Many other primate hosts are mentioned in this review, but, as already pointed out, only by their generic and/or common names. We have adopted the working classification of genera of platyrrhine primates set out in Table I. This tabulation follows Walker *et al.*'s (1964) disposition of genera in the families Cebidae and Callithricidae with only one exception: We prefer to regard *Mico* as a separate genus rather than as a synonym for *Callithrix*. If *Mico,* one of three genera of marmosets with incisiform canines, is synonymized with *Callithrix* then very probably *Cebuella* should be also (see Hershkovitz, 1964, p. 395). When a generic name used in a host — parasite record has been suppressed we provide the name used by the author: e.g., an author refers to *Hapale jacchus* as the host for a parasite; in this review his record for this host would appear either as *Callithrix* (=*Hapale*) or, rarely, as *Callithrix* (=*Hapale*) *jacchus*.

TABLE I
NEW WORLD PRIMATE GENERA

Family and genus	Common name
Cebidae	Cebid monkeys
Callimico	Goeldi's monkey
Callicebus	Titi monkeys
Aotus	Owl or night monkey
Pithecia	Sakis
Chiropotes	Sakis
Cacajao	Ukaris
Saimiri	Squirrel monkeys
Cebus	Capuchins
Alouatta	Howler monkeys
Lagothrix	Woolly monkeys
Brachyteles	Woolly spider monkey
Ateles	Spider monkeys
Callithricidae (=Hapalidae)	Marmosets
Saguinus (=Tamarin, Tamarinus, Marikina, Oedipomidas)	Marmosets, Tamarins
Leontideus (=Leontocebus)	Lion-headed marmosets
Mico	Black-tailed or silvery marmoset
Callithrix (=Hapale)	Marmosets
Cebuella	Pygmy marmoset

II. Review

A. VIRAL INFECTIONS

In order to place the few scattered findings for *Saimiri* in perspective, it will be necessary in this review to examine the records for all infections of New World primates for each parasite group. The viruses will be considered by major group, or family, following the classification of Wilner (1964): adenoviruses, arboviruses, herpesviruses, myxoviruses, papovaviruses, picornaviruses, poxviruses, reoviruses, and miscellaneous viruses. Records of infection confirmed by virus isolation are emphasized but other evidences (serological, experimental infections, tissue culture studies) of susceptibility are noted as well.

1. Adenoviruses

Records of natural or experimental adenovirus infection in New World monkeys and marosets apparently do not exist.

2. Arboviruses

Knowledge of the arboviruses of American primates has advanced rapidly since the early 1950's, largely as a result of activities at virus laboratories in Trinidad and Belém, Brazil. At least 21 arboviruses of platyrrhines have been published, cataloged, and classified; at least two others are as yet unpublished and will not be referred to in this review. Only three viruses—yellow fever, dengue (type?), and Melao (TRVL 9375)—have been reported as natural infections of *Saimiri*, and only the virus of yellow fever has been studied experimentally in squirrel monkeys. We may review the arboviruses by group:

a. Group A. The virus of eastern equine encephalitis (EEE) has not been isolated from nonhuman primates and no serological records of infection are known, but broad tissue-culture susceptibility to this virus has been demonstrated for kidney tissues from *Cebus, Alouatta, Aotus,* and *Saguinus* (=*Tamarin*) (see Hsiung *et al.,* 1964). Another group-A virus, Mucambo, related to VEE, the virus of Venezuelan equine encephalitis, has been isolated at least once from a sentinel *Cebus* monkey in Brazil (Shope *et al.,* 1964). (Many arboviruses have been isolated from sentinel monkeys, i.e., caged animals placed in natural localities where they may attract biting insects capable of transmitting viruses.)

b. Group B. Ecologically oriented studies in South and Central America over a span of more than 30 years have produced a wealth of data on the activity of the yellow fever virus in primates. Work through the 1940's is thoroughly reviewed in Strode (1951). More recent yellow fever studies have focused on an epizootic wave in Central America (Clark, 1952; Vargas-Mendez and Elton, 1953). All New World primates are assumed to be susceptible to the virus, and natural infections have been recorded for many species. Kidney tissue-culture susceptibility varies greatly, however, and in one study cited by Hsiung *et al.* (1964) only *Alouatta* tissues were susceptible while *Cebus, Aotus,* and *Saguinus* (=*Tamarin*) cultures were insensitive. Howler monkeys, *Alouatta,* are apparently highly susceptible in nature; large numbers appear to have succumbed to yellow fever on Barro Colorado Island in the Panama Canal Zone in 1949 or 1950 (Collias and Southwick, 1952). Records for squirrel monkeys include: 3 of 69 *S. sciureus* from the Brazilian states of Amazonas and Pará found serologically positive over a 15-year period (Kumm and Laemmert, 1950); 7 of 15 Colombian *S. sciureus* seropositive after a yellow fever epizootic, and 1 of 9 positive in the same region (Villavicencio) during an epizootic (Strode, 1951, p. 479); 1 of 10 *S. oerstedi* seropositive in western Panama in 1950 (Clark, 1952). Squirrel monkeys have also been experimentally infected—with a high proportion of fatalities. The animals show classic liver lesions of yellow fever at autopsy. Experimental studies are reviewed in Strode (1951, pp. 30 and 326—327).

Infection by one of the group-B viruses (type not specified) causing dengue fever has been demonstrated serologically, according to Hsiung *et al.* (1964), for *Saimiri, Cebus, Ateles, Alouatta, Aotus,* and *Saguinus* (=*Marikina*). *Cebus* kidney tissue cultures are insusceptible to the virus. Two other group-B viruses have been isolated from sentinel cebid monkeys: Bussuquara virus from *Alouatta* in Brazil and Ilhéus virus from *Cebus,* also in Brazil (Causey *et al.,* 1961). Koprowski and Hughes (1946), who studied Ilhéus virus experimentally in *Callithrix* and *Cebus,* showed that the marmosets circulate the virus much longer than the capuchin monkeys. *Callithrix* viremias persisted 5−7 days, while viremias in *Cebus* lasted only 1 day. Neither experimental host showed any signs of illness.

c. Group C. Six viruses isolated from sentinel *Cebus* monkeys near Belém, Brazil have been classified in this new arbovirus group (Causey *et al.,* 1961; Shope *et al.,* 1961). None of the viruses — Marituba, Oriboca, Apeu, Murutucu, Caraparu, and Itaqui — caused illness in the monkeys, and none have been isolated from other hosts. Nor have experimental data been published on their potential infectivity for other primates.

d. Guamá Group. Two viruses in this group — Guamá and Catú — have been isolated from *Cebus* near Belém in Brazil, neither virus causing apparent illness in the sentinel animals (Causey *et al.,* 1961). No experimental studies of infectivity for other primates have been reported.

e. Bunyamwera Group. Infections by two members of this group have been detected serologically on Trinidad: Cache Valley virus in 3 of 28 *Alouatta* (Downs *et al.,* 1961), and Kairi virus in 2 of 34 *Alouatta* and questionably in 1 of 18 *Cebus* (Anderson *et al.,* 1960a).

f. Simbu Group. Manzanilla virus was isolated from howler monkeys on Trinidad: 8 of 67 *Alouatta* were later shown to have neutralizing antibody for Manzanilla (Anderson *et al.,* 1960b). *Cebus* monkeys were "completely refractory to the virus inoculated either intraperitoneally or intracerebrally." Infection by another Simbu-group virus, Oropouche, has also been detected serologically on Trinidad in 8 of 26 *Cebus* and 9 of 26 *Alouatta.* The virus was first isolated from a man with a febrile illness on the island (Anderson *et al.,* 1961).

g. California Complex. Melao (TRVL 9375) virus of the California complex is known from Trinidad (not in primates) and Brazil where two strains have been isolated, one from a sentinel *Cebus,* the other from a young squirrel monkey (presumably a naturally infected *S. sciureus).* Except for the group-B viruses noted above this is the only arbovirus so far recorded for *Saimiri.* The list would doubtless be much longer if *Saimiri* rather than *Cebus* had been used as a sentinel animal in the Brazilian studies. Melao has not been associated with illness in monkeys.

h. Ungrouped. Tacaiuma virus, another isolate from a *Cebus* sentinel in Brazil, remains ungrouped at this writing (Causey *et al.,* 1961). It has not been associated with illness and its range of infectivity for other primates is not known.

i. Vesicular Stomatitis Group. The Indiana serotype of vesicular stomatitis virus (VSV-Indiana) has been studied in Panama where isolates have been obtained from sand flies, *Phlebotomus*, and neutralizing antibody rates are relatively high in man (Shelokov *et al.*, 1961). Antibody has also been detected in Panamanian *Ateles* and *Cebus* (Kuns, 1962).

3. Herpesviruses

a. Subgroup A. Several strains of a herpesvirus variously labeled herpes-T, herpes marmoset virus, and *Herpesvirus tamarinus* have been isolated recently from tamarin marmosets, *Saguinus* (=*Tamarinus*) *nigricollis*, owl monkeys (*Aotus*), and *S. sciureus* (Melnick *et al.*, 1964; Holmes *et al.*, 1964; Hunt and Melendez, 1966; Melendez *et al.*, 1966). The virus infection is usually fatal for *Saguinus*, and neutralizing antibodies are rarely found in these animals upon survey. Holmes *et al.* (1964) suggest that these marmosets are probably not natural hosts. Fatal infections also occur in owl monkeys (Hunt and Melendez, 1966). On the other hand, the virus is less virulent for squirrel monkeys. Isolates have been obtained from apparently healthy animals, which suggests, as Cooper (1966a) has pointed out, that *Saimiri* may be a natural host, especially in view of recent serological survey findings. These surveys have revealed low prevalence rates for neutralizing antibody in juvenile *S. sciureus*, *Ateles* sp., and *Cebus* sp., while the rates for adults of the same species are much higher (Deinhardt and Deinhardt, 1966).

b. Subgroup B. Salivary gland virus (SGV), or cytomegalic inclusion disease virus, has apparently not been isolated from New World primates but virus activity in these animals is suggested by the report of SGV-like inclusions in parotid and submaxillary glands of two *Cebus* monkeys by Cowdry and Scott (1935). Routine histological examination revealed the inclusions in much-hypertrophied cells of these salivary glands.

4. Myxoviruses

No myxoviruses have been isolated from platyrrhines. Hsiung *et al.* (1964) suggest that measles virus may be infective for New World primates —at least for tissue cultures—in view of the susceptibility of all other primates tested to date, including prosimians. A possible record of influenza in *Cebus* is noted in Ruch (1959, p. 268).

5. Papovaviruses

No papovavirus records for New World primates are known.

6. Picornaviruses

a. Enteroviruses. Hsiung *et al.* (1964) have reported susceptibilities to a number of enteroviruses for *Cebus* kidney tissue cultures. Only poliovirus type 1 infected *Cebus* cultures but the virus elicited no cytopathic effects. No *Cebus* tissue culture susceptibility was noted for: poliovirus types 2 and 3; Coxsackie A-9; Coxsackie B-1, B-2, B-3, B-4, and B-5; ECHO types 1, 2, 3, 4, 5, 6, 7, 8, 9, 11, 12, 13, 14, Bryant. Other experimental studies of polioviruses in platyrrhines, reviewed by Hsiung *et al.* (1964), suggest that susceptibility is greater to poliovirus type 1 than to the other types (which may not be infective at all).

b. Rhinoviruses. These viruses have not been reported for the platyrrhines.

c. Simian Enteroviruses (ECMO). Hsiung (1958) found *Cebus* kidney tissue culture susceptible to ECMO (2) group A.

d. Encephalomyocarditis Viruses. Roca-Garcia and Sanmartin-Barberi (1957) have isolated an encephalomyocarditis virus from two owl monkeys, *Aotus*, probably naturally infected in the Villavicencio area of Colombia. Later a pet *S. sciureus* died of the same infection after presumably acquiring the virus in the laboratory. The infection did not spread to humans in the laboratory. Autopsy of the squirrel monkey revealed lung congestion, pleuritic fluid, and histological evidence of myocarditis. The virus was recovered from the lungs, pleural fluid, and pooled liver – spleen – kidney.

7. Poxviruses

A possible occurrence of smallpox in Brazilian cebid monkeys was reported by Bleyer in 1922. At a time when smallpox was epidemic an epizootic disease involved *Alouatta* and *Cebus* in the same region. The bodies of sick and dead animals were said to have been covered with variolous pustules.

8. Reoviruses

Hsiung (1958) found what was then known as ECHO type 10 infective for *Cebus* kidney tissue cultures. This was the only "human enterovirus" in his study that elicited cytopathic effects in *Cebus* cultures. Subsequently ECHO 10 was removed from the enterovirus family and renamed reovirus type 1.

9. Miscellaneous Viruses

Experimental ocular infections by inclusion conjunctivitis virus have been produced in owl monkeys, *Aotus trivirgatus*, in San Francisco. The virus produced a mild follicular conjunctivitis in the four infected monkeys; virus was recovered from two animals 14 and 20 days following the experimental inoculations (Dawson, 1966).

B. Rickettsial Infections

Rickettsiae have neither been recorded for *Saimiri*, nor, apparently, have natural rickettsial infections been detected in other neotropical primates. Patiño-Camargo (1941) has shown, however, that *Cebus* monkeys are susceptible to experimental infection by a strain of the spotted fever agent, *Rickettsia rickettsi*, which causes in man what is known locally in Colombia as Tobia fever. Successful infection of *Cebus* suggests that *Saimiri* may also be susceptible, at least experimentally. *Bartonella bacilliformis*, causing Oroya fever and verruga peruana in man, belongs to a family allied to the rickettsiae; this organism has been reported experimentally infective for *Cebus* (Stiles and Hassall, 1929).

C. Bacterial Infections

The normal microbial flora of recently captured New World primates have not been surveyed, but scattered records are available for about a dozen genera of bacteria in newly imported or laboratory-housed animals. Little is known about the normal flora or bacterial susceptibility of *Saimiri*. Indeed at this time apparently only one paper in the literature is devoted specifically to bacterial infection in the squirrel monkey, an account of a *Pasteurella multocida* laboratory outbreak that resulted in death for 25 of 27 *S. sciureus* in a period of 10 days (Greenstein et al., 1965). Major clinical signs included unsteady gait, nystagmus, and canting of the head; pathological studies revealed invasion of the inner ear, meningitis, and acute myocarditis. The authors concluded that transmission was probably by direct contact. The infection was evidently imported (a shipment of 20 monkeys included one dead on arrival) but the geographic origin and route of shipment for the monkeys were not indicated. Smith in 1954 reported a similar apparent importation of *Pasteurella*, probably *P. multocida*, in capuchin monkeys. No experimental studies of *Pasteurella*—*P. multocida* or *P. pestis*—in New World primates have been reported or conducted to date (Meyer, 1966).

Bacteria of the coliform group have also been demonstrated in laboratory-housed squirrel monkeys. A study of experimental *Cryptococcus neoformans* infections in Panamanian *S. oerstedi* at the Gorgas Hospital was partially disrupted by deaths due in part to mechanical damage caused by the acanthocephalan, *Prosthenorchis elegans* (Takos and Thomas, 1958). Four of 10 animals died following bowel perforation and acute peritonitis. Quoting Takos and Thomas: "The serosa of the areas involved in the acute peritonitis was covered by masses of cellular exudate made up almost entirely of polymorphonuclear leukocytes. Blood cultures were made at necropsy. ... Three of the four ... had a septicemia, and pure colonies of a

gram-negative, motile organism similar to the colon bacillus were recovered. Bacterial cultures run on the inflammatory exudate yielded a mixture of organisms, chiefly of the colon-aerogenes group." Further characterization of the bacteria was not reported. The authors concluded "that
Prosthenorchis produces mechanical damage and it is only when bacteria
gain access to the submucosal tissues, probably through tunnels, that perforation takes place . . . secondary infection of the tissues by bacteria from
the bowel was probably directly responsible for both the perforation and
peritonitis."

   Saimiri is susceptible to *Mycobacterium tuberculosis*, at least in captivity, but clinical tuberculosis is relatively rare. Hill (1960, p. 300) notes that
(in his experience) patent tuberculosis in captive squirrel monkeys is primarily abdominal or generalized rather than pulmonary. Other investigators have emphasized the relatively high resistance of *Saimiri* to the disease (Greenstein *et al.*, 1965). Fiennes (1965) states that tuberculosis is rare
in squirrel monkeys and other South American primates in the gardens of
the Zoological Society of London. He has found only two records of tuberculosis in *Saimiri* at the zoo. Tubercles were present only in the spleen of
one animal, but in the lungs, spleen, and a cervical gland of the other. He
comments: "Neither monkey died of tuberculosis and the disease was possibly regressive. It was due to the human-type Mycobacterium, and occurred at the height of a serious epidemic in Old World species. I should
regard tuberculosis of squirrel monkeys as a remote hazard and only worth
the trouble of tuberculin testing if they are in contact with infected Old
World species." It seems generally agreed that New World primates are
less susceptible than Old World species, and that cebids are more susceptible than callithricids. Marmosets are not, however, "immune" to tuberculosis (Urbain, 1949; Fiennes, 1965).

   Only negative host – parasite records are available for *Saimiri* and other
bacteria. For example, no report is known of *Treponema pallidum* as a natural infection in squirrel monkeys or other neotropical primates (Ruch,
1959, p. 422). Another spirochete, *Borrelia recurrentis*, was not detected in
any of 60 *S. oerstedi* examined in Panama, while 3 of 50 marmosets,
Saguinus (=*Oedipomidas*) *geoffroyi*, from the same localities were naturally infected (Clark, 1931). In the same survey 143 other cebids were examined and found negative. The marmoset spirochete was noted to be
identical with the human relapsing fever organism and was successfully
transmitted to man, *Cebus*, *Ateles*, *Aotus*, and *Saguinus* (=*Oedipomidas*) by
blood inoculation and by *Ornithodoros* tick bite (Clark *et al.*, 1931). Presumably it could also have been transmitted to *Saimiri*.

   By serological survey and review of the literature, Minette (1966) has
shown that *Saimiri* and other cebids are probably naturally free of *Leptos-*

pira spp. Two *S. sciureus* and 120 other cebids were reported in the literature as serologically negative. Minette added negative records (for 12 serotypes) for 12 *S. sciureus*, 23 other cebids, and 38 of 39 marmosets. One
Saguinus (=*Oedipomidas*) *oedipus* was found seropositive for *Leptospira
ballum*. He suggests that the explanation for the rarity of leptospirae in
New World primates may be the result of their arboreal nature and hence
minimal contact with either contaminated soil or infected ground-dwelling
rats. That cebids are susceptible to leptospiral infection was demonstrated
by the work of Noguchi (1919): a benign infection was established in the
spider monkey, *Ateles*, while fatal infections were induced in marmosets
and *Cebus* monkeys.

A few bacterial records for other platyrrhines must be noted, for we can
assume that at least some of these microorganisms are potentially infective
for *Saimiri* as well as for their reported hosts. Acute shigellosis and *Shigella flexneri*, *Shigella dysenteriae*, and *Salmonella paratyphi* B infections
were recorded for spider monkey *Ateles* sp., at Yerkes Laboratory between
1942 and 1947 by Galton and her associates (1948). All of these infections
may have been laboratory-transmitted but presumably "natural" *Salmonella* infections in asymptomatic, newly imported marmosets are now recognized as a potential public health problem. At least 11 *Salmonella*
serotypes have been recorded from such animals (Communicable Disease
Center, 1965). Other bacteriological surveys have revealed *Paracolon* sp.,
Proteus miriabilis, and several *Staphylococcus* phage types in marmosets,
Callithrix jacchus, housed in the Primate Research Colony at the San
Diego Zoo (Cooper, 1966b). Experimental pneumococcal infections have
been induced in *Cebus capucinus* but the animal is considered moderately
(Cecil and Steffen, 1921) or highly (Stuppy *et al.*, 1931) resistant to the
Pneumococcus in comparison to macaques. Natural pneumococcal infec-
tions have not been recorded in platyrrhines.

D. Mycotic Infections

The fungi of *Saimiri* are unknown, and only one experimental study of
mycotic infection in squirrel monkeys has been reported. After observing
spontaneous *Cryptococcus neoformans* infection in captive Panamanian
marmosets, *Saguinus* (=*Marikina*) *geoffroyi*, Takos and colleagues proceeded to experimental studies of this pathogenic yeastlike fungus in *S.
oerstedi* (Takos and Elton, 1953; Takos and Thomas, 1958). Ten monkeys
were allowed to breathe an atomized spray containing the fungus. Concurrent acanthocephalan and bacterial infections resulted in the deaths of 4 of
the 10 monkeys in the study. The six other animals were sacrificed; none

died of cryptococcosis. Each sacrificed monkey showed a diffuse broncho-pneumonia at autopsy, and *Cryptococcus* was identified histologically.

Squirrel monkeys are presumably susceptible to a variety of other mycotic organisms that have been recorded from *Cebus* and *Ateles*, as follows: spontaneous *Actinomyces* infections, producing abscesses in *Cebus* and *Ateles* (see Ruch, 1959, p. 520); *Trichosporon cutaneum*, causing white piedra in *Ateles* (Kaplan *et al.*, 1958); *Microsporum distortum*, causing scaliness of the skin and alopecia in *Ateles* and *Cebus* (Kaplan *et al.*, 1957); *Microsporum canis*, causing scaling and hair loss in 10 of 21 "South and Central American monkeys" (Kaplan *et al.*, 1958); and *Microsporum audouini*, the common ringworm dermatophyte of man in the United States, causing itching, constant scratching, and hair loss in *Cebus* (Scully and Kligman, 1951).

E. INTESTINAL PROTOZOAL INFECTIONS

Although most of the genera of intestinal protozoa parasitic in man have been reported from various platyrrhines, only one of these parasites, *Trichomonas*, has so far been noted in *Saimiri*. A careful survey for intestinal protozoa would undoubtedly uncover several additional commensal species in squirrel monkeys. *Entamoeba histolytica* and *Entamoeba* spp. resembling *E. histolytica* have been reported as spontaneous infections of captive *Ateles*, *Alouatta*, and *Lagothrix*; extensive studies of experimental *E. histolytica* infections in *Alouatta*, *Ateles*, and *Saguinus geoffroyi* have also been reported (see Ruch, 1959, Chapter 4, for a review of the subject). *Entamoeba histolytica* appears more invasive—more pathogenic—in New World monkeys than in macaques and other Old World species, suggesting that the parasite is not native to the American hosts and that observed spontaneous infections were acquired in captivity. Nothing resembling *Entamoeba coli*, which is common in Old World monkeys, apes, and man, appears to have been reported from platyrrhines to date. Other amoebae of New World monkeys: *Iodamoeba bütschlii*, from *Cebus*; *Endolimax kueneni* (=*E. nana?*), also from *Cebus* (Kessel, 1928; Stiles and Nolan, 1929). The intestinal ciliate *Balantidium*, probably *Balantidium coli*, is known from *Cebus*, *Ateles*, and *Alouatta* (Kessel, 1928; Fox, 1924; Hegner, 1935).

Records for intestinal flagellates are more numerous, especially for *Trichomonas* (apparently morphologically identical with *Trichomonas hominis* of man), which has been recorded from *Saguinus*, *Aotus*, *Cebus*, *Ateles*, and *Alouatta* in addition to *S. sciureus* (Hegner, 1935; Brooks, 1963). *Giardia lamblia*, *Embadomonas intestinalis*, and *Chilomastix* sp. have all been described from *Cebus* and *Alouatta*, and *Giardia* additionally from *Ateles* (Kessel, 1928; Hegner, 1935).

F. OTHER PROTOZOAL INFECTIONS

a. Malaria. Two species of *Plasmodium, Plasmodium brasilianum* Gonder and von Berenberg-Gossler, 1908 and *Plasmodium simium* da Fonseca,
1951, have been described from American primates. No other New World
mammals are known to harbor malaria parasites of any kind (Dunn, 1965).
In nature, both species appear to be restricted to the members of the family Cebidae (Dunn and Lambrecht, 1963a). Although natural infections
have never been recorded in marmosets both plasmodial species are experimentally transmissible to these animals (Taliaferro and Taliaferro, 1934;
Deane, 1964). *Plasmodium brasilianum* will also multiply in humans exposed to the bites of infected anopheline mosquitoes, and the parasite is
capable of producing clinical quartan malaria in man (Contacos *et al.*,
1963; Contacos and Coatney, 1963). *Plasmodium brasilianum* and *Plasmodium malariae* of man are virtually indistinguishable, and *P. simium*
strongly resembles *Plasmodium vivax* of man. All available evidence
points to one conclusion: that the neotropical primates acquired malaria
from man, who introduced the parasites to the western hemisphere
from the Old World, probably after 1492 (Dunn, 1965). Little doubt remains that malaria in tropical America must be regarded as an actual or
potential zoonosis.

Many host records for *P. brasilianum* are summarized by Dunn and
Lambrecht (1963a) and many species in almost all of the cebid genera, including *Saimiri*, are recorded as hosts of *P. brasilianum. Plasmodium simium*, on the other hand, has been detected as a natural infection only in
Brazilian howler monkeys (Deane, 1964). Natural *P. brasilianum* prevalence rates for various hosts are not well established, but appear to be highest (16−29%) for Peruvian woolly monkeys, Peruvian and Colombian
squirrel monkeys, and Panamanian spider monkeys. This species has been
recognized in three species of squirrel monkeys: *S. sciureus, S. oerstedi,*
and *S. boliviensis.*

Little information is available on *P. simium* pathogenicity, except that
experimental infections by this tertian parasite in splenectomized *S. sciureus* may be severe or fatal (Deane, 1964). *Plasmodium brasilianum* pathogenicity has been thoroughly studied. Experimental infections by this
quartan parasite may be severe and produce clinical responses even in
cebid monkeys still possessed of their spleens (see Ruch, 1959, p. 325).
This pathogenicity is presumed to be a consequence of "recent" adaptation to previously unfamiliar hosts.

b. Toxoplasmosis. Records of *Toxoplasma gondii* infection in American
monkeys and marmosets are surprisingly numerous (see Ruch, 1959, pp.
297-298 and 423-424). The high degree of platyrrhine susceptibility to this

intracellular protozoan parasite is established. Spontaneous and presumably natural infections have been reported once for both *Alouatta* and *Cebus*. The howler monkey developed fever and chills; protozoa were recovered from the liver, spleen, and bone marrow. The capuchin, an emaciated and moribund infant, was sacrificed and the infection was recognized by inoculating mice with brain suspensions (de Rodaniche, 1954a). Spontaneous infections in zoo animals, usually fatal and presumably acquired from sources within the zoo, have been reported from time to time. These infections, sometimes occurring during epizootics, have affected *Ateles*, *Pithecia*, *Cacajao*, and *S. sciureus*. Experimental *T. gondii* infections have been induced in marmosets, *Saguinus* (=*Marikina*), and owl monkeys, *Aotus* (de Rodaniche, 1954b). All but 9 of 31 marmosets and 15 owl monkeys were successfully infected and succumbed to generalized disease.

c. *Trypanosomiasis (Chagas' disease)*. The important human pathogen, *Trypanosoma cruzi* and *T. cruzi*-like trypanosomes have occasionally been reported as natural infections in *Cacajao*, *Ateles*, *Cebus*, *Saguinus* (=*Tamarinus*), and *Saimiri* (Dunn et al., 1963). Forms morphologically and biologically resembling *T. cruzi* have been described under the names *T. prowazeki*, *T. lesourdi*, and *T. sanmartini*. These names and their possible synonymy with *T. cruzi* are discussed in the paper cited above, which also provides references to virtually all publications on *T. cruzi* in nonhuman primates. The reports of Marinkelle (1966) and Morales-Ayala (1961), dealing with New World primate trypanosomiasis, may be added to those cited in the 1963 study.

The squirrel monkeys, *S. sciureus* and *S. boliviensis*, of Brazil, Peru, and Colombia appear to be among the most favored hosts of *T. cruzi* — probably for ecological reasons. *Trypanosoma cruzi* infections were detected in only 8 of 223 Peruvian and Colombian primates newly imported to San Francisco in 1961 — 1962, but 5 of these infections were found in 82 squirrel monkeys (Dunn et al., 1963). At least some strains of *T. cruzi* imported into the United States in monkeys and marmosets are much more virulent for laboratory mice than are the indigenous trypanosome strains of North American vertebrates and invertebrates. Whether or not these primate strains are also more virulent for man is unknown at this time. Laboratory investigators and others who work with neotropical primates, and especially *Saimiri*, should be alert to the possible presence of this pathogenic trypanosome. There is some risk of transmission by bed bugs, by local reduviid bugs, and even by the contaminative route (i.e., saliva) (Blacklock, 1914; see Dunn et al., 1963, for further discussion of transmission mechanisms and public health implications). *Trypanosoma cruzi* is apparently nonpathogenic in its natural primate host. However, in our surveys one of the naturally infected *S. boliviensis*, studied at autopsy, was found to have numerous leishmanic forms in the heart muscle. Such infections, as in human Chagas' disease, must surely be symptomatic when the parasites are numerous.

c. *Trypanosomiasis (nonpathogens)*. Since 1909 when *T. cruzi* was described by Chagas, many other species of trypanosomes have been reported from the American primates. With the exception of an unnamed species somewhat similar to *T. conorrhini* that has recently been described by Lambrecht (1965) from *Cebus*, all of these trypanosomes may be characterized as "*T. rangeli*-like," i.e., resembling *T. rangeli*, a prevalent nonpathogenic bloodstream trypanosome reported from man in many countries of Central and South America. A recent attempt was made to bring some order into the chaotic *T. rangeli*-like array of trypanosomes by placing them in three species groups (Dunn *et al.*, 1963): the *T. rangeli*, the *T. saimirii*, and the *T. minasense* groups. Species assigned to each group are either accepted synonyms, probable synonyms, or forms closely related to the species for which the group is named. Perhaps, indeed, it will eventually be determined that only three *T. rangeli*-like species are found in primates: *T. rangeli*, *T. saimirii*, and *T. minasense*.

The *T. rangeli* group includes *T. rangeli*, *T. guatemalense*, *T. cebus*, and *T. ariarii*, the last three being generally accepted synonyms of *T. rangeli*. The known primate hosts are man and *Cebus* monkeys of Colombia and the Guianas. The *T. saimirii* group comprises *T. saimirii* and *T. diasi*, the latter probably a synonym of the former. These parasites have been described from *Saimiri* (*S. sciureus* of Brazil) and *Cebus*. All other *T. rangeli*-like forms fall in the *T. minasense* group, as probable or definite synonyms of *T. minasense*. These include: *T. mycetae*, *T. devei*, *T. escomeli*, *T. florestali*, *T. manguinhense*, *T. brimonti*, *T. advieri*, and three unnamed *T. minasense*-like trypanosomes. Many cebid and callithricid hosts are known for *T. minasense* or members of its group, and these parasites have been recorded from squirrel monkeys as follows: *S. oerstedi* (Panama), *S. boliviensis* (Peru), *S. sciureus* (Brazil, Colombia, Peru). Prevalence rates for *T. minasense* and relatives appear rather high: in the San Francisco surveys 42 of 223 Peruvian and Colombian primates and 20 of 82 *Saimiri* harbored what we identified as *T. minasense*. There are no indications that *T. rangeli*, *T. saimirii*, *T. minasense*, or their close relatives are pathogenic for man or nonhuman primates. The paper cited several times (Dunn *et al.*, 1963) in this discussion of trypanosomiasis provides full host and parasite data for all members of the three species groups, together with the criteria for the tentative establishment of such groups.

G. Cestode Infections

The characteristic cestodes or tapeworms of New World primates are those of the families Anoplocephalidae and Davaineidae. Among the 10 or 11 species so far recorded from platyrrhines only 2 (or 3) fall in other families. By far the commonest tapeworm seems to be *Atriotaenia megastoma* (Anoplocephalidae), which has been recorded from two species of *Saimiri*, from species in five other cebid genera, and from a number of marmosets (Yamaguti, 1959; Dunn, 1963, reviews the cestodes recorded in neotropical primates to that date). Other anoplocephalids include *Moniezia rugosa* in representatives of four cebid genera, *Bertiella mucronata* in three cebid species, and *Bertiella fallax* in a captive *Cebus* in Egypt. The davaineids include three species of *Raillietina* in *Alouatta* and *Callicebus* (Dunn, 1962). *Paratriotaenia oedipomidatis*, recently described from *Saguinus* (=*Oedipomidas*) by Stunkard (1965a), apparently belongs among either the anoplocephalids or the davaineids but was left unassigned pending better definition of criteria for the two families.

Other cestodes occasionally reported in platyrrhines include *Hymenolepis cebidarum* (Hymenolepididae) in *Callicebus* and *Saguinus* (=*Tamarinus*), and several dwarf tapeworms possibly assignable to the same species: a *Hymenolepis* sp. of *S. sciureus* at the Japan Monkey Center (Hayama and Nigi, 1963) and a "hymenolepid" in *S. sciureus* exported to the Netherlands from Surinam (Swellengrebel and Rijpstra, 1965). The larvae (spargana) of a diphyllobothriid cestode, *Spirometra* (=*Sparganum*) *reptans*, has also been reported several times from subcutaneous "cysts" in the marmoset, *Mico*, and in *S. sciureus*.

Only three cestodes, *Hymenolepis* sp., *S. reptans*, and *Atriotaenia megastoma* have been reported for squirrel monkeys—in *S. sciureus* for all three, and in *S. boliviensis* as well for *Atriotaenia*. Estimates of natural prevalence are not available, except for *B. mucronata* in howler monkeys (Pope, 1966), but we may note in passing that 6 of 23 newly imported Peruvian and Colombian *Saimiri* (26 %) harbored tapeworms in the San Francisco autopsy survey (Dunn, 1963). *Atriotaenia* worm burdens were light in this survey, ranging from one to eight tapeworms in the squirrel monkeys and from one to seven worms in marmosets. In the course of these dissections no signs of cestode pathogenicity in *Saimiri* or other primates were observed.

H. Acanthocephalan Infections

Acanthocephalans or thorny-headed worms of the genus *Prosthenorchis* are important parasites of neotropical primates. *Prosthenorchis elegans*, the common species, is known from *Saimiri*, *Cebus*, *Ateles*, *Callicebus*, and most of the marmosets. *Prosthenorchis spirula*, less common, has nevertheless been recorded for *Saimiri, Cebus, Cebuella, Callithrix* (=*Hapale*), and *Leontideus* (=*Leontocebus*) (Dunn, 1963). Several other "species" of *Prosthenorchis* have been described from neotropical primates and other mammals; only one, *P. sigmoides*, has been reported from *Saimiri*. The present consensus of opinion is that other primate *Prosthenorchis* spp. may be regarded as synonyms for either *P. elegans* or *P. spirula*, these being the two valid primate species (Dollfus, 1938; see also the recent notes on *Prosthenorchis* classification by Stunkard, 1965b).

In our study of newly imported South American monkeys and marmosets in 1960—1962 *P. elegans* was recorded in 32 of 65 autopsied primates, and *P. spirula* in 2 of the same 65 (Dunn, 1963). Menschel and Stroh (1963) recorded fatal *P. elegans* infections in 19 of 20 *Saguinus* (=*Oedipomidas*) *oedipus*. Many other accounts record high rates of infection in newly imported and captive primates. The cockroach, *Blattella germanica*, is a satisfactory intermediate host for both *P. elegans* and *P. spirula;* thanks to the roach, *Prosthenorchis* spreads readily in zoos, dealers' colonies, and laboratories, not only to uninfected platyrrhines but also to Old World monkeys, apes, lemurs, pottos, and other mammals (for references, see Dunn, 1963; Stunkard, 1965b). Worm burdens are often substantial, in newly captured as well as in captive animals. Takos and Thomas (1958) recorded 89, 110, 93, and 45 *P. elegans* respectively in four *S. oerstedi* that died because of the mechanical actions of the worms and secondary bacterial infection leading to bowel perforation and peritonitis (see also Section II, C on Bacterial Infections). Heavy burdens, ranging from 21 to 60 worms, were recorded in the San Francisco survey for 11 of 34 infected animals; 8 of these were *Saimiri* (Dunn, 1963). The worms may cause bowel obstruction when present in large numbers in small primates; extensive tissue reaction around the worms may contribute to this obstruction. The worms normally lie with the thorny head embedded in the bowel wall. A fibrinous nodule, readily visible on the peritoneal surface of the bowel, forms around the head. Often bowel perforation occurs at the point of attachment, probably due to secondary bacterial action in most instances (Takos and Thomas, 1958). The peritoneal cavity of the animal that has survived acute peritonitis following perforation may contain adhesions and one or more worms.

Another acanthocephalan, *Macracanthorhynchus hirudinaceus*, which is normally parasitic in pigs, has been recorded from several New World primates including *Cebus, Leontideus*, and *Saimiri* (Stiles and Nolan, 1929; Brooks, 1963). These infections are clearly exceptional and accidental; several (or all) of the records may represent misidentifications. Brooks' brief report for *S. sciureus* mentions "stool analyses," which suggests that the basis for the identification may have been the acanthocephalan egg rather than the adult worm.

I. TREMATODE INFECTIONS

Only six genera and seven or eight species of flukes or trematodes are recorded in the parasitological literature for New World monkeys and marmosets. Fairly intensive helminthological examinations of these animals over many decades have shown that trematodes as a class are not characteristic parasites of neotropical primates. Genera and species are few, prevalence rates are low, worm burdens are generally light, distribution records are extremely patchy, and most species have been recorded for only one or two host genera. Even the commonest species, *Phaneropsolus orbicularis* (Lecithodendriidae), has been recorded for only four genera — *Saimiri*, *Cebus*, *Saguinus* (=*Tamarinus*), and *Aotus* (Yamaguti, 1958; Cosgrove, 1966). Other trematode records (from Yamaguti, 1958, and Cosgrove, 1966, if not otherwise stated) are as follows: *Athesmia foxi* (Dicrocoeliidae) in *Cebus* and *Saguinus* (=*Tamarinus* and =*Oedipomidas*), and *Athesmia* sp. in *Callicebus*; *Controrchis biliophilus* (Dicrocoeliidae) in *Ateles*; *Platynosomum* sp. (Dicrocoeliidae) in *Callimico* and *Saguinus* (=*Tamarinus*); *Neodiplostomum* sp. (Diplostomidae) in *Saguinus* (=*Tamarinus*); and *Schistosoma mansoni* (Schistosomatidae) in *Saimiri* (Swellengrebel and Rijpstra, 1965). *Cebus* monkeys have also been found satisfactory as experimental hosts for both *Schistosoma mansoni* and *S. japonicum* (Pellegrino *et al.*, 1965; see also for references to earlier studies of experimental schistosomiasis in *Cebus*).

   Phaneropsolus orbicularis is the only "native" trematode so far recorded from squirrel monkeys (Cosgrove, 1966). In the course of the San Francisco surveys in 1961, however, my colleague, Vercammen-Grandjean, collected specimens of *Phaneropsolus*, possibly specifically distinct from *P. orbicularis*, from the large intestine of a *S. sciureus* of Colombian origin. He found no evidence of any pathological response to this infection (Vercammen-Grandjean, 1961). Despite careful search at autopsy of 64 other South American primates, including 22 other *Saimiri* of Peruvian and Colombian origin, no additional fluke infections were detected.

   Although *Schistosoma mansoni* is of course not native to the western hemisphere, its recent detection in one of three *S. sciureus* imported to the Netherlands from Surinam may have some epidemiological significance (Swellengrebel and Rijpstra, 1965). The authors concluded that the infection was definitely acquired in Surinam where squirrel monkeys are abundant. They noted at autopsy that ova were present throughout the "whole of the intestine in fairly large numbers, many of them viable (containing living miracidia), thus excluding the assumption that their presence was due to the monkey swallowing faeces of man or another animal containing mansoni-eggs."

J. NEMATODE INFECTIONS

The nematodes or roundworms are the most numerous of New World primate parasites. Some 30 genera and 60 more-or-less acceptable species can be listed at this time. The literature is replete with names for parasites in this class. Many scientific names proposed in years past have been reduced to synonymy by various workers, but there is still little unanimity about the classification of these worms at any level. Discussion of every species of platyrrhine roundworm is impracticable here; only the 13 species known as parasites of *Saimiri* will be examined in some detail. To provide some perspective, however, the 30 genera of nematodes and their hosts are listed in Table II. This tabulation includes all known records for natural infections and secondary infections acquired by captive animals. Major sources for this list include Yamaguti (1961), Stiles and Hassall (1929), Stiles and Nolan (1929), Ruch (1959), Yamashita (1963), and many specialized publications. The recent listing of primate parasites by Yamashita must be used with caution for it contains many typographical errors, omissions, and invalid entries (e.g., listings of the filariids, *Setaria hornbyi* and *S. pillersi*, as parasites of *Cebus* monkeys when in fact the hosts are African waterbuck of the genus *Cobus*, or *Kobus*).

Table II lists nematode genera by orders as set out by Yamaguti (1961). (Some workers do not accept all of these orders, and indeed almost every authority arranges the nematode orders and superfamilies differently, but for present purposes Yamaguti's classification provides a convenient framework.) Two mammalian nematode orders treated by Yamaguti are not represented in the neotropical primates: Dioctophymidea and Philometridea. The order Ascarididea is represented only doubtfully, by two "species" of *Ascaris* (*A. cebi* of *Cebus* and *A. elongata* of *Alouatta*) described many years ago. Whether these ascarids were natural parasites or secondarily acquired from man or other animals cannot be ascertained until additional specimens are collected. Only four species of two other orders, Rhabdiasidea and Trichuridea, are reported for platyrrhines. Representatives of the four remaining orders of nematodes — Strongylidea, Oxyuridea, Spiruridea, and Filariidea — are characteristic of the neotropical primate parasite fauna, and within these orders the following groups are particularly typical: lungworms, trichostrongylids, pinworms, physalopterids, spirurids, and dipetalonematid filarial worms.

Squirrel monkeys are recorded as hosts for nematodes in all of these orders except Ascarididea. The 13 known roundworms of *Saimiri* belong to 8 families and 10 genera; all of these genera are also represented in other primates. Among all the neotropical primates only species of *Cacajao* and *Callimico* are not recorded as hosts of nematodes also occurring in squirrel

TABLE II
NEMATODES OF NEOTROPICAL PRIMATES

Order[a]	Nematode genus[b]	Number of nematode species[c]	Host genera
Rhabdiasidea	*Strongyloides*	2	*Saimiri, Ateles, Cebus, Lagothrix Cebuella, Saguinus*
Trichuridea	*Capillaria*	1	*Ateles, Cebus*
	Trichuris	1	*Saimiri, Alouatta, Lagothrix*
Strongylidea	*Ancylostoma*	1	*Alouatta*
		("Hookworm eggs")	*Saimiri*
	Necator	1	*Ateles, Lagothrix*
	Oesophagostomum	1	*Cebus*
	Filaroides	3	*Saimiri, Lagothrix, Callithrix*
	Filariopsis	2	*Alouatta, Cebus*
	Characostomum	1	*Aotus*
	Trichostrongylus s.l.	1	*Cebus*
	Graphidioides	1	*Brachyteles*
	Molineus	3	*Saimiri, Aotus, Cebus, Pithecia Saguinus*
	Pithecostrongylus	1	*Cebuella*
	Longistriata	1	*Saimiri, Alouatta*
Oxyuridea	*Trypanoxyuris* (subgenus *Trypanoxyuris*)	7	*Saimiri, Alouatta, Aotus, Ateles Cebus, Chiropotes Lagothrix, Pithecia*
	Trypanoxyuris (subgenus *Hapaloxyuris*)	4	*Callimico Callithrix, Saguinus*
	Paraoxyuronema	1	*Brachyteles*
	Enterobius	1	*Ateles, Cebuella*
	Subulura	1	*Callicebus, Callithrix Cebuella, Saguinus*
Ascarididea	*Ascaris*	2 (?)	*Alouatta, Cebus*
Spiruridea	*Gnathostoma*	1	*Leontideus*
	Physaloptera	5	*Ateles, Callicebus, Cebus Lagothrix, Pithecia Callithrix, Leontideus*
	Abbreviata	1	*Ateles*
	Rictularia	1	*Cebus, Callithrix, Leontideus*
	Gongylonema	4	*Saimiri, Ateles, Cebus*
	Squamanema	1	*Alouatta*
	Protospirura	2	*Aotus, Ateles, Cebus*

TABLE II *(Continued)*

Order[a]	Nematode genus[b]	Number of nematode species[c]	Host genera
Filariidea	*Dipetalonema*	2	*Saimiri, Alouatta, Aotus, Ateles Brachyteles, Callicebus, Cebus, Lagothrix, Pithecia, Leontideus, Mico, Saguinus*
	Tetrapetalonema	5	*Saimiri, Alouatta, Aotus, Ateles Cebus, Saguinus*
	Parlitomosa	1	*Leontideus*
	Loa	1	*Ateles*

[a]After Yamaguti (1961).
[b]Total of 30 genera.
[c]Total of 60 species.

monkeys. Thus the *Saimiri* nematode list (reviewed below) constitutes a "typical" platyrrhine parasite assemblage.

a. Strongyloididae. Specimens of the intestinal nematode *Strongyloides* have been described from several New World primates including *S. sciureus*. The parasitic female of *Strongyloides* lives in the duodenum and upper jejunum; the species parasitizing man may be pathogenic when the infection is heavy. The parasite is soil-transmitted, i.e., contact with larvae in the soil is normally required in transmission. Two species of these parasites seem to occur in the American primates: a "spiral-ovary" species, *Strongyloides cebus*, the naturally occurring parasite of platyrrhines, including *Saimiri, Cebus, Ateles*, and *Lagothrix* (Little, 1966), and a "straight-ovary" species, *Strongyloides stercoralis* of man, which seems to occur secondarily in captive primates (records for *Cebuella* and *Ateles* in Yamashita, 1963). Little (1966) believes *Strongyloides fülleborni* is the naturally occurring "spiral-ovary" species of Old World primates. Specimens of *Strongyloides* collected from a captive tamarin marmoset, *Saguinus* (=*Tamarinus*), in San Diego have recently been identified as *S. cebus* (Dunn and Cooper, 1965).

b. Trichuridae. The only apparent record for a trichurid in squirrel monkeys is that in a note by Brooks (1963) who states that stool analyses revealed the presence of *Trichuris* (presumably eggs were the basis of the identification) in *S. sciureus* at Orange Park, Florida. These infections by whipworms, which are soil-transmitted helminths, may well have been acquired secondarily; this may also have been the case for Hayama and

Nigi's record (1963) of *Trichuris* sp. in one out of five woolly monkeys, *Lagothrix*, at the Japan Monkey Center. Old and somewhat doubtful records for *Trichuris* in howler monkeys are noted in Stiles and Hassall (1929).

Ancylostomatidae. Records for hookworms, as for whipworms, are rare; whether or not these soil-transmitted helminths are native to New World primates is still undetermined. Again the only squirrel monkey report is for "hookworm," presumably meaning hookworm eggs, in *S. sciureus* at Orange Park, Florida (Brooks, 1963). A group of newly imported monkeys were said to be heavily infected. Possibly, in this instance, trichostrongylid eggs were mistaken for those of hookworm. There is one good description of *Necator americanus* from *Ateles:* a female worm was recovered from the duodenum of the spider monkey at autopsy in Paris after death in a zoo (Dollfus and Chabaud, 1955). Buckley (1931) noted the presence of *Necator* in a woolly monkey that died in a zoo in London. The last hookworm record, dating back more than a century, is for *Ancylostoma (Ancylostoma mycetis)* from a Brazilian howler monkey (Yamaguti, 1961). Despite fairly extensive parasitological studies in recent years (e.g., Pope, 1966), no additional hookworm specimens have been collected from howlers.

Pseudaliidae. Lungworms of the genus *Filaroides* (=*Oslerus*) are rather common parasites of marmosets and cebid monkeys, and especially of *Saimiri*, in our San Francisco survey experience. The small, slender, delicate adult worms live in the parenchyma of the lung, usually close to the pleural surfaces. Upon gross inspection the infected lung may appear normal except for a few small pink or whitish and fibrotic nodules under the pleura. With care in dissection, intact worms can sometimes be drawn from these nodular sites. The area around the nodule may be stained with a brownish pigment. These small lesions encroach on only a small fraction of available ventilatory tissue, and in our experience the infections were not a cause of death, even secondarily, or of apparent respiratory embarrassment.

The species of normal occurrence in *S. sciureus* is *Filaroides gordius*, while the species in *Callithrix* is *Filaroides barretoi*, as reported by Gebauer (1933) and listed in Yamaguti (1961). Dougherty (1943) inadvertently reversed these host—parasite associations, linking *F. gordius* with *Callithrix* and vice versa. This switch has been perpetuated in several recent studies of the genus. Yamashita (1963) attempted to resolve the confusion by reporting both species as parasites of both hosts. A species of *Filaroides* was also reported from *Lagothrix* by Gebauer (1933), and two other closely related nematodes, *Filariopsis asper* and *Filariopsis arator*, have been described from *Alouatta* and *Cebus* respectively. Some workers prefer to reduce *Filariopsis* to synonymy with *Filaroides* (see Seneviratna, 1959) but Yamaguti retains the former as a good genus. At present five species of

Filariopsis and *Filaroides* are known from primates, each for a single host genus. This suggests a parallel to the host – parasite relationships of pinworms in American primates (see section on Oxyuridae below).

Trichostrongylidae. Among the vast numbers of trichostrongylid nematodes there are only seven species in five genera in the cebids and marmosets (Yamaguti, 1961; Travassos, 1937). Two of these genera are represented by three species in *Saimiri: Molineus elegans*, reported for Brazilian *S. sciureus* and *Cebus; Molineus torulosus*, also in Brazilian *S. sciureus*, *Cebus*, and *Aotus*; and *Longistriata dubia*, again in *S. sciureus* and *Alouatta* from Brazil, and in *Saguinus* (=*Tamarinus*) *nigricollis* from Peru (last host record: Dunn, 1960). A third species of *Molineus, Molineus vexillarius*, has also been described from *Saguinus* (=*Tamarinus*) (Dunn, 1961). *Molineus* is a minute parasite (3 – 4 mm long) of the duodenum and to a lesser extent the jejunum and pyloric portion of the stomach; it is sometimes present in large numbers in the slime on mucosal surfaces, but is apparently nonpathogenic in the natural host. *Longistriata dubia* is another very small nematode, conspicuously reddish-hued and coiled, of the duodenum and jejunum. Like *Molineus*, its habitat is the mucosal surfaces, and it appears nonpathogenic, at least in animals that we have examined, even though the worms are sometimes present in large numbers.

Oxyuridae. The pinworms of primates have been intensively studied, and their classification has been extensively revised in a recent series of papers by Inglis (1961; Inglis and Díaz-Ungría, 1959; Inglis and Dunn, 1964; Inglis and Cosgrove, 1965). Inglis currently accepts 12 native pinworm species in the American primates in 2 genera, *Trypanoxyuris* and *Paraoxyuronema*. Records for the human pinworm, *Enterobius vermicularis*, in spider monkeys and pygmy marmosets represent secondary infections acquired in captivity (Yamashita, 1963). The pinworms of platyrrhines have a restricted host range with one species characteristically restricted to one host genus. As Cameron (1929) noted, hosts and parasites should be expected to show parallel evolutionary trends or phylogenies under such conditions. We should also expect only one pinworm species for the genus *Saimiri* – which is the case. This species, *Trypanoxyuris* (*Trypanoxyuris*) *sceleratus*, has been recorded in *S. sciureus* from Colombia and Peru, and in *S. oerstedi* from Panama. Like the other parasites in its group, it is well adapted to its host and seemingly nonpathogenic.

Spiruridae. Although several others of the spirurid genera and species in Table II may be found in *Saimiri* sooner or later, only *Gongylonema* has been reported for this host (Yamaguti, 1961). It is particularly surprising that a species of *Physaloptera* has not yet been discovered in these monkeys, for physalopterids have often been encountered in other cebids. *Gongylonema* is a parasite of the mucosal and submucosal tissues of the esophagus; some species also invade the walls of the stomach. The worms usually produce little tissue reaction, even in unnatural hosts (see Ruch, 1959, p. 175); in their normal hosts they are presumably nonpathogens. *Gongylonema saimirisi*, the only known spirurid of squirrel monkeys, was collected from *S. sciureus* in Brazil (Artigas, 1933). This species has apparently not been recorded in other squirrel monkeys since it was described. This cannot be taken as an indication of low prevalence because it is unlikely that the esophageal mucosa is regularly scrutinized in most autopsies of primates.

Dipetalonematidae. Filariasis is perhaps the most characteristic form of parasitism in New World monkeys and marmosets. Prevalence rates are high, primates in many genera are recorded as hosts of filarial worms, and the geographical distribution of filarial infections is virtually coterminous with the distribution of primates in the American tropics (Webber, 1955; McCoy, 1936; Esslinger, 1963; Dunn and Lambrecht, 1963b). Surveys for microfilariae (filarial larvae in the bloodstream that can be detected microscopically in blood films) provide fair estimates of prevalence for primate filariasis, taken as a whole, and for several species whose microfilariae are well known. Unfortunately many other microfilariae have not as yet been associated with adult worms and cannot be identified to species. Until all of the neotropical primate microfilariae can be identified to species, surveys of primate filariasis must continue to combine careful autopsies, for the recovery of adult worms, with blood film examinations.

With the single exception of *Parlitomosa zakii* in *Leontideus*, all known filariae of platyrrhines can be assigned to two genera, *Dipetalonema* and *Tetrapetalonema* (Webber, 1955; Yeh, 1957; Dunn and Lambrecht, 1963b). *Loa loa* has been recorded once from *Ateles* in the Hamburg Zoo, but this important parasite of man and monkey in West Africa was undoubtedly a secondary infection in the spider monkey, presumably acquired in transit (see Ruch, 1959, pp. 179 and 343). Although several authorities (Webber, 1955; Chabaud, 1952) have treated the genus *Tetrapetalonema* as synonymous with *Dipetalonema*, Yeh (1957) argued convincingly for its retention as a good genus, and other data have been presented that provide strong support for Yeh's contentions (Dunn and Lambrecht, 1963b).

Four of the seven species of dipetalonematids have been found in squirrel monkeys of Brazil, Peru, Colombia, and Panama: *Dipetalonema gracile* in *S. sciureus* and *S. boliviensis*; *Dipetalonema caudispina* in *S. boliviensis*; *Tetrapetalonema marmosetae* in *S. oerstedi, S. sciureus,* and *S. boliviensis*; and *Tetrapetalonema parvum* in *S. oerstedi*. In our surveys of newly imported animals in San Francisco 87 of 194 (45%) had microfilariae. Among these animals were 83 Colombian and Peruvian *Saimiri:* 67 (81%) harbored at least one filarial species.

The adult worms of *Tetrapetalonema* commonly lie in the dorsal connective tissues and fascial planes of their hosts; their presence in these sites does not appear to harm the host. *Dipetalonema gracile* and *D. caudispina*, on the other hand, are not found in the dorsal tissues. These are parasites of the serous cavities, especially the peritoneum, and adjacent connective and subcutaneous tissues. While splenectomizing cebid monkeys, including *S. sciureus*, we have sometimes encountered numerous adult *D. gracile* moving about freely in the peritoneal cavity. The worms are conspicuous for they reach remarkable lengths — our average figures for female worms from *Saimiri* were 166 and 169 mm in length. *Dipetalonema gracile* can be pathogenic for squirrel monkeys: "The adult worms were most often found free in the peritoneal cavity or bound up in the mesentery. A few were found in the pleural spaces; several in the pericardial sac . . .; and two in the loose connective tissues of the inguinal regions . . .. In the light peritoneal infection (less than half a dozen worms) an inflammatory response is rare, but larger worm populations often provoke fibrinous exudative reactions. Adhesions sometimes bind parts of the mesentery to the peritoneal wall; the worms are occasionally found entwined in these adhesive bands. Large masses of worms permanently matted together and entangled in the mesentery were seen in several squirrel monkeys. Pleural adhesions were usually present in animals with pleural space infections" (Dunn and Lambrecht, 1963b). Some of the more dramatic peritoneal reactions may have been due in part to old bowel perforations associated with *Prosthenorchis elegans* infections, but we were unable to prove this to our satisfaction, and reactions in the pleural space similar to those in the peritoneum could only have been caused by the filariae themselves.

K. ARTHROPOD INFESTATIONS

A remarkable and diverse array of endo- and ectoparasitic arthropods has been described from the platyrrhines. With few exceptions these parasites are known only from the neotropical region, and only from primates. Although no records exist for fleas (Hopkins, 1957a), and tick infestation is evidently rare, the pentastomid worms, botfly larvae, lice, and mites are well represented. The arthropod list is less diverse for *Saimiri* but nontheless includes a pentastomid and a series of unusual mites.

Ticks. The hard ticks must be rare and transient ectoparasitic visitors on New World primates. The only record that has come to attention is a half-century-old report of *Ixodes loricatus* on *Ateles* of Mexican origin (Cooley and Kohls, 1945). Among the soft ticks, species of *Ornithodoros* have been used in successful experimental transmission of *Borrelia recurrentis* in Panama (Clark *et al.*, 1931). Accounts of natural *Ornithodoros* attacks on platyrrhine monkeys and marmosets are lacking, but *B. recurrentis* infections in wild-caught *Saguinus geoffroyi* suggest that these Panamanian marmosets, at least, are probable hosts for *Ornithodoros*. As noted in Section II,C on Bacterial Infections, natural spirochetal infections have not been reported for *Saimiri*.

Mites. The American primates have thus far yielded nine species of mites to acarologists, but it is becoming evident that workers in the past have overlooked many mites in obscure locations. Recent studies by Lavoipierre (1964a) of mites of the hair follicles of *Saimiri*, and by Fain (1959, 1964) of mites inhabiting the nasal cavities of *Saimiri* and *Callithrix*, suggest that additional species await discovery as studies are extended to other platyrrhine genera.

Mite — host records for the neotropical primates follow: Trombidiformes: *Demodex* sp. of *S. sciureus* in hair follicles, including the depths of the follicle (Lavoipierre, 1964a). Mesostigmata: *Pneumonyssus stammeri* in the lungs of *Lagothrix* (see Ruch, 1959, p. 279, for a comment on the apparent rarity of pulmonary acariasis in New World monkeys). Sarcoptiformes: Four species of sarcoptiforms belonging to two genera have recently been described for the first time from *S. sciureus*. *Audycoptes greeri* and *A. lawrenci* (Audycoptidae) were collected from the upper part of specialized hair follicles known as sinus-hair follicles (Lavoipierre, 1964a). The host was a laboratory-housed *S. sciureus* from eastern Peru. Although the mites were undoubtedly native to this host Lavoipierre considered the infestation heavier than might have been expected for a free-ranging host. With regard to pathogenicity he remarks: "*Audycoptes* spp. probably feed directly on the product of the sebaceous gland which is a fatty material known as sebum and which is said to lubricate the surface of the skin. Interference with this natural process leads, in heavy infestations with audycoptids, to a breakdown in the defenses of the follicles and subsequent secondary infection with microorganisms."

Sarcoptiform mites have also been reported from the nasal cavities of several *S. sciureus* that died at the Antwerp Zoo soon after importation from South America. Two species of these nasal mites, *Mortelmansia longus* and *Mortelmansia brevis*, were described by Fain in 1959; apparently no pathogenic effects of infestation were noted. Fain (1964) has also described a species of this sarcoptiform, *Mortelmansia duboisi*, from the same nasal sites in a marmoset, *Callithrix* (=*Hapale*) of Brazilian origin. Two other sarcoptiform species, described by Lavoipierre (1964b), complete the present acarine record for American primates. The first of these, *Dunnalges lambrechti*, was collected from newly imported Peruvian tamarin marmosets, *Saguinus* (=*Tamarinus*). Lavoipierre comments: "The tamarins were very heavily infected and showed some skin changes, in particular a discrete hyperkeratinization; there did not appear to be any evidence of depilation." The other mite, *Rosalialges cruciformis*, represented by only two specimens of the female, was collected from the skin of a Peruvian owl monkey, *Aotus*, which was dead on arrival by air in San Francisco.

Pentastomids. The larvae of these wormlike endoparasitic arthropods have been found encysted, usually in the liver, in several monkey and marmoset intermediate hosts. An old record for *Porocephalus (Porocephalus clavatus)* in *S. sciureus* from "South America" is listed by Stiles and Nolan (1929). Larvae were recovered from the liver, mesentery, and lungs of the infected animal. Other records include *Porocephalus crotali* in *Saguinus*, *Linguatula serrata* and *Linguatula* sp. in *Callicebus*, and *Porocephalus (=Armillifer) armillatus* in *Cebus* (Desportes and Roth, 1943; Stiles and Nolan, 1929). These infections appear to be infrequent and accidental in New World primates although data on their prevalence are not available. We encountered no pentastomids during autopsies of 65 animals in San Francisco (Dunn, 1963); nor did Pope (1966) find them in her autopsy studies of 84 *Alouatta* from northern Argentina.

Botfly larvae. The status of myiasis in New World primates is rather extraordinary. Parasitic maggots are known only from howler monkeys, *Alouatta*, yet the records for such parasitism in howlers are numerous (Townsend, 1935). Cuterebrid larvae or maggots of the genus *Alouattamyia* (several species, including one known formerly as *Cuterebra baeri*) have been collected from many howlers in Panama, British Guiana, and several localities in Amazonian Brazil. In at least one of these areas primates of other genera examined at the same time were found free of infestation. The range of *Alouattamyia* flies may not extend into northern Argentina, for Pope (1966) does not mention myiasis in her review of postmortem findings for 302 wild-caught howlers from this region. The maggots of these host-specific flies are reportedly subcutaneous parasites, mainly of the throat region (Townsend, 1935).

Lice. Squirrel monkeys are not represented among the numerous platyrrhine hosts so far recorded for lice. Mallophagan lice of the amblyceran superfamily are apparently restricted to owl monkeys. A host-specific species, *Aotiella (=Gyropus) aotophilus* (Gyropidae), has often been collected from *Aotus* (Hopkins, 1949, 1957b). Hopkins believes that this occurrence is secondary, although not recent, since the family to which this genus belongs is otherwise represented only on South American hystrichomorph rodents. The ischnoceran division of the Mallophaga is represented on *Alouatta*, *Ateles*, and *Brachyteles* by at least two species of trichodectid lice, *Cebidicola (=Trichodectes) armatus* and *Cebidicola semiarmatus*

(Hopkins 1949, 1957b). Eventually, lice of this genus may well be reported from *Saimiri*.

Anopluran lice of the genus *Pediculus* have often been collected from wild-caught and captive spider monkeys and howlers (Hopkins 1949, 1957b; Pope, 1966); records for other genera (*Pithecia, Cebus, Saguinus*) are doubtful, probably resulting from contamination in Hopkins' opinion. Although several species have been described, all forms of *Pediculus* from New World monkeys are close to *Pediculus humanus* of man. Most authorities agree that these ectoparasites were acquired by monkey from man after his entry into the western hemisphere (see Hopkins, 1949, for extensive discussion of this point).

III. Comment: Ecology, Behavior, and Phylogeny

Although the primates of the American tropics are hosts for numerous and diverse parasitic forms, the gaps in knowledge are great for almost every parasitic group. Deficiencies in the present record are particularly evident for the viruses, bacteria, and fungi. Among the viruses only those in the arthropod-transmitted group have received much attention—and even knowledge of these arboviruses is fragmentary. Additional arboviruses doubtless await detection, and much also remains to be learned about the natural host distribution, prevalence, geographical distribution, and pathogenicity of those that are presently known. The record for other viruses is, as already indicated, almost nonexistent. Bacterial, mycotic, and rickettsial infections have received much less attention than viruses; almost all of our data for these organisms are derived from experimental work or studies of captive animals.

The protozoa of the blood and tissues are far better known, in part because these parasites can often be recognized with relative ease by simple investigative methods. Intensive study of malaria and Chagas' disease in many parts of the Americas has also stimulated subsidiary investigation of primate counterparts of the human parasites. Most of the species of intestinal protozoa normally occurring in platyrrhines have probably been reported at least once, but knowledge of host distribution is sketchy. The larger ectoparasites are among the first parasites to be collected from a host; we may assume that present records are relatively meaningful and that, for example, the apparent absence of fleas really means that fleas rarely (if ever) parasitize these animals. On the other hand, as Lavoipierre (1964a,b) has shown, sparse records for the mites of hair follicles and other obscure sites merely reflect limited collecting to date from these anatomical locations. The helminths, like the blood protozoa, are better known

than most groups. Most helminths are large enough and sufficiently conspicuous to ensure their collection at autopsy; only the smallest forms and
those normally resident in obscure locations, such as *Gongylonema* in the
esophageal wall, are likely to be seriously under-represented in collections.

Despite the deficiencies in the record outlined here—deficiencies that
apply to *Saimiri* as to all other cebids and marmosets—something may be
gained from inspection of numerical summaries of the known parasite as-
semblages. These are presented in Tables III and IV—for all platyrrhines,
for *Saimiri* alone, for all members of the family Cebidae, and for all of the
Callithricidae. The review, and the tables, cover 165 kinds of platyrrhine
parasites: 117 species of protozoa, helminths, and arthropods; 6 species of
fungi in 4 genera; 1 *Rickettsia;* 1 *Bartonella;* 10 genera of bacteria (many
species and types); and 30 viruses. Against this grand total of 165 there are
43 kinds of parasites recorded for *Saimiri:* 34 species of protozoa, helminths, and arthropods; 1 fungus; 3 bacterial genera; and 5 viruses.

The viruses and the genera of other parasites are tallied in Table III
while in Table IV the breakdown is extended to include species as well as
genera for the major categories of protozoa, helminths, and arthropods.
Several records in Table III, especially among the viruses and bacteria,
represent experimental demonstrations of susceptibility to agents, rather
than natural infections. Table IV, however, includes very few experimental
infections.

The records for *Saimiri* in Table IV represent 36% and 29%, respectively, of all known genera and species of arthropods, helminths, and protozoa
in the platyrrhines. About 40% (25/63) of genera and 33% (34/103) of species known for the Cebidae have also been reported for squirrel monkeys.
Saimiri is typically cebid in parasite pattern, as we also noted above in re-
viewing the nematodes.

Almost all genera and species of arthropods, helminths, and protozoa
recorded for platyrrhines appear in the Cebidae; only 6 genera and 14 species are unique to the marmosets. Twenty-seven of the 33 genera and 28 of
the 42 species in marmosets occur also in cebids. Thus the marmosets
share to a large extent the same kinds of organisms that parasitize the cebids, with one important difference: many cebid parasite species (75) and
genera (36) are not known to occur in the marmosets. Few of the genera
missing from hapalids appear to be phylogenetically host-specific. This difference is, therefore, probably not a product of phylogenetic factors, and
must be explained in ecological terms if it can first be shown that marmosets have received about as much attention from parasitologists as have the
cebid monkeys. Although this is not the place for a discussion of marmoset
ecology, behavior, and parasitism we note in passing that arboreal animals
that come to the ground occasionally (i.e., some cebids, including *Saimiri*)

TABLE III

THE PARASITES OF NEOTROPICAL PRIMATES: SUMMARY OF ALL
RECORDS INCLUDING THOSE DEMONSTRATING HOST SUSCEPTIBILITY BY
EXPERIMENTAL INFECTION, TISSUE CULTURE, OR SEROLOGY

Parasite	All platyrrhines	Saimiri	All Cebidae	All Callithricidae
		Number of genera		
Rickettsia and Bartonella	2	–	2	–
Bacteria	10	3	7	7
Fungi	4	1	4	1
Protozoa	11	4	11	5
Arthropods	13	4	12	4
Helminths	45	17	40	24
	85	29	76	41
No. of viruses	30	5	30	5

should be expected to harbor a greater variety of parasites than animals that rarely leave their arboreal environment (i.e., the marmosets). The same may be said for omnivorous primates (i.e., some cebids, again including *Saimiri*) as opposed to animals of specialized diet (i.e., insect-eating marmosets).

Some of the parasites of *Saimiri* provide specific ecological and behavioral clues. As noted elsewhere, records for spargana (*Spirometra reptans*) suggest that free-ranging squirrel monkeys occasionally eat either frogs or small snakes—likely sources of these larval cestode infections (Dunn, 1963). Other cestodes and acanthocephalans found in *Saimiri* point to a substantial component of insects in the natural diet, since these parasites must have been acquired by eating insect intermediate hosts. A study of prevalence rates for trypanosome infections in platyrrhines has suggested that at least some *T. minasense* infections are acquired by squirrel monkeys and some of the other platyrrhines by ingestion of infected insects (Dunn *et al.*, 1963). A disposition to include arthropods in the diet may also account for certain disparities in the ectoparasite records. With one exception (*Aotiella* on *Aotus*) the predominantly vegetarian primates (*Ateles*, *Brachyteles, Alouatta*) are the only known natural hosts for the larger ectoparasites: ticks, botfly larvae, *Pediculus, Cebidicola*. Among the animals that apparently include insects in their regular diet—marmosets, *Saimiri*, and other small cebids—the only known ectoparasites are acarines so minute that even their hosts would scarcely be able to see them. Can we conclude, or perhaps even demonstrate experimentally, that the vegetarians

TABLE IV

THE PARASITES OF NEOTROPICAL PRIMATES: SUMMARY OF GENERIC AND
SPECIFIC RECORDS FOR ARTHROPODS, HELMINTHS, AND PROTOZOA[a]

Primate	Intestinal protozoa	Blood and tissue protozoa	Arthropods	Acantho-cephalans	Cestodes	Trematodes	Nematodes	Total
All platyrrhines								
No. genera	8	3	13	2	7	6	30	69
No. species	8	8[a]	19	3	11	8	60	117
Saimiri								
No. genera	1	3	4	2	3	2	10	25
No. species	1	6	6	3	3	2	13	34
All Cebidae								
No. genera	8	3	12	2	6	5	27	63
No. species	8	8	16	3	10	7	51	103
All Callithricidae								
No. genera	2	3	4	2	4	4	14	33
No. species	2	5	4	3	4	4	20	42

[a]For this tabulation "*T. rangeli*-like" forms are assigned to three species groups or "species": *T. rangeli*, *T. saimirii*, and *T. minasense*.

are indifferent to the presence of the larger ectoparasites, while the omnivorous and insectivorous animals promptly dispose of any chance
arthropod visitors?

As patterns of parasitism emerge more clearly it may also be possible to
use these data in assessing degrees of arboreality in various geographical
and ecological settings. Minette (1966) has suggested that minimal contact
with contaminated soil (and infected ground-dwelling rodents) may explain
the apparent rarity of leptospiral infections in platyrrhines. If this is so,
future studies should reveal higher rates of prevalence or at least sporadic
leptospiral infections in those animals, including *Saimiri*, that do visit the
ground intermittently. The presence or absence of certain trematode infections may also serve to indicate contact with the ground, for certain trematodes are clearly not transmitted up in the trees. As with the leptospirae,
perhaps the relative scarcity of records for fluke infections in American
primates is a reflection of their general arboreality. If, for example, Swellengrebel and Rijpstra's record (1965) for *Schistosoma mansoni* in a
squirrel monkey represents a natural infection, it is certain that the animal
became infected through contact with water at ground level—by drinking,
by touching the water, or perhaps even by falling in. Other indirect generalizations about certain aspects of platyrrhine behavior may emerge as we
learn more about the life cycles and natural cycles of transmission of the
neotropical parasites. Diet and relative arboreality have been mentioned;
parasite data may also point to or help to confirm reports of nesting—as in
Aotus. The mallophagan louse, *Aotiella*, is not a nest-dwelling parasite, but
its restriction to owl monkeys may be partially a consequence of the nes-
tling proclivities of the host. The nesting habit may also help to explain the
presumed spillover of these lice from hystrichomorph rodents to owl monkeys (Hopkins, 1957b).

Prevalence rates for certain parasites, such as the filarial nematodes,
transmitted by insect vectors may also be affected by the behavior of the
hosts. One might expect, for example, that night-biting insects would trans-
mit parasites more efficiently to sleeping animals than to nocturnally active
creatures, i.e., *Aotus*. It will be interesting to learn what host behavioral
factors enter into the apparent specific affinity that cuterebrid botflies
have for *Alouatta*. I think we must assume this to be a case of "ecological
host-specificity" (Audy, 1960) rather than "phylogenetic host specificity"
(Dunn, 1966). Inglis's work, cited in Section II, J on nematodes, provides
the outstanding example of the latter type of specificity among the parasites of platyrrhines. The pinworm species in the genus *Saimiri* conforms to
the pattern first noted by Cameron (1929) and later explored by Inglis: *Trypanoxyuris (T.) sceleratus* is uniquely a parasite of squirrel monkeys and
one of seven pinworms of cebid monkeys that form a "cebid" subgenus.

Other pinworms, of marmosets, form a second, more primitive, "hapalid" (or "callithricid") subgenus. Interestingly, the parasite of *Callimico, T. (H.) goeldii*, falls in the "hapalid" rather than the "cebid" subgenus, one bit of evidence in favor of the placement of *Callimico* among the Callithricidae rather than the Cebidae. As the parasites of platyrrhines become better known, other examples of phylogenetic host specificity may be recognized but an instance of host — parasite parallelism more striking than that of the pinworms and their primate hosts is unlikely to emerge.

ACKNOWLEDGMENTS

Some of the studies discussed in this review were supported in part by research grant TW 00144 to the University of California from the ICMRT Program, Office of International Research, National Institutes of Health, U.S. Public Health Service, and in part by contract DA-49-193-MD-2291 from the U.S. Army Medical Research and Development Command with sponsorship by the Commission on Parasitic Diseases, Armed Forces Epidemiological Board.

REFERENCES

Anderson, C. R., Aitken, T. H. G., Spence, L. P., and Downs, W. G. (1960a). Kairi virus, a new virus from Trinidadian forest mosquitoes. *Am. J. Trop. Med. Hyg.* **9**, 70-72.

Anderson, C. R., Spence, L. P., Downs, W. G., and Aitken, T. H. G. (1960b). Manzanilla virus: A new virus isolated from the blood of a howler monkey in Trinidad, W. I. *Am. J. Trop. Med. Hyg.* **9**, 78-80.

Anderson, C. R., Spence, L. P., Downs, W. G., and Aitken, T. H. G. (1961). Oropouche virus: A new human disease agent from Trinidad, West Indies. *Am. J. Trop. Med. Hyg.* **10**, 574-578.

Artigas, P. de T. (1933). Sobre o parasitismo do *Saimiris sciureus* por um Gongilonema (*G. saimirisi n. sp.*) e as possibilidades de infestação humana. *Rev. Soc. Paulista Med. Vet.* **3**, 83-91.

Audy, J. R. (1960). Parasites as 'ecological labels' in vertebrate ecology. *Proc. Centenary Bicentenary Congr. Biol., Singapore, 1958* pp. 123-127. Univ. Malaya, Singapore.

Blacklock, B. (1914). On the multiplication and infectivity of *T. cruzi in Cimex lectularius*. *Brit. Med. J.* **I**, 912-913.

Bleyer, J. G. (1922). Ueber Auftreten von Variola unter Affen der genera Myoetes und Cebus bei Vordringen einer Pockenepidemie im Urwaldgebiete an den Nebenflüssen des Alto Uruguay in Südbrasilien. *Muench. Med. Wochschr.* **69**, 1009-1010.

Brooks, B. A. (1963). More notes on *Saimiri sciureus*. *Lab. Primate Newsletter* **2**, 3-4.

Buckley, J. J. C. (1931). On two new species of *Enterobius* from the monkey *Lagothrix humboldtii*. *J. Helminthol.* **9**, 133-140.

Cameron, T. W. M. (1929). The species of *Enterobius* Leach, in primates. *J. Helminthol.* **7**, 161-182.

Causey, O. R., Causey, C. E., Maroja, O. M., and Macedo, D. G. (1961). The isolation of arthropod-borne viruses, including members of two hitherto undescribed serological groups, in the Amazon region of Brazil. *Am. J. Trop. Med. Hyg.* **10**, 227-249.

Cecil, R. L., and Steffen, G. I. (1921). Studies on pneumococcus activity. I. Active immunization of monkeys against pneumococcus type I pneumonia with pneumonoccus type I vaccine. *J. Exptl. Med.* **34**, 245-258.

Chabaud, A. G. (1952). Le genre *Dipetalonema* Diesing 1861: Essai de classification. *Ann. Parasitol.* **27**, 250-285.

Clark, H. C. (1931). Progress in the survey for blood parasites of the wild monkeys of Panama. *Am. J. Trop. Med.* **11**, 11-20.

Clark, H. C. (1952). Endemic yellow fever in Panama and neighboring areas. *Am. J. Trop. Med. Hyg.* **1**. 78-86.

Clark, H. C., Dunn, L. H., and Benavides, J. (1931). Experimental transmission to man of a relapsing fever spirochete in a wild monkey of Panama—*Leontocebus geoffroyi* (Pucheran). *Am. J. Trop. Med.* **11**, 243-257.

Collias, N., and Southwick, C. (1952). A field study of population density and social organization in howling monkeys. *Proc. Am. Philo. Soc.* **96**, 143-156.

Communicable Disease Center. (1965). Salmonella Surveillance Reports, No. 39, pp. 2-3 and No. 40, pp. 4-5. U.S. Public Health Service, Atlanta, Georgia.

Contacos, P. G., and Coatney, G. R. (1963). Experimental adaptation of simian malarias to abnormal hosts. *J. Parasitol.* **49**, 912-918.

Contacos, P. G., Lunn, J. S., Coatney, G. R., Kilpatrick, J. W., and Jones, F. E. (1963). Quartan-type malaria parasite of New World monkeys transmissible to man. *Science* **142**, 676.

Cooley, R. A., and Kohls, G. M. (1945). The genus *Ixodes* in North America. *Natl. Inst. Health Bull.* **184**.

Cooper, R. W. (1966a). Herpes-T. *Herpesvirus tamarinus. Lab. Animal Dig.* **2** No. 2, 10-13.

Cooper, R. W. (1966b). Personal communication.

Cosgrove, G. E. (1966). The trematodes of laboratory primates. *Lab. Animal Care* **16**, 23-39.

Cowdry, E. V., and Scott, G. H. (1935). Nuclear inclusions suggestive of virus action in the salivary glands of the monkey, *Cebus fatuellus. Am. J. Pathol.* **11**, 647-658.

Dawson, C. R. (1966). Personal communication.

Deane, L. M. (1964). Studies on simian malaria in Brazil. *Bull. World Health Organ.* **31**, 752-753.

Deinhardt, F., and Deinhardt, J. (1966). The use of platyrrhine monkeys in medical research. *Symp. Zool. Soc. (London)* **17**, 127-152.

de Rodaniche, E. (1954a). Spontaneous toxoplasmosis in the whiteface monkey, *Cebus capucinus*, in Panama. *Am. J. Trop. Med. Hyg.* **3**, 1023-1025.

de Rodaniche, E. (1954b). Susceptibility of the marmoset, *Marikina geoffroyi*, and the night monkey, *Aotus zonalis*, to experimental infection with Toxoplasma. *Am. J. Trop. Med. Hyg.* **3**, 1026-1032.

Desportes, C., and Roth, P. (1943). Helminthes récoltés au cours d'autopsies pratiquées sur différents mammifères morts à la ménagerie du Muséum de Paris. *Bull. Musée Hist. Nat., Paris* **15**, 108-114.

Dollfus, R. P. (1938). Étude morphologique et systématique de deux espèces d'acanthocéphales, parasites de lemuriens et de singes. Revue critique du genre *Prosthenorchis* Travassos. *Ann. Parasitol.* **16**, 385-422.

Dollfus, R. P., and Chabaud, A. G. (1955). Cinq espèces de nématodes chez un atèle mort à la ménagerie du muséum. *Arch. Musée Natl. Hist. Nat.* **3**, 27-40.

Dougherty, E. C. (1943). The genus *Filaroides* van Beneden, 1858, and its relatives: preliminary note. *Proc. Helminthol. Soc. Wash. D.C.* **10**, 69-74.

Downs, W. G., Spence, L., Aitken, T. H. G., and Whitman, L. (1961). Cache Valley virus, isolated from a Trinidadian mosquito, *Aedes scapularis. West Indian Med. J.* **10**, 13-15.

Dunn, F. L. (1960). Unpublished survey records.

Dunn, F. L. (1961) *Molineus vexillarius* sp. n. (Nematoda: Trichostrongylidae) from a Peruvian primate, *Tamarinus nigricollis* (Spix, 1823). *J. Parasitol.* **47**, 953-956.

Dunn, F. L. (1962). *Raillietina (R.) trinitatae* (Cameron and Reesal, 1951), Baer and Sandars, 1956 (Cestoda) from a Peruvian primate. *Proc. Helminthol. Soc. Wash. D.C.* **29**, 148-152.

Dunn, F. L. (1963). Acanthocephalans and cestodes of South American monkeys and marmosets. *J. Parasitol.* **49**, 717-722.

Dunn, F. L. (1965). On the antiquity of malaria in the western hemisphere. *Human Biol.* **37**, 385-393.

Dunn, F. L. (1966). Patterns of parasitism in primates: Phylogenetic and ecological interpretations, with particular reference to the Hominoidea. *Folia Primatol.* **4**, 329-345.

Dunn, F. L., and Cooper, R. W. (1965). Unpublished records.

Dunn, F. L., and Lambrecht, F. L. (1963a). The hosts of *Plasmodium brasilianum* Gonder and von Berenberg-Gossler, 1908. *J. Parasitol.* **49**, 316-319.

Dunn, F. L., and Lambrecht, F. L. (1963b). On some filarial parasites of South American primates, with a description of *Tetrapetalonema tamarinae* n. sp. from the Peruvian tamarin marmoset, *Tamarinus nigricollis* (Spix, 1823). *J. Helminthol.* **37**, 261-286.

Dunn, F. L., Lambrecht, F. L., and du Plessis, R. (1963). Trypanosomes of South American monkeys and marmosets. *Am. J. Trop. Med. Hyg.* **12**, 524-534.

Esslinger, J. H. (1963). Primate filariasis in Colombia. *Proc. 7th Intern. Congr. Trop. Med. Malaria, Rio de Janeiro, Brazil, 1963* Vol. II, pp. 152-154.

Fain, A. (1959). Deux nouveaux acariens nasicoles chez un singe platyrrhinien *Saimiri sciurea* (L.). *Bull. Soc. Roy. Zool. Anvers* **12**, 3-12.

Fain, A. (1964). Les Lemurnyssidae parasites nasicoles des Lorisidae africains et des Cebidae sub-américains. Description d'une espèce nouvelle. (Acarina: Sarcoptiformes.) *Ann. Soc. Belge Méd. Trop.* **44**, 453-458.

Fiennes, R. N. (1965). Incidence of Tb in squirrel monkeys and marmosets. *Lab. Primate Newsletter* **4**, 10.

Fox, H. (1924). Balantidium in red howler (*Alouatta seniculus*). *Rept. Lab. Comp. Pathol., Philadelphia* p. 27.

Galton, M. M., Mitchell, R. B., Clark, G., and Riesen, A. H. (1948). Enteric infections in chimpanzees and spider monkeys with special reference to a sulfadiazine resistant *Shigella*. *J. Infect. Diseases* **83**, 147-154.

Gebauer, O. (1933). Beitrag zur Kenntnis von Nematoden aus Affenlungen. *Z. Parasitenk.* **5**, 724-734.

Greenstein, E. T., Doty, R. W., and Lowy, K. (1965). An outbreak of fulminating infectious disease in the squirrel monkey, *Saimiri sciureus*. *Lab. Animal Care* **15**, 74-80.

Hayama, S., and Nigi, H. (1963). Investigation on the helminth parasites in the Japan Monkey Centre during 1959-1961. *Primates* **4**, 97-112.

Hegner, R. (1935). Intestinal protozoa from Panama monkeys. *J. Parasitol.* **21**, 60-61.

Hershkovitz, P. (1964). Book review: "Primates. Comparative Anatomy and Taxonomy. Vol. V," by W. C. Osman Hill. *Am. J. Phys. Anthropol.* **21**,[N. S.] 391-398.

Hill, W. C. O. (1960). "Primates. Comparative Anatomy and Taxonomy," Vol. IV, Part A. Edinburgh Univ. Press, Edinburgh.

Holmes, A. W., Caldwell, R. G., Dedmon, R. E., and Deinhardt, F. (1964). Isolation and characterization of a new herpes virus. *J. Immunol.* **92**, 602-610.

Hopkins, G. H. E. (1949). The host-associations of the lice of mammals. *Proc. Zool. Soc. London* **119**, 387-604.

Hopkins, G. H. E. (1957a). Host-associations of Siphonaptera. *In* "First Symposium on Host Specificity Among Parasites of Vertebrates," pp. 64-87. Inst. Zool., Univ. Neuchatel, Neuchatel.

Hopkins, G. H. E. (1957b). The distribution of Phthiraptera on mammals. *In* "First Symposium on Host Specificity Among Parasites of Vertebrates," pp. 88-119. Inst. Zool., Univ. Neuchatel, Neuchatel.

Hsiung, G.-D. (1958). Some distinctive biological characteristics of Echo-10 virus. *Proc. Soc. Exptl. Biol. Med.* **99**, 387-390.

Hsiung, G.-D., Black, F. L., and Henderson, J. R. (1964). Susceptibility of primates to viruses in relation to taxonomic classification. *In* "Evolutionary and Genetic Biology of Primates" (J. Buettner-Janusch, ed.), Vol. 2, Chapter 8, pp. 1-23. Academic Press, New York.

Hunt, R. D., and Melendez, L. V. (1966). A pathologic study of herpes-T in the owl monkey *(Aotus trivirgatus)*. *Pathol. Vet. (Basel)* **3**, 1-26.

Inglis, W. G. (1961). The oxyurid parasites (Nematoda) of primates. *Proc. Zool. Soc. London* **136**, 103-122.

Inglis, W. G., and Cosgrove, G. E. (1965). The pin-worm parasites (Nematoda: Oxyuridae) of the Hapalidae (Mammalia: Primates). *Parasitology* **55**, 731-737.

Inglis, W. G., and Diaz-Ungria, C. (1959). Nematodes parasitos vertebrados venezolanos. I. Una revision del genero *Trypanoxyuris* (Ascaridina: Oxyuridae). *Mem. Soc. Cienc. Nat. La Salle* **19**, 176-212.

Inglis, W. G., and Dunn, F. L. (1964). Some oxyurids (Nematoda) from neotropical primates. *Z. Parasitenk.* **24**, 83-87.

Kaplan, W., Georg, L. K., Hendricks, S. L., and Leeper, R. A. (1957). Isolation of *Microsporum distortum* from animals in the United States. *J. Invest. Dermatol.* **28**, 449-453.

Kaplan, W., Georg, L. K., and Ajello, L. (1958). Recent developments in animal ringworm and their public health implications. *Ann. N.Y. Acad. Sci.* **70**, 636-649.

Kessel, J. F. (1928). Intestinal protozoa of monkeys. *Univ. Calif. (Berkeley) Publ. Zool.* **31**, 275-306.

Koprowski, H., and Hughes, T. P. (1946). The virus of Ilhéus encephalitis. Physical properties, pathogenicity and cultivation. *J. Immunol.* **54**, 371-385.

Kumm, H. W., and Laemmert, H. W., Jr. (1950). The geographical distribution of immunity to yellow fever among the primates of Brazil. *Am. J. Trop. Med.* **30**, 733-748.

Kuns, M. L. (1962). Unpublished Ph. D. Thesis, University of Wisconsin.

Lambrecht, F. L. (1965). An unusual trypanosome in *Cebus griseus* F. Cuvier, 1819, from Colombia, South America. *Rev. Inst. Med. Trop. São Paulo* **7**, 89-98.

Lavoipierre, M. M. J. (1964a). A new family of acarines belonging to the suborder Sarcoptiformes parasitic in the hair follicles of primates. *Ann. Natal Museum* **16**, 1-18.

Lavoipierre, M. M. J. (1964b). A note on the family Psoralgidae (Acari: Sarcoptiformes) together with a description of two new genera and two new species parasitic on primates. *Acarologia* **6**, 342-352.

Little, M. D. (1966). Comparative morphology of six species of *Strongyloides* (Nematoda) and redefinition of the genus. *J. Parasitol.* **52**, 69-84.

McCoy, O. R. (1936). Filarial parasites of the monkeys of Panama. *Am. J. Trop. Med.* **16**, 383-403.

Marinkelle, C. J. (1966). Observations on human, monkey, and bat trypanosomes and their vectors in Colombia. *Trans. Roy. Soc. Trop. Med. Hyg.* **60**, 109-116.

Melendez, L. V., Hunt, R. D., Garcia, F. G., and Trum, B. F. (1966). A latent herpes-T infection in a squirrel monkey *(Saimiri sciureus)*. *Symp. Zool. Soc. (London)* **17**, 393-397.

Melnick, J. L., Midulla, M., Wimberly, I., Barrera-Oro, J. G., and Levy, B. M. (1964). A new member of the herpesvirus group isolated from South American marmosets. *J. Immunol.* **92**, 596-601.

Menschel, E., and Stroh, R. (1963). Helminthologische Untersuchungen bei Pincheäffchen *(Oedipomidas oedipus)*. *Z. Parasitenk.* **23**, 376-383.

Meyer, K. F. (1966). Personal communication.

Minette, H. P. (1966). Leptospirosis in primates other than man. *Am. J. Trop. Med. Hyg.* **15**, 190-198.

Morales-Ayala, F. (1961). Hallazgo del *Trypanosoma cruzi* Chagas, 1909 en el mono *Saimiri boliviensis* de la amazonia Peruana. *Rev. Brasil. Malariol. Doencas Trop. Publ. Avulsas* **13**, 99-105.

Noguchi, H. (1919). Etiology of yellow fever. II. Transmission experiments on yellow fever. III. Symptomatology and pathological findings in animals experimentally infected. *J. Exptl. Med.* **29**, 565-584 and 585-596.

Patiño-Camargo, L. (1941). Nuevas observaciones sobre un tercer foco de fiebre petequial (maculosa) en el hemisferio americano. *Bol. Ofic. Sanit. Panam.* **20**, 1112-1124.

Pellegrino, J., Katz, N., Oliveira, C. A., and Okabe, K. (1965). Rectal biopsy and mucosal curettage in *Cebus* monkeys experimentally infected with *Schistosoma mansoni* and *Schistosoma japonicum. J. Parasitol.* **51**, 617-621.

Pope, B. L. (1966). Some parasites of the howler monkey of northern Argentina. *J. Parasitol.* **52**, 166-168.

Roca-Garcia, M., and Sanmartin-Barberi, C. (1957). The isolation of encephalomyocarditis virus from *Aotus* monkeys. *Am. J. Trop. Med. Hyg.* **6**, 840-852.

Ruch, T. C. (1959). "Diseases of Laboratory Primates." Saunders, Philadelphia, Pennsylvania.

Scully, J. P. and Kligman, A. M. (1951). Coincident infection of a human and an anthropoid with *Microsporum audouini. Arch. Dermatol. Syphilol., N.Y.* **64**, 495-498.

Seneviratna, P. (1959). Studies on the family Filaroididae Schulz, 1951. *J. Helminthol.* **33**, 123-144.

Shelokov, A. I., Peralta, P. H., and Galindo, P. (1961). Prevalence of human infection with vesicular stomatitis virus. *J. Clin. Invest.* **40**, 1081-1082.

Shope, R. E., Causey, C. E., and Causey, O. R. (1961). Itaqui virus, a new member of arthropod-borne group C. *Am. J. Trop. Med. Hyg.* **10**, 264-265.

Shope, R. E., Causey, O. R., de Andrade, A. H. P., and Theiler, M. (1964). The Venezuelan equine encephalomyelitis complex of group A arthropod-borne viruses, including Mucambo and Pixuna from the Amazon region of Brazil. *Am. J. Trop. Med. Hyg.* **13**, 723-727.

Smith, H. C. (1954). Pasteurellosis in monkeys. *J. Am. Vet. Med. Assoc.* **124**, 147-148.

Stiles, C. W., and Hassall, A. (1929). "Key-Catalogue of Parasites Reported for Primates (Monkeys and Lemurs) with their Possible Public Health Importance," Hyg. Lab. Bull. No. 152. Public Health Serv., Washington, D.C.

Stiles, C. W., and Nolan, M. O. (1929). "Key-Catalogue of Primates for which Parasites are Reported," Hyg. Lab. Bull. No. 152. Public Health Serv., Washington, D.C.

Strode, G. K., ed. (1951). "Yellow Fever." McGraw-Hill, New York.

Stunkard, H. W. (1965a). *Paratriotaenia oedipomidatis* gen. et sp. n. (Cestoda), from a marmoset. *J. Parasitol.* **51**, 545-551.

Stunkard, H. W. (1965b). New intermediate hosts in the life cycle of *Prosthenorchis elegans* (Diesing, 1851), an acanthocephalan parasite of primates. *J. Parasitol.* **51**, 645-649.

Stuppy, G. W., Falk, I. S., and Jacobson, M. A. (1931). The intratracheal inoculation of monkeys with pneumococci. *J. Prevent. Med. Baltimore*, **5**, 81-88.

Swellengrebel, N. H., and Rijpstra, A. C. (1965). Lateral-spined schistosome ova in the intestine of a squirrel monkey from Surinam. *Trop. Geograph. Med.* **17**, 80-84.

Takos, M. J., and Elton, N. W. (1953). Spontaneous cryptococcosis of marmoset monkeys in Panama. *A.M.A. Arch. Pathol.* **55**, 403-407.

Takos, M. J., and Thomas, L. J. (1958). The pathology and pathogenesis of fatal infections due to an acanthocephalid parasite of marmoset monkeys. *Am. J. Trop, Med. Hyg.* **7**, 90-94.

Taliaferro, W. H., and Taliaferro, L. G. (1934). Morphology, periodicity, and course of infection of *Plasmodium brasilianum* in Panamanian monkeys. *Am. J. Hyg.* **20**, 1-49.

Townsend, C. H. T. (1935). "Manual of Myiology," Part II. São Paulo.

Travassos, L. (1937). Revisao da familia Trichostrongylidae Leiper, 1912. *Monogr. Inst. Oswaldo Cruz* **1**, 1-512.

Urbain, A. (1949). Deux cas de tuberculose spontanée d'origine aviare chez singe africain: cercopithéque grivet (*Cercopithecus aethiops L.*) et chez un singe americain; ouistiti à pinceaux blancs (*Hapale jacchus L.*). *Bull. Acad. Vet. France* **22**, 349-351.

Vargas-Mendez, O., and Elton, N. W. (1953). Naturally acquired yellow fever in wild monkeys of Costa Rica. *Am. J. Trop. Med. Hyg.* **2**, 850-863.

Vercammen-Grandjean, P. H. (1961). Personal communication.

Walker, E. P., Warnick, F., Lange, K. I., Uible, H. E., Hamlet, S. E., Davis, M. A., and Wright, P. F. (1964). "Mammals of the World," Vol. I. Johns Hopkins Press, Baltimore, Maryland.

Webber, W. A. F. (1955). The filarial parasites of primates: A review.I. — *Dirofilaria* and *Dipetalonema.* II. — *Loa, Protofilaria* and*Parlitomosa,* with notes on incompletely identified adult and larval forms. *Parasitology* **49**, 123-141 and 235-249.

Wilner, B. I. (1964). "A Classification of the Major Groups of Human and Lower Animal Viruses," 2nd ed. Cutter Labs., Berkeley, California.

Yamaguti, S. (1958). "Systema Helminthum. Vol. I. The Digenetic Trematodes of Vertebrates," 2 parts. Wiley (Interscience), New York.

Yamaguti, S. (1959). "Systema Helminthum. Vol. II. The Cestodes of Vertebrates." Wiley Interscience, New York.

Yamaguti, S. (1961). "Systema Helminthum. Vol. III. The Nematodes of Vertebrates." 2 parts. Wiley (Interscience), New York.

Yamashita, J. (1963). Ecological relationships between parasites and primates. I. Helminth parasites and primates. *Primates* **4**, 1-96.

Yeh, L. S. (1957). On a filarial parasite, *Deraïophoronema freitaslenti* n.sp., from the giant anteater, *Myrmecophaga tridactyla* from British Guiana, and a proposed reclassification of *Dipetalonema* and related genera. *Parasitology* **47**, 196-205.

CHAPTER 3

Observations of Squirrel Monkeys in a Colombian Forest

Richard W. Thorington, Jr.

I. Introduction

Squirrel monkeys (*Saimiri*) have an extensive range in South America (see the general range map in Hill, 1960, p. 300) and are found in some regions of Panama and Costa Rica (Hall and Kelson, 1959, p. 226). Over this range they occur in a variety of habitats and are common in many different forests. The animals have evolved in these habitats in response to various selective pressures. The characteristics of *Saimiri* are thus adaptations to these habitats and are best understood functionally and causatively within the framework of the ecology of the animals. (This touches the general thesis of proximate and ultimate cause in biology which has been discussed lucidly and persuasively by Mayr, 1961.)

This rationale provides the basis for a useful framework of interrogation (a *Fragestellung*) for both laboratory and field investigations of *Saimiri*. This framework is (1) the determination of the species characteristics, especially the differences betweeen squirrel monkeys and other platyrrhine monkeys; (2) the functions of these characteristics; and (3) their significance to wild squirrel monkeys: i.e., the manner in which they are adaptations to the South American habitats of squirrel monkeys. Within this framework, laboratory and field studies of *Saimiri* can be integrated to form a body of knowledge about *Saimiri* and their evolution. This information is not only of intrinsic interest but can also make *Saimiri* more useful in research.

Habitats that appear similar in different parts of the Amazon and Orinoco drainages are very different botanically (e.g., see Aubréville, 1961) and zoologically, and it is misleading to consider the environment of squirrel monkeys as uniform. In these habitats in different parts of South America, squirrel monkeys differ, but the degree of geographic variation has not yet been precisely delineated. The differences of opinion regarding the number of species in the genus (e.g., Fiedler, 1956; Cabrera, 1957; Hill, 1960; also see Chapter 1) reflect both different concepts of the species category and our lack of knowledge of geographic variation of the characteristics of *Saimiri*. Most of the details of geographic variation will be elucidated by laboratory research and museum work. To relate these facts to the geographic variation of habitat will require a thorough understanding of the biology of *Saimiri* and many field studies by investigators with different backgrounds and interests. Thus, the present study can serve only as an introduction to the ecology of *Saimiri*.

II. The Study Site

This study was carried out in the llanos of Colombia, east of San Martin (3° 40′ N latitude, 73° 20′ E longitude). The area has been briefly described by Mason (1966). In this area the llanos consists of grassland and gallery forests which occur along river banks and escarpments. The abrupt border between forests and the grassland is maintained by grazing and by fire. Many of the forests have been diminished in recent years by burning, undertaken to increase the utilizable range. However, the presence of cattle in the llanos reduces hunting pressures on the monkey populations, which makes the region much more favorable for behavioral studies than many areas in the Amazon valley where beef is expensive or unavailable.

The forest in which the study was carried out is "Monte Seco" on Hacienda Barbascal. The study site is 250 yards wide and approximately 700 yards long, with a north—south orientation. It is connected by an isthmus of palms and low trees to a more extensive tract of forest to the south. The troop of squirrel monkeys studied never crossed into this more extensive tract although another troop occasionally entered the study area through this isthmus. A road effectively forms the northern boundary of the forest, although a few trees exist on the north side of the road, and the squirrel monkeys sometimes crossed the road. On the east and west the forest is bounded by grassland. The nearest forests to the east and west are each about a half mile distant. The canopy of the forest ranges from 60 ft to 125 ft averaging 80—100 ft in height. The east side of the forest is more open and is penetrated by cattle trails. The west side of the forest is quite dense and has many trees festooned with vines. Two ravines cut southwest through the forest from the eastern edge to the western edge and join the main ravine which runs along the western edge of the forest. Vegetation in and along these ravines is dense.

Five species of monkeys inhabited the forest. The *Saimiri* were the most common. A troop of five tufted capuchins (*Cebus apella*), several pairs of titis (*Callicebus moloch*), several pairs of night monkeys (*Aotus trivirgatus*), and five howler monkeys (*Alouatta seniculus*) were also regular inhabitants of this forest.

III. Methods

This study represents approximately 500 hours of observations made during a 10-week period in January, February, and March of 1965. Observations were concentrated in the morning hours when the animals were most conspicuous, and in the middle and late afternoon. The monkeys were observed through 7 × 50 mm binoculars and the data recorded in a notebook. Attempts to quantify the observations with a stop watch were of limited success. These quantifications were biased by the ease or difficulty of observing *Saimiri* under different conditions.

Trails were cut or existing trails enlarged down the east and west sides of the forest and cross trails were made at every 100 yards. These enabled me to move quickly and quietly through the forest disturbing the monkeys minimally. Early in the study it was not possible to remain within 100 yards of the *Saimiri* in open parts of the forest or within 50 yards of them in denser areas. I would position myself in front of the troop and allow them to move past me, then either follow them at a distance or move to a position in front of them again. They gradually adapted to my presence in the forest, and after a week it was possible to make close observations of undisturbed animals. However, some of the animals particularly the females, did not adapt to my presence readily. It was easy to recognize by their actions and vocalizations when the *Saimiri* were disturbed by my presence. At times immature or adult males approached within 10 ft to study me but usually they kept to a distance of at least 20 or 30 ft.

Recognition of individual animals was a problem at first. It became possible to recognize the adult animals in the troop but never to recognize all of the juveniles as individuals.

Temperature and relative humidity were determined with a sling psychrometer. Measurements were taken at irregular intervals, four to six times daily, in the vicinity of the *Saimiri* at an elevation of 6 ft. In the early morning when the air was still, the temperature and humidity in the canopy may have differed somewhat from that recorded. During the rest of the day there was considerable movement of air within the forest and only slight gradients of temperature and humidity seemed likely.

IV. Observations

A. TROOP SIZE AND SUBDIVISION

The troop of *Saimiri* observed consisted of 18 animals at the beginning of the study and was increased by four births during the 10-week period. These included 3 adult males, 5 adult females, and 10 juvenile animals estimated to be one to 3 years old. The animals did not stay together. They would generally sleep in the same group of trees at night but would separate into smaller groups during the day. They might rejoin in the middle of the day but would again separate as they recommenced foraging. On 88 occasions accurate counts were obtained of the size of these groups. On 41 of these occasions, group size was between five and eight animals. The mode was seven animals in a group. Fourteen or more animals were counted in a group on only seven occasions but this in part resulted from the difficulty of obtaining an accurate count of this many *Saimiri*.

This is a much smaller troop than is commonly described for *Saimiri*, however, it is not possible at present to give an accurate average of troop size of wild *Saimiri*. My hesitance to accept "estimates" uncritically is due to the fact that the troop of 18 animals studied was variously estimated as a troop of 50 to 100 animals. Also, estimates are usually formed on the basis of brief contact with the animals and thus provide no clue to the permanence or impermanence of the grouping.

The troop divided into groups that were sometimes unisexual; e.g., the pregnant females, the females with young, or the adult males. Juvenile animals would frequently associate with the adult females. Since juveniles could not be distinguished from one another, it was not possible to determine whether these associations were constant and perhaps represented familial bonds. No particular order of travel was evident other than the fact that the adult females frequently initiated movement of the troop away from me. This seemed to reflect only their timidity, for they were not in the front of groups disproportionately frequently when they were intercepted.

B. GENERAL ACTIVITY AND BEHAVIORAL THERMOREGULATION

The temperature and humidity of the forest during the 10 weeks the troop was studied in recorded in the accompanying graphs (Figs. 1 and 2). During the dry season, the temperature ranged from 70° to 90°F. The relative humidity was 90−95% in the morning and fell as the temperature rose during the day. The absolute humidity remained relatively constant. On rainy days at the beginning of the wet season the temperature did not range as high; the relative humidity was 100% in the early morning and would quickly become 100% shortly after the onset of rain.

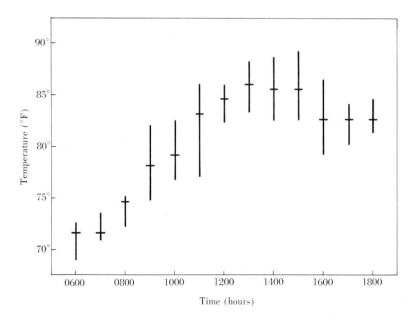

FIG. 1. Temperature fluctuations throughout the day in Monte Seco. Medians of 1-hour periods; two-thirds of all measurements fall within the range indicated.

Like most diurnal mammals squirrel monkeys were most active in the early to midmorning and middle to late afternoon. In the middle of the day they were less active and generally rested for 1−2 hours. In the early morning they would range to the tops of the trees and sometimes were active at the very top of the canopy. Later in the day they moved below the canopy and sometimes came within a few feet of the ground. They commonly spent the middle of the day in the dense thickets of the western side of the forest. In this way the squirrel monkeys avoided intensive solar radiation and concentrated their activity during times of day when the temperature ranged between 70° and 80°F. As the temperature rose to 85° or 90° the squirrel monkeys became inactive and somnolent.

The resting postures of squirrel monkeys vary during the course of the day in response to the temperature. In the early and midmorning, resting squirrel monkeys sit in a typical huddled position with their tails over their shoulders. Toward the middle of the day they more frequently stretch out on branches letting their legs dangle. During the rest period in the heat of the day all the squirrel monkeys rest in the stretched-out position. These postures have obvious thermoregulatory functions. The sprawled position increases the effective surface area from which heat can be lost by the

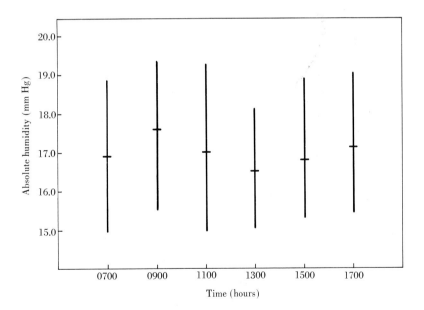

FIG. 2. Fluctuations in absolute humidity throughout the day in Monte Seco. Averages of 2-hour periods; two-thirds of all measurements fall within the range indicated.

animal to its environment. In a huddled position an animal presents less surface area and therefore will lose heat more slowly.

On only one occasion was an animal observed sunning itself. This was a pregnant female which stretched out on a branch for 4½ minutes in a patch of sun one morning when the temperature was 75°F.

At the approach of a storm the squirrel monkeys retreated into thickets and assumed the huddled position. Only in very dense downpours did they stay in these thickets, however. More often they moved about quite freely foraging both in the rain and after, although they appeared to avoid the denser vegetation when the forest was dripping wet.

C. BEHAVIOR OF PREGNANT AND POSTPARTURIENT FEMALES

Four females of the troop delivered during the course of my study. The newborns were first observed on February 6, February 19, February 27, and March 8. These dates are close to the dates of parturition. One female of the troop was still pregnant, but near term, at the end of the study on March 28. These delivery dates correspond to the normal end of the dry season and the beginning of the wet season in this part of Colombia. The most notable characteristic of the behavior of the pregnant and nursing females was that they were less active than the other animals. They frequently traveled together and more frequently associated with the *Cebus* troop. They were more shy and hence more difficult to observe than were the other *Saimiri*.

The lesser activity of these females was evident in the longer periods of inactivity and the slower manner in which they foraged. They might sit in one place for 4−8 minutes at times of day when the other *Saimiri* would seldom sit still for more than 10 or 15 seconds. The one occasion on which I observed behavior that might be interpreted as sunning involved a pregnant animal. When the postparturient animals rested, the infants would nurse. While foraging, the pregnant and postparturient females would spend more time in a single tree than the other animals, which meant that they did less actual traveling. This may explain their increased association with the *Cebus* troop which also traveled more slowly through the forest.

The pregnant females and females with young appeared to be attractive to the younger *Saimiri* which sometimes would approach and smell the female or the newborn. The pregnant or nursing females would frequently travel together with several of the juvenile members of the troop. They did not disassociate themselves from the males of the troop as did the animals observed by DuMond and Baldwin at Monkey Jungle (see Chapter 4). Nor were any animals other than the mothers observed carrying the infants.

Some of the females were hypersensitive to disturbances to which the other *Saimiri* had adjusted. When disturbed they would initiate movement of the troop by their movements and their vocalizations. Their dominant role in the determination of troop movement and direction seemed to be limited to times when they were disturbed.

The infants spent most of their first few weeks clinging to the backs of their mothers, shifting position only to reach the teats for nursing. They appeared to use the basal two-thirds of their tails in clinging to their mothers, for it was wrapped tightly around the female while the distal one-third dangled. By the age of 4 weeks the infants were much more explorative, but were never observed to leave their mother's body (see Chapter 8).

D. Feeding Behavior

Saimiri eat many buds, fruits, nuts, and a wide variety of insect matter. The stomach contents of three wild-shot animals were examined, all of which included insects. Fooden (1964) reported insects among the contents of stomachs of 2 of 12 *Saimiri* collected in Surinam. One of his animals had eaten only insects just prior to being collected.

At dawn, shortly after the animals wakened, they moved to a nearby fruiting tree to feed. After feeding there intensively for a few minutes, they would move on to another fruiting tree and feed there for a few minutes. As the morning progressed they would feed less intensively on the fruit-bearing trees and would spend more time moving from one tree to another, at which time they would be foraging for insects. The *Saimiri* would seldom spend more than a few minutes feeding in any fruiting tree. The average length of time spent by an individual in a given tree was 3 minutes, although a good fruiting tree might be full of *Saimiri* for a much longer period of time. Only in a tree with small fruits which were diffusely distributed did animals feed for as long as 7½ minutes. Frequently the *Saimiri* would eat fruit right where it was, but not uncommonly they carried it in one of their hands to another place to eat it. This latter behavior was noticeable particularly when a more dominant animal moved nearby. There appeared to be more dominance interactions in fruiting trees than elsewhere. Animals were more visible to each other in most of the fruiting trees than they were when foraging in the foliage, and there were more opportunities to steal food. These interactions between feeding animals contrast with the situation at Monkey Jungle, where the animals are provisioned.

During most of their waking hours *Saimiri* seem to be incessantly active, much more so than other monkeys in the forest (e.g., *Callicebus* or *Cebus*). They are always moving about investigating their environment, seldom remaining long in one place. This foraging behavior is particularly characteristic of their movements between fruiting trees. Typical behavior includes pouncing upon and unrolling dead leaves, the close investigation of palm fronds, and the manner in which the animals peer here and there as they momentarily sit on a branch. It is difficult to determine how much food the *Saimiri* obtain while foraging, for they forage most in the dense foliage, but at times they find one or two items to masticate every minute. *Saimiri* were observed to eat large insects, such as 2-inch caterpillars, and were heard catching cicadas on occasion, but most of their fare seemed to be smaller. Usually they ate what they found quickly. Thus there was little opportunity for a more dominant animal to steal food from another. Also, visibility in the foliage where they forage is less, and correspondingly social contact during foraging activities appeared to be slight, in contrast to that between animals in the fruiting trees. In foraging each animal followed a different route, although the members of a foraging group remained near each other. This is probably the basis of the fragmentation of the troop into smaller groups.

This technique of foraging does not require the concentration of the animals over extended periods of time. Their attention span seemed to be far less than that of the *Cebus* that were feeding in the same habitat (Thorington, 1967). The attributes that would seem most important to a squirrel monkey are the ability to notice slight movement, the ability to discriminate cryptically colored and shaped insects, and the agility to reach them quickly and catch them.

In the course of feeding and foraging *Saimiri* occasionally used their tails in a quasi-prehensile manner. When hanging by their feet to reach for some item of food, they looped their tails over a branch for additional support. When normally moving through the forest or fleeing quickly they used their tails for balance but did not use them as a fifth limb for support. This suggests the hypothesis that the prehensile tail of platyrrhines evolved as an adaptation for feeding.

E. VOCALIZATIONS

It was not possible to discriminate as precisely between the various vocalizations of *Saimiri* as did Winter *et al.* (1966) in the laboratory (see also Chapter 9). Since they provide spectrograms of the diverse calls, I shall attempt to correlate my observations with their descriptions.

The *Saimiri* were quite vocal in the early morning and the late afternoon and rather quiet toward the middle of the day. They were more vocal when they were close together and in sight of each other, as in fruiting trees, and quieter when they were foraging in dense foliage.

"Seee" calls, described by Winter *et al.* as "peep" calls, were given fairly commonly under several different circumstances. The "isolation peep" a long seee call with a falling inflection, was given by *Saimiri* on those few occasions when isolated animals or single *Saimiri* with some *Cebus* were observed. These were very similar to calls given by tamarins, *Saguinus midas*, under similar circumstances (Thorington, unpublished). In this context they are clearly contact calls of an animal seeking others. Similar calls, perhaps the "long peeps" of Winter, were sometimes given by members of a moving group of *Saimiri* as they foraged, or by an animal in a resting group shortly before the group began to move. In the first case it appeared that the calls were given when the animals were separated from one another, as when one group was foraging on the north side of the road and another group on the south side, or when two groups were separating or coalescing. Usually a foraging group of *Saimiri* was quiet. In the second case, the long peep call was used to initiate the movement of the group. Peep calls were among the first heard in the morning as the animals prepared to leave their lodging area and move to a fruiting tree. At times of intense agonistic interaction between the *Saimiri* the animals would give peep calls and the group would move off, which would break up the fighting and dominance interactions. At other times when the alarm calls of one animal did not elicit the response of the other animals (e.g., when they were directed at me and the other animals were quite accustomed to my presence), the alarmed animal would give long peeps and the whole group would leave the area. These long peep calls, like the isolation calls, were infectious and were answered by other animals of the group as they all started to move.

Other elements of the peep series were not evident in the field. Vocalization given by animals in play such as the "play peeps" described by Winter *et al.* was not detected. Only a chitter call was noticed in response to hawks and toucans, not the alarm peep that Winter described.

There were two alarm calls used by the *Saimiri*. One was given in response to a terrestrial predator, the other to avian predators. It was not clear whether the terrestrial-volant dichotomy or the necessary immediacy of response was the important characteristic of the evoking stimulus. The call given for a terrestrial predator, evoked both by me and by a tayra, can be onomatopoetically termed a "chunk" call. This seems to correspond to Winter's "yap" call. It alerted the other members of the troop nearby, who might call or not depending on their own response to this stimulus. The call given in response to hawks and toucans was a "chitter" that could not be distinguished from the very common chittering call given in captivity under rather different circumstances. This seems to correspond to the "twitter" or "trill" calls of Winter. The call is very infectious and is taken up by all the other members of the group as soon as one of them starts it. All animals are immediately on the alert and ready to dash out of the way of the bird. A similar call was given by subordinate animals of the group after the dominant animal chased one of the others. Thus, the call seemed to be given under general conditions of alarm and excitement, which differ from the contexts in which Winter *et al.* recorded it in the laboratory.

Saimiri give a variety of vocalizations in agonistic situations as described by Winter *et al.* These were very evident in the field but it was difficult to define the specific context in which the calls were given. It was frequently difficult to determine which animal gave the call. Precise studies of social interactions of squirrel monkeys may be difficult to effect in the wild, particularly with unmarked animals.

F. OTHER INTRASPECIFIC BEHAVIOR

1. Penile Display

Genital displays were observed approximately six times during the study. The dominant male gave a penile display apparently directed at me once. On another occasion he displayed to the next most dominant male from a distance of 9 inches. This second male displayed, apparently at me, 1 minute later. In two other cases, one male displayed to another under less well-defined circumstances. A juvenile male approached a female and her infant, abducted his left leg, and probably displayed to the infant. The female then moved away from him. On several other occasions, animals were observed to abduct their thighs or to have erections but these were not clearly displays and were not interpreted as being displays. My impression is that the penile display was not commonly given in this troop of *Saimiri* at that time of year.

2. Play

Young *Saimiri* were observed to play on several occasions. Playing seemed to be more common during the middle of the day when the adults were resting and the troop remained in one place. Play behavior took several forms among these juvenile animals but it principally involved hanging by the hind legs and wrestling, or mock biting and chasing. No vocalizations were observed to be given by the juveniles as they played, as described by Winter *et al.* (1966). All the play observed took place in trees. Since the troop was surprised very near the ground on only one occasion, it is doubtful that any play took place on the ground, as reported by DuMond (see Chapter 4) among the *Saimiri* at the Monkey Jungle.

G. SELF-CARE

1. Grooming with Urine

Both male and female *Saimiri* urinate on their hands and then rub their hands on the soles of their feet (see von Castell and Maurus, 1967). This behavior was noted seven times, mostly among males. Never did it take the elaborate grooming pattern of *Cebus apella* (see Nolte, 1958) nor did it occur under similar circumstances (Thorington, 1967). In several cases it terminated self-grooming. The animals scratched several times, then urinated on their palms and rubbed them on their feet. There was no indication that this behavior has olfactory or other social significance. Its role in the self-care of the animals is not very clear either.

2. Scratching

No mutual grooming was observed among the *Saimiri* watched. On several occasions animals sat close to one another and groomed but each groomed himself only. The self-grooming generally took the form of scratching and took place at all times of day, though perhaps it was more common in the late morning when foraging activity became more casual than earlier in the day. The amount of scratching increased notably when the animals were wet. I did not observe the *Saimiri* to shake, as did the *Cebus* when they were wet. Rather they expressed water from their fur by scratching and by rubbing against branches. In particular, when they were wet they rubbed their backs against branches and scratched their sides with their hands or feet. Under some conditions they shook water off their heads; under other conditions they scratched their heads when they were wet.

H. INTERSPECIFIC ASSOCIATIONS

1. Reactions to Other Monkeys

The *Saimiri* and *Cebus* associated with one another occasionally. Usually there was little interaction between the two species and the association appeared to be casual. Some facts hint that it is more than a chance association, however. Animals of one species temporarily isolated from conspecifics seemed to seek out and remain with a troop of the other species. *Cebus* and *Saimiri* congregated in a fruiting tree tended to move out of it in the same direction. The *Cebus* usually moved more slowly through the forest as they foraged than did the *Saimiri*, with the exception of the pregnant female *Saimiri* or females with young. These associated with the troop of *Cebus* more frequently than did the other groups of *Saimiri*. Several times young *Cebus* threatened some of the *Saimiri*, and on three clearcut occasions the *Saimiri* went out of their way to avoid conflict with a young *Cebus*. On several other occasions vocal interchanges between the two species were heard, suggesting more pronounced agonistic exchange. These situations could not be defined but I suspect that they probably involved competition for fruit or nuts. Young *Saimiri* sometimes studied the foraging behavior of *Cebus* at close range without the latter exhibiting concern. The *Saimiri* did not associate with the *Alouatta* or *Callicebus* in the forest. However, a lone male *Saimiri* in a nearby forest actively associated with the *Callicebus* in that forest (cf. Mason, 1966).

2. Reactions to Birds

At the sight of flying hawks and toucans, the *Saimiri* gave an alarm call that evoked the immediate response and attention of all the animals of the troop. Occasionally small hawks would follow above the canopy and catch insects which the *Saimiri* stirred up in their foraging activities. The *Saimiri* did not adjust to this behavior but gave their alarm chatter whenever the hawks swooped at them. A flying toucan was also an object of immediate concern to the *Saimiri*. A sitting hawk or toucan seemed to be ignored, but on one occasion it was observed that the dominant male *Saimiri* clearly foraged less while a toucan was present than both before and after. On another occasion it approached a toucan that had just perched near the troop. The toucan flew away. It is quite possible that these large toucans are predators of young *Saimiri*, and it is not unlikely that they could do considerable damage to an adult *Saimiri* if they took it by surprise.

V. Discussion

A. FEEDING

Saimiri are generalized feeders and eat a wide variety of forest products. It remains for future field work — both observations of feeding animals and studies of stomach contents — to demonstrate whether they specialize on certain foods in some parts of their range or at some times of the year. Analyses of stomach contents alone can be misleading because of diurnal changes in feeding habits. In this study, stomach contents of animals collected very early in the morning would have comprised mostly fruit and few insects. Animals collected later in the day would have had proportionately more insects in their stomachs.

The nutritional significance of the feeding and foraging behavior of *Saimiri* can be stated only imprecisely. From the fruit the animals derive carbohydrates and moisture. The vitamin and protein content of these fruits is unknown. The insects probably provide most of the protein in the diet. To tie the field observations more precisely to nutritional studies in the laboratory will require calorimetric and other nutritional studies of the foods and of the stomach contents of animals collected in the wild. In the absence of sunlight *Saimiri* probably utilize vitamin D_2 inefficiently and may require vitamin D_3, as is the case for other platyrrhines (Hunt *et al.*, 1966, 1967). The high gastric acidity of fasted *Saimiri* (Brodie and Marshall, 1963a,b) and the brevity of their gastrointestinal tracts (Hill, 1960; Fooden, 1964) suggest that their digestive physiology may be especially interesting.

There are several ecological implications to the generalized feeding habits of *Saimiri*. As described elsewhere (Thorington, 1967) *Saimiri* did not seem to compete with *Cebus apella* for food. Although both species ate many of the same fruits, these were plentiful. Probably more critical was the proteinaceous portion of the diet of each — derived principally from insects. The foraging procedures of the two species were different and thus the kinds of insects caught and eaten were different. For this part of their diets they did not seem to compete at all. *Saimiri* and *Callicebus* may compete somewhat since they forage for insects in similar ways. Supporting this hypothesis is the fact that *Callicebus* were not as common in Monte Seco as they were in neighboring forests that did not contain *Saimiri*. However, competition for food and other forms of ecological competition between platyrrhine monkeys need more study before such hypotheses can be critically evaluated.

B. SIGNIFICANCE OF FORAGING BEHAVIOR

The foraging behavior of squirrel monkeys seems to be a significant determinant of their social behavior and of their troop structure. While foraging, the animals are more isolated from one another visually, and agonistic behavior is correspondingly restricted. Thus the intercalation of periods of feeding in fruiting trees and foraging in foliage causes social interaction to be intermittent. Since efficient foraging for insects requires each animal to take a different path through the forest, it is probably the basis of the fragmentation of the troop into subgroups during the day.

These two characteristics of social interaction, its intermittence and the subdivision of the troop in the wild, are difficult to duplicate in captivity. It is unclear how studies will be biased when *Saimiri* are maintained continuously in close contact with each other. This would appear to be a less stressful situation to the *Saimiri* than is the isolating of individuals, but it definitely produces quite a different social situation from that which exists in the wild. The tendency of pregnant females and females with young to disassociate from the adult males of the troop probably reflects their slower rate of travel through the forest, not an active avoidance.

The foraging behavior gives functional significance to the data on visual acuity and discrimination for *Saimiri* (Woodburne, 1965a,b). The ability to discriminate between different shapes and to learn the discriminations quickly is of obvious value to an animal that forages for insects in the manner of *Saimiri*. Squirrel monkeys seem to be adapted to the job of selecting and noting the significant features of a very complex environment. They do not manipulate objects in their environment frequently, and they discriminate at a distance. These observations correlate with the experimental results of Peterson and Rumbaugh (1963) who found that *Saimiri* discriminate no better when they are allowed to handle the test objects than when they cannot. Before their results are extrapolated to other primates (Meyer *et al.*, 1965) the utilization of haptic clues probably should be tested in species which customarily manipulate more than *Saimiri*.

C. RESPIRATORY WATER LOSS

In the forest Monte Seco, the relative humidity varied during the day as the temperature varied but the absolute humidity fluctuated little. The total range of measurements taken during the 10 weeks was 11.4−21.4 mm Hg. The average value was 17 mm Hg, which is equivalent to relative humidities of 90% at 70°F and 65% at 80°F. The average respiratory water loss of *Saimiri* in the forest can be estimated on the basis of the following assumptions:

(1) The basal metabolic rate of *Saimiri* is normal for mammals of their size (cf. Kleiber, 1961, pp. 179 and 382; Malinow and Wagner, 1966). (2) The average metabolic rate of *Saimiri* is 25% above basal. (3) *Saimiri* utilize an average of 25% of the oxygen in inspired air (cf. Nimms, 1955, p. 826). (4) *Saimiri* expire saturated air at approximately 93°F.

Under these conditions a *Saimiri* weighing 750 gm will respire approximately 13 liters of air per hour and (at an environmental humidity of 17 mm Hg) will lose approximately 300 mg of water per hour from his respiratory tract. (Physical data for these calculations were taken from Lange, 1952, pp. 1446, 1505, and 1506.)

It has been intimated that a high humidity is necessary for the healthy maintenance of squirrel monkeys in captivity (Hill, 1960, p. 300; Bantin, 1966). Bantin reported troublesome respiratory infections at $75 \pm 3°$ F and 30−35% relative humidity. The respiratory water loss under these conditions is 50% above the average loss in the wild (based only on assumption 4). Such relationships between humidity and respiratory infections are not well understood. The exchanges of heat and water between the inspired air and the upper respiratory tract are described by Walker and Wells (1961) but the effect of these changes on the respiratory mucosa and the mechanism of any increased susceptibility to infection are not known (Proctor, 1964). Proctor suggests a mechanism whereby a sudden change to breathing drier air could increase susceptibility. This is perhaps relevant to the experiences described by Bantin and Hill. In our laboratories *Saimiri* have adapted to very low humidities (absolute humidity less than 4 mm Hg) when acclimated gradually.

VI. Conclusions

On the basis of a 10-week study of squirrel monkeys in a Colombian forest, the following tentative conclusions are drawn:
(1) *Saimiri* associate in troops which subdivide and rejoin daily. (2) Sub-
divisions of the troops may be unisexual or bisexual. (3) The animals feed
on many fruits, nuts, buds, and berries. They commonly forage for insects.
Their feeding and foraging behavior significantly influences troop structure and movement and the social interaction between the animals. (4) In
their diurnal pattern of activity and in some of their postures, *Saimiri* exhibit behavioral thermoregulation. They seemed less influenced by
climatic vicissitudes such as rain and cold than were *Callicebus* and
Alouatta.

ACKNOWLEDGMENTS

This study was supported by N.I.H. Grant FR 00168-03 to Harvard University. I am grateful
to Dr. J. C. S. Paterson, Director of the ICMRT program in Cali, Colombia and to Dr. William
A. Mason, who made this study possible. The hospitality of the Botero family, owners of
Hacienda Barbascal, is gratefully acknowledged.

REFERENCES

Aubréville, A. (1961). "Étude écologique des principales formations végétales du Brésil et
    contribution à la connaissance des forêts de l'Amazonie Brésilienne." Centre Technique
    Forestier Tropical, Nogent-sur-Marne (Seine), France.
Bantin, G. C. (1966). Establishment of a squirrel monkey colony. *J. Inst. Animal Technicians*
    17, 66-73.
Brodie, D. A., and Marshall, R. W. (1963a). Gastric content of fasted primates: A survey. *Sci-
    ence* **141,** 174-175.
Brodie, D. A., and Marshall, R. W. (1963b). Fasting gastric content of the squirrel monkey
    (*Saimiri sciurea*). *Am. J. Physiol.* **204,** 681-685.
Cabrera, A. (1957). Catalogo de los mamiferos de America del Sur. *Ciencias Zool.* **4,** 1-307.
Fiedler, W. (1956). Übersicht über das System der Primates. *Handbook Primatol.* **1,** 1-266.
Fooden, J. (1964). Stomach contents and gastro-intestinal proportions in wild-shot Guianan
    monkeys. *Am. J. Phys. Anthropol.* [n.s.] **22,** 227-231.
Hall, E. R., and Kelson, K. R. (1959). "The Mammals of North America." Ronald Press, New
    York.
Hill, W. C. O. (1960). "Primates," Vol. IV, Part A. Edinburgh Univ. Press, Edinburgh.
Hunt, R. D., Garcia, F. G., and Hegsted, D. M. (1966). Vitamin D requirements of New World
    primates. *Federation Proc.* **25,** 545.
Hunt, R. D., Garcia, F. G., and Hegsted, D. M. (1967). A comparison of vitamin D_2 and D_3 in
    New World primates. I. Production and regression of osteodystrophia fibrosa. *Lab. Animal
    Care* **17,** No 2, 222-234.
Kleiber, M. (1961). "The Fire of Life." Wiley, New York.
Lange, N. A., ed. (1952). "Handbook of Chemistry." Handbook Publ., Sandusky, Ohio.

Malinow, M. R., and Wagner, R. (1966). Oxygen uptake in squirrel monkeys (*Saimiri sciurea*). *Lab. Animal Care* **16,** 105-108.

Mason, W. A. (1966). Social organization of the South American monkey, *Callicebus moloch:* A preliminary report. *Tulane Studies Zool.* **13,** 23-28.

Mayr, E. (1961). Cause and effect in biology. *Science* **134,** 1501-1506.

Meyer, D. R., Treichler, R. F., and Meyer, P. M. (1965). Discrete-trial training techniques and stimulus variables. *In* "Behavior of Nonhuman Primates" (A. M. Schrier, H. F. Harlow, and F. Stollnitz, eds.), pp. 1-49. Academic Press, New York.

Nimms, L. F. (1955). Gas exchange and transportation. *In* "A Textbook of Physiology" (J. F. Fulton, ed.), pp. 825-842. Saunders, Philadelphia, Pennsylvania.

Nolte, A. (1958). Beobachtungen über das Instinktverhalten von Kapuzineraffen (*Cebus apella L.*) in der Gefangenschaft. *Behaviour* **12,** 183-207.

Peterson, M. E., and Rumbaugh, D. M. (1963). Role of object-contact cues in learning set formation in squirrel monkeys. *Perceptual Motor Skills* **16,** 3-9.

Proctor, D. F. (1964). Physiology of the upper airway. *In* "Handbook of Physiology" (Am. Physiol. Soc., J. Field, ed.), Sect. 3, Vol. I, pp. 309-345. Williams & Wilkins, Co Baltimore, Maryland.

Thorington, R. W., Jr. (1967). Feeding and activity of *Cebus* and *Saimiri* in a Colombian forest. *In* "Progress in Primatology" (D. Starck, R. Schneider, and H. J. Kuhn, eds.), pp. 180−184. Fischer, Stuttgart.

von Castell, R., and Maurus, M. (1967). Das sogenannte urinmarkieren von totenkopfaffen (*Saimiri sciureus*) in abhangigkeit von umweltbedingten und emotionalen faktoren. *Folia Primatol.* **6,** 170-176.

Walker, J. E. C., and Wells, R. E., Jr. (1961). Heat and water exchange in the respiratory tract. *Am. J. Med.* **30,** 259-267.

Winter, P., Ploog, D., and Latta, J. (1966). Vocal repertoire of the squirrel monkey (*Saimiri sciureus*), its analysis and significance. *Exptl. Brain Res.* **1,** 359-384.

Woodburne, L. S. (1965a). Geometrical shape discrimination by *Saimiri sciureus*. *Psychon. Sci.* **3,** 307-308.

Woodburne, L. S. (1965b). Visual acuity of *Saimiri sciureus*. *Psychon. Sci.* **3,** 309.

CHAPTER 4

The Squirrel Monkey in a Seminatural Environment

Frank V. DuMond

1. Introduction

A. THE IMPORTANCE OF FIELD STUDIES

Interest in systematic field studies of nonhuman primates has been late in developing. Carpenter (1934) pioneered this field with his now classic study on the behavior and social relations of the howler monkey (*Alouatta palliata*) on Barro Colorado Island. Yet basic questions regarding the normal social environment likely to be critical to the emotional development of these highly social animals, and those regarding the physical environment which provided the forces that shaped the evolution of each primate species, can only be answered through such field research.

Until recently, the only New World primate that had been covered in depth was the howler monkey which was studied by Carpenter more than 30 years ago, and more recently by Altmann (1959). The great increase in interest in the squirrel monkey as a laboratory primate and the subsequent history of reproductive failure in captivity clearly point to the need for the establishment of basic information from the field. Field studies would provide a foundation to guide future attempts to induce these primates to reproduce in the laboratory at close to their potential fecundity and to serve as a reference area for any behavioral studies that might be carried out in that setting.

B. BREEDING SUCCESS IN A SEMINATURAL ENVIRONMENT

A colony of squirrel monkeys has been living in a seminatural environment at the Monkey Jungle near Miami, Florida since 1960 and has achieved what I feel approaches a normal annual birth rate of 70−80%. This facility offers a unique opportunity to observe the behavior of this primate in an environment that very closely approximates the field environment and yet offers certain advantages for control and experimentation.

The contents of this chapter are the results of 11 months of intensive observations of this colony in addition to intermittent observations over the past 6 years.

II. The Environment

A. THE MONKEY JUNGLE

The Monkey Jungle is a commercial zoological park devoted to primates. Its primary objective is the naturalistic display of primates in semifree-ranging environments and the establishment of these primates in social units comparable to those encountered in the field.

The facility consists of a 15-acre "hammock" or subtropical jungle. The total area has been divided into two separate sections: one accommodates a colony of about 100 java macaques (*Macaca irus*) and the other (called the "Rainforest") is a simulation of a tropical American "wet forest." The latter serves as the environment for the squirrel monkeys and four other species of western Amazon basin primates.

B. PHYSICAL CHARACTERISTICS OF THE ENVIRONMENT

The Monkey Jungle is situated in the extreme lower east coastal region of southern Florida at approximately 25.4° N latitude and 80.2° W longitude, or about 20 miles south of Miami.

The climate may be characterized as subtropical. There is an average annual rainfall of between 58 and 60 inches, the major precipitation occurring in the summer from June through September. The annual rainfall is greatly affected by equatorial air masses moving up from the warm Caribbean waters in the form of easterly waves or full-blown hurricanes that may add 20 or more inches of rainfall to any given year in which several of them occur. The relative humidity rarely drops below 30% and rises to above 90% during all but a very few nights of the year. The annual mean relative humidity is 72% and the mean maximum daily relative humidity is 92% for the year.

The mean annual temperature is 75° F. The lowest temperatures usually occur several times each winter for very brief periods and may drop to below freezing for an hour or less just before sunrise. It is during these transitory cold spells that the relative humidity drops below 30% for a very brief period.

While these periods of cold weather have clearly demonstrated a negative effect on the health of the more delicate primates in captivity, they have so far presented no obvious sustained problems for the squirrel monkey colony; such a cold spell, however, may have been associated with an episode of an acute fulminating pneumonia in the colony that caused the death of at least four adult males (all wild born) during the winter of 1965.

C. NATURAL ECOLOGICAL CHARACTERISTICS OF THE SQUIRREL MONKEY AREA

The Rainforest environment consists of a 4-acre hammock or subtropical hardwood growth of jungle (Fig. 1). These hammocks or jungle islands dot the extreme southern tip of the Florida peninsula and extend into the Keys.

FIG. 1. Aerial view of the environment. Hammock or jungle can be seen in center surrounded by fruit groves. Fenced trapezoidal area marked A in upper center of the hammock is the Rainforest. The rectangular area in the middle of the hammock and below the Rainforest is the area occupied by the Java monkey *(Macaca irus)* colony. Marker indicates 300 ft.

On the mainland, they are generally surrounded by open pine land or savanna-type lowland. The jungle ecology is comparable to that of the Caribbean and tropical American deciduous forest. These hammocks are, in most instances, the northern limit of the range of growth for the broad-leaf trees found in them whose southern range extends into Central and South America.

The indigenous broad-leaf growth provides a considerable part of the diet of the primates that live in this environment and includes *Ficus, Coccoluba, Lysiloma, Erythrina, Chrysophylla, Simarouba, Bursera, Pisonia, Psychotria* (wild coffee), *Sideroxylon, Chiococca, Hamelia, Psidium,* and *Quercus* to name a few of the major genera, all of which are represented in tropical American deciduous and wet forests.

The indigenous animal population of the Rainforest consists primarily of Florida Everglades wildlife: raccoons, opossums, skunks, rodents including squirrels, several species of snakes (the yellow rat snake, *Elaphe quadrivittata*, predominates) hawks, owls, several species of small birds, tree frogs, lizards, snails, and a great variety of insects.

None of the native animals has been intentionally eliminated from the environment. In general, there is a minimal interaction between the native animals and the monkeys. Occasionally, a snake is sighted and causes a great gathering, mainly of curious juvenile squirrel monkeys who run to the scene at the sound of the alarm chirp given by the first juvenile who sees it, and all watch intently from a short distance. Hawks are apparently a threat but there is very little opportunity for any other small animal predator to catch a squirrel monkey as they are constantly alert to their surroundings and are quick to respond to an alarm or distress call or flight reactions of the others.

D. Modifications to the Natural Environment

The natural hammock with its indigenous flora forms an excellent foundation for the development of a tropical American wet forest. To this end the environment has been substantially modified by the addition of more than 100 species of South American forest palms, 20 species of philodendron, 15 species of surface aroids, and heavy plantings of an unidentified South American *Ficus* introduced as an additional food source. More than 50 other species of tropical American forest trees have been introduced in the hammock. All were carefully selected from extensive studies of new world rainforest and wet forest ecologies so that the appearance of the environment contrasts considerably with that of the unaltered native hammock.

To support these truly tropical introductions, the entire area of 4 acres has been supplied with an irrigation system which is turned on for 2 hours every other morning. This provides more than 180 inches of moisture (rainfall plus irrigation) annually.

Although the primary purpose of this major modification was for the creation of the visual effect of a "living museum" for the public, it has provided a more lush tropical environment for the nonhuman primate inhabitants. Many of the introduced plants have been incorporated into the diet of the monkeys, and the increased humidity and plant growth provided by the irrigation system have certainly helped to increase the insect population on which the squirrel monkey feeds.

In this simulated tropical environment, a reproducing group of seven red uakaris *(Cacajao rubicundus)*, a reproducing colony of eight white-lipped tamarins *(Saguinus fuscicollis)*, and a group of five red howlers *(Alouatta seniculus)*, all from the western Amazon Basin, have been successfully established.

The entire Rainforest is surrounded by a 7-ft fence which has the upper 30 inches covered with smooth metal to prevent climbing and escape. This has proved effective during the most critical stages of introduction when the monkeys are most apt to flee. Later, after they become well established, some learn to scale the fence and venture out for brief periods but do not leave the general area.* The jungle canopy reaches a height of 70 ft in areas not destroyed by recent hurricanes, where it is only about 40 ft high. There is a 4-ft-wide walking trail about a quarter of a mile in length which winds through the Rainforest. The trail is open and unprotected.

E. Colony Ecology

The Rainforest was sufficiently similar to the natural environment from which the squirrel monkeys had been collected so that minimal reorientation to the new environment was required. This undoubtedly facilitated the rapid establishment of an apparently normal social unit.

There are several subecologies in the Rainforest including the tall climax central area, the low scrub areas around the periphery, and the second growth areas where recent hurricanes have destroyed the upper canopy. The *Saimiri* use all of these areas during their daily activities and in their search for food, behavior that might be expected to occur in the field where the jungle comes tumbling down at river banks and elsewhere to form different ecologies.

The colony which now consists of approximately 110 animals utilizes almost all of the cubic area every day although it usually is not dispersed over more than a half acre at any one time. The time of year, time of day, and weather influence the colony as to how much time it spends in a given subecology. However, in most cases, the daily routes periodically pass through the "feeding stations" and loop out to other areas of the Rainforest. During extremely hot weather, the colony tends to remain closer to the jungle floor; after a rain and in the cool of the late afternoon or early morning they move up to higher levels, sometimes to the very top of the canopy. In the winter breeding season, however, they spend a great deal of time on the ground and during colder weather they follow the sun from the east side in the morning to the south side and then to the southwest side in the later afternoon with the periodic loops to the feeding stations.

The colony is provisioned at two separate locations. One is under a roofed shelter located at the east side, originally planned as a cold weather shelter but which was never needed. At 10:30 A.M. a feeding of a vitamin-enriched mixture of bread soaked in milk and eggs is put out along with Wayne monkey diet and a pan of whole milk. The squirrel monkeys customarily arrive at this station at least 30 minutes prior to feeding time and

---

* There has been a group of seven extra-colony males which I have termed "bachelor" males that live outside the fenced area most of the year but have never left the 15-acre jungle area.

consume everything but the Wayne monkey diet less than 5 minutes after it is put out. Those that are still hungry reluctantly take the monkey pellets.

The main feeding station is more centrally located and consists of two small platforms located in trees 20 ft apart. A mixture of bananas, apples, peanuts, grapes, fresh fruit in season, and oranges is given six times a day at hourly intervals to the ringing of a dinner bell which the monkeys have learned to associate with the feedings. The food levels are adjusted according to the foraged food levels which fluctuate seasonally so that nearly all the food is consumed within 15 minutes after each feeding. The great variety of food offered is probably not necessary for the monkeys' well being nor is the frequency of the feedings. These procedures were adopted to accommodate visitors and to discourage the monkeys from soliciting food from the public.

As mentioned above, a considerable portion of the monkeys' diet is foraged out of the jungle environment. The growing tips of a great variety of native and introduced plants and trees are eaten; *Ficus, Lysiloma,* and *Cecropia* seem to be popular. Mature leaves are rarely eaten. The squirrel monkey has a particular predilection for flowers of almost any plant: orchids, bromiliads, *Erythrina, Malvaviscus, Sanchesia,* to name a few. The fruit of several trees is eaten, e.g., wild coffee, *Ficus, Psidium, Lysiloma* and *Exothea* (ink wood). The *Saimiri* spend a considerable amount of time in the low scrub at the Rainforest periphery searching for insects under dead wood and low-lying leaves, catching small flying insects that may fly up in their paths, and unfolding wrapped leaves left by certain web-making insects.

The monkeys have recently become attracted to a small terrestial snail (*Zachrisia provisoria*) from Cuba which is most destructive to foliage. They lick the open ends from which the snails have withdrawn, carry them around, steal them from one another and perhaps eat them; as a result, the snail population has been considerably diminished.

Although I have seen other captive squirrel monkeys that would avidly eat finches, I have not observed any of the Rainforest troop eating birds or other small animals.

Squirrel monkeys do not ordinarily appear to drink from streams or bodies of water but learn to recognize certain trees with water holes in them formed by rotting areas where branches have broken off, and have been observed to make purposeful excursions to them when in the vicinity. They insert their hand or forearm, withdraw it, and lick the water off their fur or out of the hand. They also lick rain and dew directly from the leaves.

F. POSSIBLE EFFECTS OF ARTIFICIAL FACTORS ON BEHAVIOR AND SOCIAL STRUCTURE

Although the normal home range of wild *Saimiri* troops is not known, it is probable that free-living animals in their search for food tend to range over a wider area than is provided at the Monkey Jungle. DeVore and Hall (1965) noted that in an abundance of food primate colonies tended to have smaller ranges. Baboons, for example, which usually ranged several miles, reduced their range to the immediate area of certain fruiting trees when these provided ample food. It is my opinion that the artificial feeding in the Rainforest has reduced the *Saimiri* colony's range considerably from that of a normally foraging troop.

Several features of the Rainforest colony's behavior suggest that in the field squirrel monkeys are likely to develop a definite territorial range to which they tend to confine themselves (see Chapter 3): our animals repeatedly use the same jungle routes; they habituate the same watering trees; despite repeated excursions by subjects of all ages beyond the fenced area, all have returned; and finally, the "bachelor" male group which lives for most of the year completely outside the fenced area (roaming freely over the entire 15 acres and sometimes beyond into adjacent property) habitually return to the same group of royal palms for night lodging.

It might be expected that the close quarters of the feeding area would pose an unnatural social stress in the colony as certainly would be expected among macaques or baboons. However, there has been no observed evidence of competition for food or space at the feeding stations. The youngest animals eat contentedly beside adult males with no observable tension. Feeding seems definitely on a "first come, first served" basis.

The monkeys are almost totally undisturbed by the presence of human observers. Many times, the public will pass through an area on the path where a group of juveniles are playing. The monkeys barely move enough to keep from being stepped on and resume play immediately as soon as the people pass. On the other hand, however, the *Saimiri* have not developed any attachments to humans but have remained generally indifferent even to those people with whom they are in regular contact.

Although the various species of primates in the Rainforest come from the same geographic location and presumably would be in occasional contact with each other in their natural habitat, we would not expect that they would be in such constant close association as they are here. However, there has been no indication that this interspecific contact effects intraspecific interaction or exerts any pressures on it. There is no observable competition between the species for food at the station.

In summary, it seems likely that this environment provides the most favorable habitat for the establishment of colonies of tropical American primates possible in the United States at this time. Within this environment these primates have an excellent opportunity to form natural societies and exhibit behavior very closely approximating that which might be found in the field. At the same time relatively controlled close observations of the animals can be made for long periods and under facilitating conditions not commonly found in the field.

III. Observational Methods

A. EARLY OBSERVATIONS

Squirrel monkeys were the first species established in the Rainforest and there was intensive initial observation following their introduction. The primary emphasis was on problems encountered during orientation to gain information pertaining more to husbandry than to behavior per se.

Very shortly after the squirrel monkey introduction some of the other species were introduced. Since the *Saimiri* group adjusted so well and presented no problems, while the other groups subsequently introduced experienced difficulties, very little time was spent on observations of *Saimiri* during the next several years except for the recording of reproduction data.

B. INTENSIVE OBSERVATION PERIOD

Intense and fairly continuous observation was initiated in June, 1966 and is still under way. As of this writing, over 270 hours of observations made on 121 different days have been logged. Observation periods were from 1 hour in length to nearly a full day. The colony was observed at various times of day and under a variety of weather conditions. As mentioned above, the colony animals are thoroughly conditioned to human presence and we are confident that the observer's presence had a negligible effect on their behavior.

C. EXPERIMENTAL PROJECTS

One of the difficulties experienced in understanding the squirrel monkey has been that social structure and interrelations are very subtly expressed and difficult to determine. it was felt that by introducing some unusual stresses into the colony that some of its social organization might present itself more clearly under these conditions.

Two of the experimental projects consisted of introductions of newly imported wild adults into the colony. First, a single adult male was introduced; then, a group of three males and five adult females that had lived as a group for 6 weeks prior to introduction so that they might attain a certain amount of group identity was introduced.

IV. Chronology of Introduction and Adaptation to the Environment

A. INTRODUCTION AND ADAPTATION

On August 3, 1960, shortly after the retaining fence was completed, a single adult male from Iquitos, Peru (the "Roman" variety described by McLean, 1964: see also Chapter 1) was released in the Rainforest. When he was sighted, still within the Rainforest 3 days later, a group of six animals (two males and four females) from Iquitos was also released. They were extremely timid at first, but by August 16 it was determined that they were all still in the 4-acre area and were coming for food put out for them.

On August 16, 1960, 30 adult or nearly adult squirrel monkeys (11 males and 19 females), also from Iquitos and all probably not in captivity more than 10 days to 2 weeks, were introduced into the Rainforest. The plan was to include enough wild-caught adults in the group so that there would be a good supply of experienced mothers and breeding males that had received the benefits of any social experiences that might be necessary to establish a stable social structure with normal reproduction. By August 18, only 2 days after introduction, the new group had learned where the food was put out and was very much settled down. The larger group was much less nervous than the first seven had been, possibly due to their greater number.

The whole group seemed quite well adapted to the new environment and feeding schedules by September 9, 1960, when a very severe hurricane struck, inflicting major damage to the Rainforest. Winds up to 140 mph were experienced with the heavy wind and rain lasting 10−12 hours. The jungle was largely defoliated and probably 15% of the large trees were blown down. The following morning the wind was still blowing 60−70 mph and not a monkey was in sight. I had anticipated some loss of monkey population from the storm, either by injury or by escape over damaged fence areas. They had only been in the Rainforest 3½ weeks when the hurricane struck and it seemed unlikely that they could have become very well adapted to this particular jungle. Fortunately, none of this happened. There was no evidence of loss or escape due to the hurricane. As has been the case after more recent hurricanes, many of the monkeys' forest routes were destroyed. They approached the feeding area and came to the ground where a familiar route tree had been blown down. It took only a few days to develop new routes and apparently the monkeys were none the worse for the storm.

The next problem concerned the monkeys' survival of our winters in the Rainforest. By mid-February, 1961, they had withstood our coldest weather with no apparent ill effects and a number of the females were obviously pregnant. The first birth was recorded February 24, 1961. By April 6, there were 6 mothers carrying infants and more than half of the estimated "crop" of 8 to 10 had arrived.

During this time, other species were being introduced into the Rainforest and it was striking that the squirrel monkeys exhibited no observable interest, curiosity, or any other reaction to the new arrivals. They did not even seem to notice them at the feeding station as they crowded in for their share of food.

B. EVALUATION OF ADAPTATION TO THE ENVIRONMENT

The introduction and establishment of the squirrel monkey colony was uneventful and surprisingly trouble-free. The remains of three animals were found within the first 6 months. They were too badly decomposed to determine the sex and the last one discovered was only a skeleton. Considering the possibility that the remains of several monkeys might not have been discovered, I estimated that the total introduction loss did not exceed 5 or 6, leaving 31 or 32 out of the original 37 liberated.

Since the first birth occurred on February 24, 1961, by counting back the estimated 24 weeks of gestation (Beischer and Furry, 1964), it is clear that they started mating activities by September 10, or immediately after the hurricane struck. None of this first mating season was observed as we were totally occupied for the 6 weeks after the storm clearing out damage. The above record certainly indicates extremely rapid adaptation to the new environment.

V. Reproductive Patterns

As already noted, the first birth season began February 24, 1961 with most births coming in late March; by the end of April, all of the 8 to 10 of the first birth season had been delivered. The whole birth season was thus about 8 weeks in duration.

Throughout the six birth seasons so far recorded, there has been no direct evidence of infant mortality in the colony. However, it seems unlikely that with an estimated total of 100 live births there would be no mortality at all. There is reason to suspect that an isolated stillbirth or infant death could go undiscovered. Nonetheless, no remains have ever been discovered even though the area is regularly cleaned and maintained. The peer play groups that develop after the birth season seem to contain substantially the same number of animals as were estimated to have been delivered in that birth crop. Except for the first year, the estimated number of infants recorded during a given birth season has approached at least 70—80% of the estimated number of adult females in the colony capable of re-

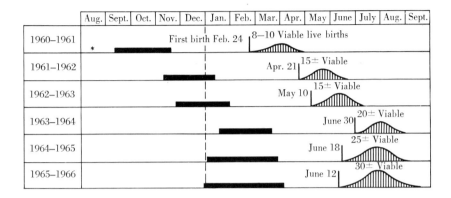

FIG. 2. Reproduction record of the squirrel monkey colony living in a seminatural environment indicating the shift in the reproductive cycle from 1960 through 1966. Total of 37 monkeys introduced (*), 14 males and 23 females, less 6 animals that died. Solid line, mating season; hatched area, birth season (high portion indicates birth peak).

producing. This is an indication of the high fecundity of the group. Some infant mortality must be assumed but it must be considered negligible.

Figure 2 graphically illustrates the statistics of the entire 6-year reproduction record. The first season's crop only included 8 to 10 infants indicating that about half of the colony females gave birth the first year. There were some that did not appear mature in the group and some might have either aborted or not have been well enough adjusted to the new environment. However, in 1962, most of the females did produce viable infants, as was also the case the following year. The next jump in the number of births occurred in 1964 with the addition of mothers born to the colony during the 1961 season. From then on, the number of births each year has increased with the addition of new mothers maturing with each new season. From this, the age at which a female *Saimiri* reaches puberty can be estimated at about 3 years. Those born in March, 1961 would have been approximately 36 months old in March, 1964 at the height of the 1964 mating season.

A. SEASONALITY OF THE REPRODUCTIVE CYCLE AND THE
   SEASONAL SHIFT

It has been reported that many primates have discrete reproductive seasons (Lancaster and Lee, 1965). As noted elsewhere in the volume (Chapter 5), the squirrel monkey also demonstrates a marked seasonality in its reproduction. Figure 2 clearly illustrates that in the Monkey Jungle the birth season is confined to a very short period of 8−12 weeks with a definite peak in the middle.

The rigidity of this seasonality in *Saimiri*, however, is particularly worthy of note as there has never been a birth recorded outside of the discrete periods shown on the chart. It is of particular interest that those females that failed to give birth in the 1961 season did not become impregnated until the 1961 – 1962 mating season (mid-November through mid-January) and that the newly matured females that became mothers for the first time in 1964 – 1965 – 1966 all became impregnated only during the mating seasons of those years.

There has been a very definite and well-defined shift in the time of year of the mating and birth seasons since the establishment of the newly imported colony. The birth peak shifted from late March – early April in 1961 to late July – early August by 1964. The birth season then stabilized and remained the same in 1965 and 1966. Even though the birth spread became somewhat wider as the number of births increased, it can be seen that the peak birth period has remained stable.

The squirrel monkeys from Iquitos, Peru are reported by the local importers to arrive in Miami with clinging infants during late December, January, and February. A personally conducted survey of 3300 freshly imported animals distributed over a 12-month period confirmed these reports. The first abortions and stillbirths in newly imported *Saimiri* are observed during December. During January, the incidence of stillbirths and abortions rises sharply. Females imported during pregnancy are under such stress that live births in this species are rare in importers' compounds. The original members of the Monkey Jungle colony were probably caught in the early part of the July – September Iquitos mating season and were released during the middle of the same season. The stress of transit apparently did not markedly upset their reproductive rhythm and mating began in the local environment during the last part of the Iquitos mating season. This could explain the slightly later occurrence of our first birth season as compared to the Iquitos environment. All conceptions evidently occurred after arrival, as the first birth of the 1961 season was 27 weeks after introduction, which is 3 weeks longer than the estimated gestation period of 24 weeks.

It is expected that a given species in a given environment will evolutionarily "select" the optimum time for the most critical phases of the reproductive cycle so as to insure species perpetuation. There is some indication that the *Saimiri* newborn with a weight of 90 – 125 gm is almost twice as large in proportion to the mother as most other primates at birth (see Chapter 6). Thus, the rapid growth stage of development in the third trimester of pregnancy would understandably represent an unusually heavy demand on the mother to consume large amounts of nutrients to support this rapid fetal growth and carry her through delivery and lactation. Thus, one might expect gestation to terminate during a period when the forest diet might be enriched with flushes of growth.

These periods of tropical forest growth flushes are usually associated with the seasonal increases in rainfall of a given area as they are in southern Florida. Figure 3 illustrates climatological comparisons between the lower east coast Florida environment and the western Amazon Basin. These curves are based on long-term records secured from the United States Weather Bureau for the western Amazon Basin and the local data from the Miami station, together with those values recorded at a facility approximately 1 mile from the colony site for the actual years that the *Saimiri* colony has been at the Monkey Jungle.

It will be noted that an interesting correlation between rainfall and reproductive season emerges when the precipitation cycles of the western Amazon basin and southern Florida are compared. The stable birth season occurs near the top of the precipitation curve in both environments and the mating season during the dry period.

Regarding the initiation of mating behavior itself, which of course begins several months prior to the birth season, it has been shown that in various species, including primates (Lancaster and Lee, 1965), variations in the light—dark cycle are critical to the regulation of breeding. However, our *Saimiri* derive from an area about 4° below the equator where the deviation in absolute light—dark cycle is only ±11 minutes throughout the year. Thus if photic mechanisms are influential in regulating squirrel monkey breeding seasonality, the sensitivity of this species to minimal changes in illumination are remarkable indeed.

The actual triggering mechanism for mating cannot be positively determined until more data on reproductive cycles from other environments can be obtained. Information is presently being sought on mating seasons of *Saimiri* from other latitudes that also have differing climatologies. Thorington (Chapter 3) reports a birth season similar to Iquitos during February, March, and April in San Martin, Colombia which is 4° *above* the equator and in the same, though greatly attenuated, light—dark cycle as Miami. However, the rainy season for the area is March, April, and May and the estimated mating season occurs during the dry period. Mating seasons occur in the valleys of the precipitation curves for all three environments reported. Some environmental stimuli such as changes in the quality of solar illumination or vegetative growth cycles must be present prior to the mating season to trigger hormonal preparation for reproduction. A further discussion of the female reproductive cycle in *Saimiri* is presented by Rosenblum (Chapter 5).

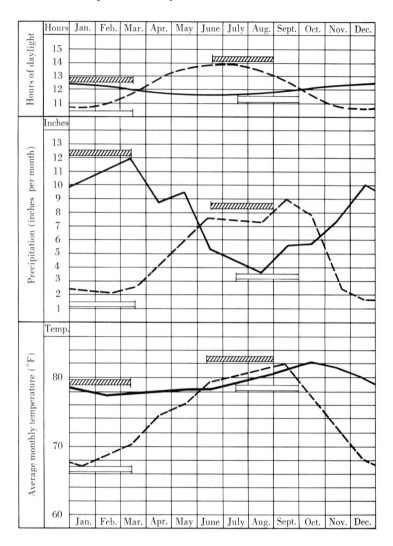

FIG. 3. Climatological comparison of the western Amazon Basin with the local Miami environment, showing the correlation of the birth season with the peak rainfall periods in both environments. The light—dark cycle for Iquitos, Peru has a maximum deviation of ± 11 minutes (sunrise to sunset). Solid line, hours of daylight, precipitation, and temperature for the Amazon Basin; broken line, hours of daylight, precipitation, and temperature for Miami; hatched line, birth seasons; open line, mating seasons. [U.S. Department of Commerce (1941-1950, 1951-1960) and Kendrew (1953); data from all three were averaged together.]

B. The "Fatted" Males

Male *Saimiri* manifest a parallel seasonal cyclicity in their spermatogenic cycle which is signaled by the appearance of "fatted" males in the colony. Figures 4a and 4b show a male in the fatted state during the mating season and the same male "nonfatted" 6 months later. This seasonal acquisition and loss of what appears to be a secondary sexual characteristic had been observed in the colony for several years before the nature of it was understood. In surveying the animals arriving from the field in local compounds, it was noted that during the summer, particularly in July and August (the height of the Iquitos mating season), adult males were arriving with a characteristic heaviness about the shoulders, upper forelimbs, and torso that has been noted in recent years among adult colony males during the winter months (the local mating season). Among the freshly imported *Saimiri* surveyed during the remainder of the year no fatted males were recorded.

Testicular samples were taken from fatted (mating season) and nonfatted (nonmating season) males arriving in Miami from Iquitos during September, November, December, February and March (1966−1967). One

FIG. 4a. "Fatted" male, "Scar Eye," colony male in the local environment taken mid-January, 1967. Note the heaviness about the shoulders and upper forelimbs and parting of the fur on the forelimbs. (Photograph by Frank DuMond.)

nonfatted male was trapped in September, 1966 out of the "bachelor" male group in the Rainforest to help verify the existence of a reproductive season in the local male population.

The fatted male testicular preparation (Fig. 5a) shows very active spermatogenesis with many spermatozoa imbedded in the syncitium lining the tubule lumina. The tubular cell structure is well developed with numerous cells in all stages of spermatogenesis. The nonfatted male preparation (Fig. 5b) illustrates advanced testicular regression but with evidence of prior spermatogenesis, as a considerable amount of sperm was found in the epididymis, presumably from the prior mating season. The seminiferous tubules show evidence of marked regression. They are smaller in actual size with no mitotic activity in evidence and tubule lumina are greatly enlarged, virtually clear of cells. The tubule wall is reduced to the basal layer of sertoli cells and spermatogonia. Samples taken during the early regression phase illustrated masses of detached cells which apparently sloughed off leaving the greatly enlarged lumina as shown in Fig. 5b. The evidence of prior spermatogenesis as demonstrated by masses of spermatozoa present in the epididymis of all regressed testicles clearly indicates a cyclical spermatogenesis in male *Saimiri*.

FIG. 4b. Photograph of the same animal taken 6 months later, July, 1967 when in the nonfatted state. Note the slenderness about upper forelimbs and shoulders; for further comparison note the relationship of head size to the shoulder area in the two conditions. (Photograph by Frank DuMond.)

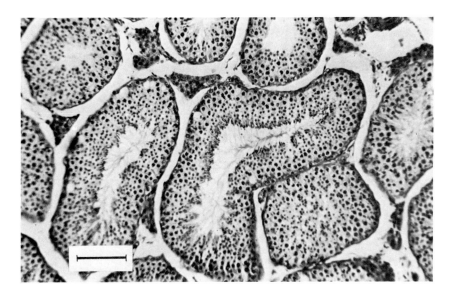

FIG. 5a. Testis sample taken from a fatted male from Iquitos, Peru September 19, 1966 (late mating season in the western Amazon Basin) showing seminiferous tubules in cross section. Tubules show very active spermatogenesis. Note the well-defined cell structure, the many spermatozoa imbedded in syncytium at the border of the lumana, and the abundance of germ cells in all stages of spermatogenesis. Marker indicates 100 μ. (Photomicrograph by Frank DuMond.)

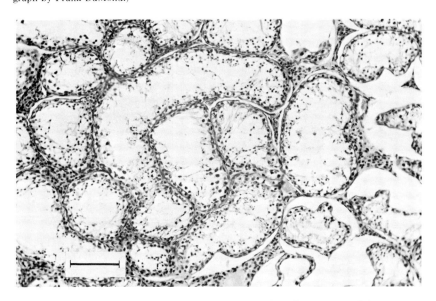

FIG. 5b. Testis sample taken from a nonfatted male from Iquitos, Peru February, 1967 illustrates the dormant period of maximal regression. Tubule lumina are greatly enlarged and are virtually clear of cells. The tubule wall consists of a single basal layer of sertoli cells and spermatogonia with no evidence of mitotic activity. Marker indicates 100 μ.

Body measurements indicated a considerably greater amount of subcutaneous fat in fatted males than in nonfatted males (average skin-fold thickness of 4.0 mm as compared to 1.2 mm). In addition, the fur was more fluffy, possibly due to a stretching of the skin by the layer of subcutaneous fat. The fatted male weights averaged 937 gm as compared to 715 gms for the nonfatted males, however, the bone length measurements were comparable and roentgenograms established that the epiphyses on the nonfatted males were all closed, indicating that they were mature animals.

Further support for the association of the fatted condition with spermatogenesis and for considering this state as an indication of increased hormonal activity has been gained from recent behavioral studies in the colony described below.

VI. Population Dynamics and Colony Composition

POPULATION DYNAMICS

When the group was created there was a homogenous population consisting of all adult or nearly adult animals. The first juvenile one (juveniles less than 1 year old) peer group did not develop until late 1961, some 5 or 6 months after the first birth season, and the juvenile two (juveniles more than 1 year old) peer group did not develop until 1962. Close ("aunt") relationships between infant-carrying mothers were not observed until the 1964 birth season along with the entry of the colony-born mothers into the reproductive female group. The initial entrance of first-time fatted máles into the adult male group was not observed until the 1966 – 1967 mating season. It became obvious that even after 6 years anything approaching normal population dynamics in this young colony was just beginning to develop.

Since squirrel monkeys are born in such discrete seasons, there is a progression of rather well-defined segments of the population moving along toward maturation. It has been estimated that females reach puberty at about 36 months and that although males may become reproductively capable at sometime near or shortly after 36 months, they apparently need an additional 2 years to develop into the socially mature fatted males observed during the mating season. As indicated, the first colony-born fatted males were observed in the 1966 – 1967 mating season. These were males that were presumably born in 1961. They could have been males of a later birth season but this seems unlikely. If it is accepted that some males survived from the 1961 crop and that the 1966 – 1967 mating season marked the first appearance of colony-born males becoming socially mature, then the age that this occurs can be placed at between 60 and 67 months.

VII. General Behavior

A. INDIVIDUAL NONSOCIAL BEHAVIOR

1. Locomotion

Squirrel monkeys display typical quadrupedal pronograde locomotor characteristics, in most instances running, leaping, landing, hopping, ascending, and descending on all fours. When about to make a very long leap they will sometimes assume a stance not unlike a typical standing broad jumper, though with the knees more flexed and with the arms hanging down and swinging slightly to the rear; then the leap is made with a powerful thrust from the legs. At times, when descending rapidly down a thick trunk or limb that is slightly inclined from the vertical, they slide down sideways, standing on all fours and facing outward at about a 45° angle from the plane of the direction of motion. This may be done while descending a smooth-barked, nearly vertical trunk with much greater speed than in the normal head-first method.

Saimiri can travel at great speeds through the jungle, particularly over established routes for which distances and the relationships of limbs and trees have apparently been well learned. It is not unusual for them to make a pinpoint landing on a small branch no larger than a quarter of an inch in diameter from a height of 30 feet above. They can turn their body in flight so as to land in perfect alignment on the distal end of a branch using its springiness to break the impact. Pregnant females and mothers carrying infants, although a little more cautious, also have been observed to make similar leaps.

2. Postural Behavior

Two characteristic postures, the huddle and the sprawl, are observed in the squirrel monkey. In the huddle they crouch on their hind legs, hunch their back, and support the upper torso with flexed arms as they incline more or less forward. The tail is brought around underneath so that the animal is sitting on the base of it with the end curled around to the front and over one shoulder. This is very similar to the position used during the night sleep period; during the latter, the tail is always wrapped over the body and is never allowed to hang below.

In the sprawl the animal straddles a branch, resting on the ventral surface, letting the limbs and tail dangle below (Fig. 6). Occasionally, one arm is flexed and brought up on the branch. This position is very common in the summer when the weather is warm but is never used for night sleep. Mazur and Baldwin (1966) established a definite temperature relationship between the ratio of huddles to sprawls observed. As the temperature ap-

FIG. 6. Young squirrel monkey in typical sprawl posture which is associated with warm temperatures and a very relaxed and tranquil emotional state. (Photograph by Frank DuMond.)

proached 90°F the percentage of sprawls to huddles rose sharply to 85—90%. The sprawl is apparently a body heat—radiating mechanism while the huddle is associated with conserving body heat (see Chapter 3). Observations indicate certain emotional factors also seem to be associated with the huddle—sprawl relationship. The sprawl is usually associated with a very relaxed unstressed monkey; a sick monkey does not usually assume the sprawl posture. The huddle posture is not only assumed in cool weather but by sick animals as well and it is also the position assumed when in the presence of a more dominant monkey. The sprawl is a position in which a monkey is vulnerable to other animals falling or landing on it and is a position from which the subject is less prepared for quick movement than from the huddle in which all four limbs are flexed and in solid contact with the perch. I have not observed captive squirrel monkeys living in fairly crowded quarters assume the sprawl position even when temperatures are high.

Most observers indicate that squirrel monkeys tend to have an alopecic area at the base of the tail. This apparently is a problem only in captivity when a combination of poor sanitation and increased huddling may lead to the development of sores on the base of the tail (see Chapter 14).

Squirrel monkeys do not often walk or stand bipedally. They do occasionally if they are carrying something large enough to require both hands but they are very prone to drop anything that they cannot carry in their mouths or very easily in one hand. When in the grass area around the jungle perimeter they may stand up for short periods, apparently in order to see over the grass and weeds.

There is also the interesting behavior of "back-rubbing" which involves a bipedal stance (see also Chapter 3). This behavior is often seen immediately following rainfalls and is generally accomplished by the animal standing in a fork of a tree limb and doing a sort of knee bend up and down, making contact with the upright bark surface with the back. Fatted males are observed to back-rub even when it is dry; the significance of this behavior is not as yet clear.

3. Tail Use

The tail is nonprehensile but is used for balancing and stabilizing the animal as it moves about and for support or bracing. As can be seen in Fig. 7, it may be partially wrapped around a limb and used for support. The use of the tail by *Saimiri* neonates is discussed by Rosenblum in Chapter 8.

4. Manipulation

The hand of the squirrel monkey is used by the animal in such nonlocomotive activities as searching for and uncovering insects, catching flying in-

FIG. 7. A subadult male demonstrates an almost prehensile use of its tail as he wraps it around the post to help support him in extending his body. (Photograph by Frank DuMond.)

sects, handling food, and carrying small objects. When *Saimiri* are handling an object, they characteristically assume a semihuddle position, squatting on their haunches thus freeing the hands for manipulative activities. Some of the bachelor male group that spend much of their time outside the Rainforest and thus are not as well provisioned, have become very adept at catching peanuts thrown to them by the public.

Because of their almost totally quadrupedal manner of locomotion, it is apparently difficult for a squirrel monkey to carry other than the smallest objects very effectively while on the move, and an object carried is frequently dropped. The hands are used quite a bit in low-level aggression. A mother for example, chastising her infant, may pull the hair on top of the baby's head or back, and juveniles do a lot of arm wrestling while playing.

5. Investigative Behavior

Squirrel monkeys do not exhibit as much investigative behavior as do many other primates. New construction, the introduction of a new monkey of another species, or even camera equipment left by the public does not seem to attract the squirrel monkey's attention. In general, *Saimiri* show very little sustained interest in objects that can neither be eaten nor pose a threat to their well being.

6. The "Foot Wash"

Squirrel monkeys frequently are observed to execute a stereotyped behavior pattern which we have termed the "foot wash." This is accomplished while the animal is in a crouched or sitting position. After shifting the body weight to one foot and positioning the other foot slightly flexed under the genital area, the hand on the same side is brought down in palm contact with the footpad. It is then rubbed or wiped with the foot as several drops of urine are released and rubbed between the pad surfaces of the foot and hand. This may alternate to the other foot and hand.

The foot wash is practiced by both sexes of all ages. Infants have been observed foot washing at several weeks of age while clinging to the mothers back. Many observations of this practice suggest that it is an indication of mild arousal in the animal. In the fatted males, the foot wash may explode into violent stereotyped kicks suggesting a higher state of arousal. The foot wash seems to be a very basic reaction pattern in the squirrel monkey (Castell and Maurus, 1967), and has also been observed in other species of South American monkeys, particularly in the brown capuchin (*Cebus apella*).

B. ACTIVITIES AND ARBOREALITY VERSUS TERRESTRIALITY

Although squirrel monkeys are considered arboreal animals, in the Rainforest they spend a considerably greater amount of time on the ground foraging and playing than was originally reported elsewhere. However, in any stressful situation, they move rapidly to the trees. They find a substantial quantity of insects on the ground and in the premating and mating season spend more than half of the day on the ground, the adults foraging and socially interacting, while the juveniles play.

The play activities of the juveniles seem specifically adapted as a ground activity. They seek out uncluttered areas where there is little underbrush and spend long periods in play groups running, hopping on each other, and wrestling playfully (Fig. 8). This type of play is difficult to enact in the trees. When play occurs in the trees, it is quite often in the form of a play pair hanging by their feet and arm wrestling. Play off the ground usually occurs at low levels, no more than 10 feet from the ground and quite often this form of play, once initiated, quickly turns into ground play as the animals tumble toward the ground while wrestling. This contrasts with the almost exclusive arboreal play patterns observed in uakari and howler monkeys in the same area.

Despite all this terrestrial activity, *Saimiri* to a certain extent, are not at ease on the ground and seem always ready to rush upward. When a group is on the ground, a single animal that becomes frightened and bolts upward for any reason causes the whole group to flee upward several feet. If no real danger materializes, all return to the ground and resume their activities, only to have the same thing happen again a few minutes later. This relative uneasiness on the ground leads to speculation that wild groups of squirrel monkeys would not be found on open ground more than a very few feet from the protection of the trees and would probably be ecologically confined by any open ground barrier of more than perhaps 100 yards in width. It should further be noted that our *Saimiri* never sleep or rest on the ground but always return to the security of the trees for this purpose.

Weather also has a considerable influence on the amount of time spent on the ground. During the summer, very warm weather seems to keep them out of the upper levels of the trees away from exposure to the sun during midday, but in the late afternoon, as the sun descends, the group generally returns to the higher levels. After a rain, there is usually a migration to higher levels where they are observed to lick water from the leaves and back-rub against the trees as described earlier.

C. Daily Route Patterns and Activity Rhythms

The squirrel monkeys' day typically begins at sunrise. They can still be seen in their huddle groups just prior to dawn though are easily aroused at this time. As the daylight approaches, some individual huddle groups break up momentarily and reform, or the animals stir restlessly for a few minutes.

FIG. 8. Typical ground play group comprised of juvenile ones (10−11 months old). While only five animals are included in this picture, the whole play group consisted of more than a dozen animals stretched out over a 20−30 foot length of the walking trail. (Photograph by Frank DuMond.)

As daylight becomes stronger, huddle groups, one or two at a time, break up and the animals start moving out from the lodge area (sleeping sites). Within 15 minutes nearly the whole group has dispersed, radiating out in a wide flow pattern. At this time, the colony may be very widely scattered in pairs, triads, or even slightly larger groups, probably representing the original sleep-huddle groups.

The first hour of activity consists mainly of foraging and licking the morning dew off the leaves in the upper jungle canopy. There is not much social interaction during this high-level forage activity.

Toward the end of the first hour, the general movement usually progresses toward the area of the morning feeding station where the colony dispersal gradually is reduced and the groups coalesce. The next hour or two before the morning feeding is spent with the adults resting in huddle groups or sprawls. The juveniles, however, rest for a shorter period of time and form play groups near the station. As feeding time approaches, the entire group becomes very highly aroused; social interactions increase and some fighting is observed in the play groups.

The morning provision is consumed in a matter of several minutes and the group then migrates away from the station, quite often to the north.

During the mating season adult females and males comprise a ground forage group in which from time to time sexual interactions occur, involving either male-to-male displays or male-female encounters. The juveniles interrupt their foraging activity with play which becomes widespread. As one play pair forms others join in and a play group of five or six wrestling pairs may be seen. Group movement is very slow and random.

This slow migration usually brings the colony toward the area of the next feeding station by the time of the 11:45 A.M. feeding. After passing through the feeding station, the group usually moves to the west and north with the initial movement fairly rapid toward the periphery or western and northern edge of the jungle. During the winter this excursion often extends out beyond the perimeter of the jungle and into the grass-weed area beyond. They may spend more than an hour foraging, slowly migrating toward the south in the low peripheral scrub and on the cleared area.

The routes and activity for the remainder of the day consist of patterns of large loops formed by passes through the feeding stations at feeding time and excursions back out toward various areas of the jungle and back again (Fig. 9). Season and weather conditions exert an influence on troop route patterns and activity rhythms. During very warm weather there is usually a long rest period in mid-afternoon when colony activity subsides and most of the colony can be seen sleeping in small huddle groups or in solitary huddles and sprawls. At times during very hot weather many monkeys will seek shelter under the large philodendron leaves that cover the trunks of many of the trees.

During a rain activity decreases sharply; most of the groups seek shelter under the philodendron leaves and can be seen peeking out from under the large leaves either singly or in huddle pairs. Some may huddle out in the open but during a hard rain most seek this shelter when it is nearby. At times a juvenile will apparently be rejected by a group and after a series of vocalizations will rush out to find another sheltered area. After the rain ceases, the groups move up to the higher levels again.

After the last feeding at 5:00 P.M., one last excursion out from the station is made. Small groups may return to the feeding station several times for another provision. The remainder of the day is typically spent in foraging in the upper canopy. During the summer when there are several hours of daylight left after the last feeding there is usually a period of considerably increased social interaction near the central forest area at medium levels.

The squirrel monkeys do not start bedding down procedures until it is nearly dark, sometimes so dark that they can hardly be seen. The huddle groups form either as pairs or as small groups probably comprised of animals from the same subgroups. During the birth season mothers sleep in one area and seem to be coupled with other mothers or closely associated females (aunts). There is a period of 15−20 minutes of shuffling around and changing partners which sometimes erupts into mild disturbances. The animals gradually settle down and soon all are quiet. There is some indication that for the first several hours of sleep they are very easily aroused but as the night progresses sleep apparently becomes deeper and they are more difficult to disturb.

Although the philodendron leaves are used as shelter from both sun and rain during the daytime the terminal ends of smaller branches of the taller trees are typically selected for sleeping. The same trees are habitually selected for lodging, at least for several months at a time. Whether or not the huddle groups are composed of the same animals night after night is not definitely known but there is some evidence that sleep partners may have some permanency: the five experimental females have been observed together as one huddle group at night on each of five different observations over a 5-month period.

D. RELATIONS WITH MAN

As would be expected, new imports, once free in the jungle, are at first very much afraid of humans and do their best to keep considerable distance between any humans and themselves. Lateral distance seems more important to them than vertical distance; even though a monkey may be 70 feet high in the canopy it will move laterally even at the expense of having to descend to a lower level when it sights a human directly below. Squirrel monkeys are very much aware of being watched. If afraid of the observer, males will sometimes turn their heads away to avert ones' stare though they will glance back every few seconds much as they do to a more dominant male while they huddle.

There seems to be a relationship between the size of the group and the ease with which *Saimiri* become accustomed to human presence. Although my observations are obviously quite limited, it would appear that very small and very large groups may adapt most readily. The medium-sized groups that I have observed (compared with our largest group of 30) tended to form more cohesive units which seemed to be much more subject to the contagion of the fear of any one group member. Within the larger and smaller groups individuals are less inhibited by the negative reactions of any partners that may have developed specific fears of humans. These individuals thus are free to accept the food and related reinforcements presented by humans; they serve thereby ultimately to draw the rest of their group into positive associations with humans.

E. RELATIONS WITH OTHER NONHUMAN PRIMATES

It has already been noted that the *Saimiri* respond minimally to the other species of primates in the Rainforest. The young uakaris frequently play with the young *Saimiri*, sometimes even carrying them on their back for short periods. The marmosets have also been observed associated with *Saimiri* play groups. However, interspecific interaction among the adults has been minimal. Once a half-grown uakari stole a bag of peanuts that one of the experimental males had in turn stolen from one of the visiting public, but no overt response to the uakari was observed. On another occasion, a young uakari attempted to initiate play with one of the fatted males who reacted with a very annoyed "raucous squawk," and although he did not run away the male moved out of the uakari's reach while vocalizing. No interactions at all between the *Saimiri* and the howlers in the jungle have been observed.

F. RELATIONS WITH NONPRIMATE ANIMALS

The squirrel monkey shows very little interest in any of the animals in the environment that do not pose an obvious threat. The young will intently watch and follow a snake whereas the adults respond minimally. I once saw a hawk settle down on a tree that was in the midst of a "rest-forage" group; this elicited harsh staccato "chirps" from the group, and all the monkeys in the exposed upper level of the jungle descended to lower more protected levels and watched intently until the hawk left. It is likely that very few animals actually saw the hawk approaching and vocalized, and it was the calls that alerted the others. This call seemed different from either those heard directed at a snake or the startle peeps that cause ground forage groups to rush upward.

Raccoons and opossums seem to move about without disturbing the squirrel monkeys very much. Once a domestic cat got inside the fenced area and was unable to get out for several weeks. The monkeys were considerably disturbed by the cat and would respond to its presence with alarm chirps.

VIII. Social Behavior

A. SUBGROUPS

1. Seasonal Dynamics of Saimiri Behavior

Rather discrete subgroups are observed within the colony which tend to be somewhat socially independent, particularly at certain times of the year; there is, however, some relationship between the subgroups and a loose cohesiveness of the entire colony that exists throughout the year. The unusual characteristic of the organization of the squirrel monkey colony involves the relationships between and within the subgroups which constantly change, month by month, as the colony rhythmically passes through the several phases of the annual reproductive cycle (Fig. 10).

2. The Adult Male Group and the Fatted Males

The adult male squirrel monkeys are the least social members of the colony. Paternal relations with infants or juveniles have not been observed in the adult males. Adult males have never been observed playing with, grooming, or directly exerting any influence or controls over the activities of the rest of the colony. There is a seasonal rhythm of behavior associated with the mating season when the males acquire the secondary sexual characteristics we have termed the fatted condition. With this changed state they acquire certain traits of masculine behavior that suggests increased androgen production along with the recommencement of spermatogenesis. The first indications of the onset of this period are observed in the Rainforest in early November as the males begin to vocalize more and move with a little more confidence through the colony. During the rest of November the males continue to vocalize and are sometimes answered by the females. In early December ("premating" season) a weight gain is noticeable and a stereotyped series of interactions begins through which a dominance hierarchy is established among the males. These interactions are typified by frequent gatherings of the fatted males and involve penile display interactions and highly aroused males rushing together, vocalizing, and bumping each other.

In the penile display episodes a dominant male presses his opened thigh against the shoulder and head area of a crouching submissive male (the crouching is the only demonstration of deference observed). Other fatted males usually rush to the scene and join in, also displaying to the subordinate male. The initial stage is characterized by great tension among the fatted males. Males whose status is still uncertain are very volatile and display episodes with them may erupt explosively into actual fights. Some of the penile display variations described by Ploog *et al.* (1963) such as the "open" stance, the double thigh display, and the stiff leg dragging, seem to be examples of juvenile display activities which are more variable, while the fatted males are more stereotyped in their display activities.

As is described in detail below, during the summer of 1966 several experimental subjects were placed in the colony. It is not known what influence the introduction of the experimental males may have had on that year's dominance-establishment phase. Several males were observed to be severely cut up but wounded males have been noticed in past years during

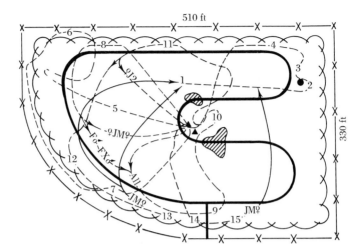

FIG. 9. Typical daily route pattern during premating and mating season when the colony generally moves together and is not as separated as it is during the birth season.

1, 8:30 A.M.; 2, 9:30 A.M.; 3, 10:30 A.M.; 4, 11:30 A.M.; 5, 12:00 P.M.; 6, 12:30 P.M.; 7, 2:30 P.M.; 8, 3:30 P.M.; 9, 4:30 P.M.; 10, 4:45 P.M.; 11, 5:30 P.M.; 12, 6:00 P.M.; 13, 6:30 P.M. (bedding down, ♀, J1, M♀ sleep groups); 14, 6:30 P.M. (bedding down, F♂, FX♂ sleep groups); 15, 6:30 P.M. (bedding down, ♀, J2 sleep groups); −, daybreak initial dispersal pattern (6:30 A.M.); ---, group route.

Key to symbols: ♀, Adult females; M♀, mothers with infants; A♀, aunts; X ♀, experimental females; NE♀, nonestrus females; C♂, colony adult males; FX♂, fatted experimental males; F♂, fatted colony males; B♂, bachelor males; J1, juvenile under 1 year; J2, juvenile over 1 year; ▲, afternoon feeding station; ●, morning feeding station; ⟋⟋⟋⟋ edge of jungle; —X—fence; ▬▬▬ trail (foot); ⟋⟋⟍ major aggression; ⟋⟋⟍ minor aggression; ⌀ small pit; ⬭ waterfall and piranha pit.

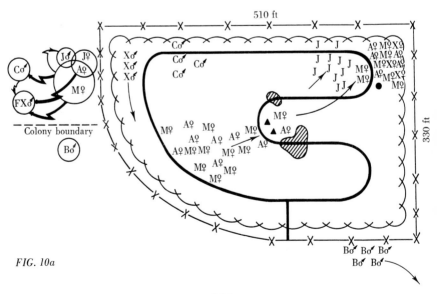

FIG. 10a

116

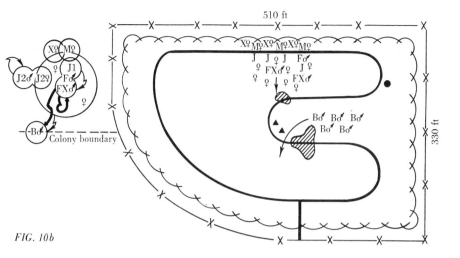

FIG. 10b

FIG. 10. Seasonal dynamics of subgroup relationships. Figures on the right illustrate actual sample locations recorded on specific observations. The number of subgroup symbols represent locations and relative concentrations and are not intended to represent actual numbers of animals. Figures on the left are diagramatic interpretations of the colony subgroup structure and relationships for the particular phase of the annual cycle in which the observation on the right was made. The subgroup relationships illustrated occurred while the experimental animals were integrating into the colony. Some of the aggression intensities seem somewhat lowered when no strange animals are in the troop. *a*. Typical midbirth season subgroup distribution in the environment. *b*. Typical premating season subgroup distribution in the environment. *c*. Typical mating season subgroup up to January 14, 1967. See legend to Fig. 9 for key to symbols.

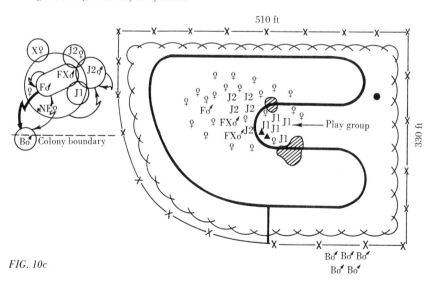

FIG. 10c

this phase. At the beginning of this period "Scar Eye," a colony male was dominant, and assumed the dominant role in all displays in which a dominance could be determined (Table I). Two levels of dominance were recorded, those in which one male clearly was in the most dominant role and those in which the dominance seemed to be shared by another male. Scar remained dominant from November 5 to December 3 although he was observed to have minor wounds on November 23. "Silver Belt" also was wounded at that time. On December 3 Scar was injured so badly that during recovery he withdrew from all colony interactions. After about a week of convalescence, he recovered sufficiently to begin interacting again with the other fatted males. He, however, had lost his dominant status and in the ensuing weeks was not observed in a dominant role in the displays. Table II shows a tabulation of 39 display interactions and dominance roles of the four fatted males recorded from December 3 through January 14, 1967.

As indicated in Table II Scar went from the most dominant to the least dominant position as a result of the fight in which he was so severely wounded. "Pink Belt" went from the most submissive to the most dominant position. Silver seemed to remain in the number two position and Charlie, who was unranked before the rearrangement, was now in third place. Silver never approached Pink to initiate a display but would enter into displays that Pink had initiated to either Charlie or Scar. In these, he would display to the already submissive male, keeping the submissive male between himself and Pink. Although Silver displayed to Charlie and Scar, Charlie displayed only to Scar, and Scar displayed to no one. In a display that involved all four males, Pink and Silver would be outside and Charlie and Scar would have the middle positions, each accepting a display from

TABLE I
Dominant and Submissive Roles Observed in
Four Fatted Males Prior to Scar Eye's Loss of Status[a]

Fatted Male	Scar Eye	Silver Belt	Charlie	Pink Belt
Number of penile displays participated in	9	4	4	9
Number of times most dominate participant	6	0	0	0
Number of times shared dominance with others	0	1	Unknown	1
Number of times submissive	0	0	1	5

[a]From November 5 to December 3, 1966.

TABLE II
DOMINANT AND SUBMISSIVE ROLES OBSERVED IN
FOUR FATTED MALES AFTER SCAR EYE'S LOSS OF STATUS[a]

Fatted Male	Pink Belt	Silver Belt	Charlie	Scar Eye
Number of penile displays participated in	24	19	21	21
Number of times most dominate participant	7	2	4	0
Number of times shared dominance with others	11	14	6	0
Number of times submissive	0	0	6	20

[a] From December 3, 1966 to January 14, 1967.

an outside dominant male. During times at which the hierarchy was well established the previously observed tension diminished. Scar seemed completely at ease in his new submissive role and even was observed apparently soliciting displays from Pink by approaching him and assuming the submissive crouch posture.

One indication of the reduced tension was the diminished occurrence of a characteristic kick which might be termed an "arousal state kick," and that was observed only in the fatted males (McLean, 1964, denotes this behavior as a scratch). The kick seemed to be an involuntary reflex action that usually occurred just before or just after a display or sexual episode. The animal, sitting in a semicrouch posture, would violently thrust out a leg with the toes first traveling up under the armpit and then straight out, three or four times, and then alternate legs. Sometimes the animal would continue through two or three alternations and on all observed occasions there was at least one alternation so that both legs were involved. Occasionally the kicks would be so violent that the animal would actually knock himself off balance. The kick seemed to start out very much like the foot wash (see Section VII, A, 6) with the hand on the sole of the foot of the same side, then it would explode into the kick. Once, I was within 2 feet of a kicking male and observed a jet of urine ejected with each leg alternation. Following unsuccessful sexual approaches to females but mostly during periods when the hierarchy was unstable kicks were very frequently observed, in the latter case about one per hour of observation. During January, however, the kicks became less numerous and from January 9 through January 16 only one kick was observed during 22 hours of observation. The displays were less intense with reduced antagonism or tension and a "harsh purring" sound often replaced the raucous squawks and "chucks" heard in displays during December. At times a display would merge into a huddle group in which the involved males would remain resting for 10—15 minutes, something not observed during November and December. There were indications, however, that the hierarchy did not remain stable in the following months although it is not yet clear what accounted for this continued instability.

What is so interesting about the display-dominance hierarchy phenomenon is that the dominance standing of a male seemed to have virtually no implications in its social life within the colony when the males were not actively participating in a display episode. The most submissive male, Scar, would eat with absolute composure side by side with Pink, and during sexual interactions Scar at times was more actively involved than any of the other more dominant males. Females and juvenile ones would frequently chase dominant males but the dominant males did not chase any member of the group. It is worthy of note, however, that the dominant males did direct aggressive behavior toward the separate bachelor male group (see below). When Scar was still dominant it was he that aggressed the bachelors, whereas after he fell to the most subordinate position it was the other males that assumed this role.

During the period of dominance establishment, the fatted males began interacting sexually with the females. Early in the premating season most females began passively accepting these approaches, or even at times seemed to solicit approaches. These sexual interactions frequently occurred just before or just after displays and could also be characterized as rather stereotyped episodes. Usually more than one male became involved in these interactions; they characteristically began with one or more males approaching a female, sometimes making "affection purr" calls similar to the calls of females to young during the birth season. Once a sexual interaction was initiated, other fatted males in the immediate area ran over and joined in the behavior which consisted of lip-to-lip contacts alternated with genital sniffing or inspection. At times one male would display to the female while positioning his body in order simultaneously to sniff the genital area. The several males involved crowd around the female and all attempt to make some close contact with her, one smelling the genitalia from the side, another from underneath, while another male might make lip-to-lip contact.

Sometimes a different approach was observed in which the male began by making soft rapidly repeated "chirps" or "twitters" while looking at the female and rapidly retracting the ears to the side of the head three or four times. The female would respond with "contact chirps" and might approach the male. If a sexual interaction developed then other males would run over and the interaction took on the appearance of the other episodes.

In most cases, the females remained relatively passive to these investigations and indeed, when a female seemed to actively solicit the interaction, the fatted males tended to reject it. An interesting aspect of these premating season sexual interactions was that during the first 2 months none were observed to culminate in copulation. The first copulation was observed January 7, although obviously their actual onset may have occurred somewhat prior to that date.

The actual copulation patterns observed so far have almost all been multiple social interactions. They began with a mount with none of the courtship preliminaries described above. The other fatted males within sight all rushed to the scene and began making lip contact, genital sniffs (even during copulation), and in general, interacting with the pair during the episode as much as they could, although the other males usually did not attempt actually to interfere with the mounting male. Immediately after the copulation, the males quite often joined in a display episode. In February John Baldwin observed five instances of complete copulation that involved only the coital pair; the other fatted males were not in the area and thus did not enter the interaction. Baldwin has suggested that these more private copulations, being less subject to distraction of other partners, may more regularly result in ejaculation although further observations of these behaviors must be made before final conclusions can be drawn.

Observations in the latter half of the mating season revealed a somewhat different pattern of reproductive behavior than that observed earlier. Perhaps toward the end of the season most of the females were already pregnant and no longer in estrous. In any event, during this period several or all fatted males would become sexually interested in and compete to mount a single female on a given day. Curiously, although the obviously dominant male might keep others from successfully mounting her, she might reject his approaches. Other times the dominant male was accepted but was interrupted by the behavior of a subordinate male and so still had difficulty in completing the act. What was interesting in these cases was that the aggressive contacts that were made by the dominant male did not develop into serious "shriek" fighting.

The reproductive behavior observed indicates that while mating activity between a pair tends to draw others to it, extra animals can have a disruptive affect on successful completion. Frequently other females, probably nonestrous, broke up copulations, juveniles soliciting nursing, and competing males also disrupted copulations.

A female seems to exhibit a preference as to which male she permits to mount her although this may or may not be the dominant male. A male may make a number of rejected approaches, at times executing a sort of "courtship dance." As he approaches the female he leans or lunges forward, then sharply pivots to one side just before touching her. This behavior may be repeated several times in an approach as the female moves away. As we have seen, the preferred male may also have a number of mounts interrupted by other animals. During these rather frustrating situations the male frequently displays to other males and does kicks between attempts to mount. Apparently the male squirrel monkey, even if dominant and favored, encounters obstacles to copulation not often observed in other primates, for example, the *Macaca irus* colony in the other section of the jungle.

As the birth season approaches, a marked change in male behavior is observed which becomes more pronounced as mid-birth season is reached. The males lose the fatted condition and diminish in size. Display interactions, kicks, and sexual interactions diminish or cease and the males withdraw as a group into virtual isolation. As the females begin to deliver their young, the males are actively aggressed by the females and are excluded from the central part of the social unit which now is comprised of the mother – infant group.

On August 13 I observed a group of about 15 mothers with infants together with some pregnant females, which were foraging in a centrally located ficus tree. Scar and several other males approached and as they neared the mother – infant group, a chorus of aggressive chucks was heard whereupon the males stopped. During the next 15 minutes the males remained about 40 – 60 feet from the female group. When one or more of the males moved in the direction of the female group, the aggressive chucks were heard again; when they moved in the direction away from the group no vocalizations were heard. This sequence occurred three times until finally the males moved west and away from the female group.

There were several observations of a male rushing down to the feeding station filled with mothers with their infants. On seeing the group of mothers the male stopped short and then crossed over to the other feeding station. It seemed that the male was reluctant to enter such a closely packed group of mothers whether at the feeding station or not.

From June through most of October the status of the adult male subgroup in the colony declines considerably and thus during the birth and infant-carrying time of year the colony becomes completely female dominated.

Another indication of the seasonal change in colony organization was observed during the introduction of the experimental males (see Section IX). The one introduced on July 16 was aggressed primarily by the females and not by the males. On the other hand, the group of three males introduced later was aggressed by Scar and his group of males and it was the males, first Scar and then the experimental males, that aggressed the bachelor male group during the premating and mating seasons. It seems that only when the males are becoming fatted and dominant are they involved in aggressing intruders to the colony.

3. The Female Subgroup

Most active social behavior occurs within and around the female subgroup. It is in this subgroup that most of the affiliative behavior, collective defensive behavior, and grooming occurs (although grooming is infrequently seen even among females).

When many females are pregnant in May and early June, the female subgroup begins to reform its separate identity. The males, while not yet actively aggressed, are not seen as closely associated with the females as during the mating season. When the first births occur in mid-June, the mothers become very shy and tend to seek the more sheltered, thick-foliaged areas of the Rainforest.

It is also during this time that older female juveniles probably leave the "juvenile-two" play group and become associated with the infant-carrying mothers in a very close relationship for which the term aunt, used by others, seems appropriate. Aunts then, are often young, nulliparous females that are either pregnant for the first time or were just too young to become pregnant during the past mating season.

During the first half of the birth season, most of the mothers are seen with an aunt which follows her, nuzzles the infant, fondles it, and is permitted to carry it around for short periods. A considerable mutual "affection" seems to exist between mother and aunt and observations of hand contact, lip-to-lip contact, resting together either huddling or one leaning on the other, are frequent. Occasionally, however, the mother objects to the aunt's taking the baby for some reason and momentarily aggresses her.

As the mother group becomes larger, it adheres more closely together and the males are more actively excluded. The older juvenile males are also seldom seen with the mother group but do not seem to be as aggressively excluded. The mothers travel together as a rather close unit (Fig. 11), arriving as a group at the feeding station; at times 10 or more each wait their turn in line on a particular route limb to make the jump to the feeding station tree. They leave the feeding station as a unit and even sleep together in the same trees, typically arriving and bedding down at the same time.

Toward the end of the birth season the aunts are not as frequently seen as are mothers with other mothers. Many of the aunts probably gave birth themselves and are still associating with the mothers, but even the non-pregnant aunts are less in evidence.

During the whole birth season, ground activity is at a minimum. The females in the latter half of the season become considerably bolder in mov-

FIG. 11. Group of five mothers with infants at afternoon feeding station calmly feeding side by side with two red howlers. (Photograph by Frank DuMond.)

ing to the ground, probably due to the greater numbers of mothers acting as a group. However, the more tangled areas at the middle levels are still selected for rest periods. Mother—infant congregations are easily detected as the mothers and aunts continually make the affectionate purr call, to the infants.

There have been occasional observations of behaviors, in all likelihood reflecting dominance activity and general arousal, in which adult females have been observed displaying to another female or mother in a manner very much like the male penile display. Adult females have also been observed to assume the copulatory position with another adult female (Fig. 12).

4. Maternal Behavior*

As with so many other aspects of squirrel monkey life, casual observation of the mother—infant relationship suggests that for the most part the mother's behavior appears to be almost entirely passive with respect to her infant. However, under close scrutiny and particularly in unusual situations, the mothers seem capable of a considerable amount of active maternal care involving assistance, protection, and manipulation of the infant's

*See also Chapter 7.

124

FIG. 12. Adult female assuming the male coital position with another female. (Photograph by Frank DuMond.)

activity. Normally, the baby clings on the mother's back and it is in this position that the young squirrel monkey spends the first few weeks of life. The mother is able to go about her daily activities, forage, climb, run, and leap with minimal attention to her infant. When the baby nurses, it pokes its head forward and laterally under one of her arms which she raises somewhat, permitting the baby to nurse (Fig. 13).

It is not known at what age the mothers in our situation permit aunts to take the baby but it does occur quite early, probably around the third week. As I have indicated above, in most cases the aunt follows the mother and often nuzzles the infant, while making frequent affectionate purr calls. Aunts have been seen to nuzzle the inside thigh area of the infant who may then do a thigh spread (as in a penile display) to the aunt under this stimulus. An infant on one occasion did a foot wash after the thigh spread. Mothers also nuzzle their own infant on an aunt's back and two infant-carrying mothers may nuzzle each others' babies, making the affectionate purr calls. Frequently such mothers make lip-to-lip contact with each other as well. The baby may crawl on the aunt while she nuzzles it, or the aunt may manually lift the baby off the mother's back.

I have made several observations of mothers rescuing infants from aunts who, for the most part are young animals and apparently lack suffi-

FIG. 13. The two mothers carrying infants illustrate the customary infant positions. On the right, the typical dorsal riding position and on left, the typical nursing position with the baby's head under the mother's arm. (Photograph by Frank DuMond.)

cient experience to protect the infant in all situations. On one occasion a female with undeveloped nipples (thus assumed to be an aunt) was noticed carrying an infant. She appeared to be alone with the infant, which seemed unusual. As she sat on a branch the baby climbed off her back and crawled about a foot away. In order to test the aunt's maternal reactions, I approached the pair making gestures toward the infant. As the infant became frightened and vocalized, the aunt made no move to retrieve it but looked at me somewhat curiously. Almost immediately, the mother was seen rushing over from about 20 yards away; she ran to her infant and retrieved it. Similarly, during the experimental introductions, when a new fatted male was brought into the area and the colony was highly aroused, a mother was observed to run to an aunt very excitedly and forcibly lift the infant off her back (using both hands) and move from the area.

Mothers and aunts may cooperate in infant care as the following observation illustrates: A mother and an aunt that was carrying the infant were traveling as a pair. The mother was nuzzling the infant making affectional vocalizations. As the pair approached a grey squirrel in their route, the mother violently shook a small branch causing the squirrel to move away. A few moments later the baby was off the aunt's back alone, as both the mother and aunt had gone about 15 feet ahead. As the grey squirrel was returning to where the baby had been left, the aunt ran to the baby and presented her shoulder to it, making a purr call as the infant climbed on.

The mother or aunt seem to have no trouble in inducing the infant to climb on when desired. There are several methods by which this is accomplished. In many cases the purr call alone is sufficient to bring the baby toward the mother. As the baby approaches, the female crouches with one shoulder lowered against it. This retrieval position is also sufficient by itself to make the young squirrel monkey climb on. In one instance, a mother that did not want her baby to join a play group of older juveniles kept retrieving the infant in this way but it kept climbing off, attempting to join the play group. The baby climbed on almost automatically each time the mother crouched against it.

Young *Saimiri* are first observed attempting to eat solid food in the Monkey Jungle when 4−6 weeks old. The infant begins testing some of the food as the mother eats at the feeding station (Fig. 14).

The close association of the mothers with each other permits early formation of peer groups. The first peer play group was observed on August 12, although the infant born on June 12 had already started some play with

FIG. 14. Mother with infant at the feeding station. As the mother eats, the baby learns the location of the food and samples the most preferred choices. (Photograph by Frank DuMond.)

the younger juveniles of the previous birth season. At the early stages the mothers remain very close to the play group. The mothers often seem anxious to prevent younger infants from playing with the older juveniles. Several observations were recorded in which a juvenile two joined in a juvenile one play group and a mother rushed in making an aggressive bark to the juvenile two offender, who was effectively chased away. At times during play, even when only juvenile ones are involved, an infant will suddenly get the worst of the situation, start intense vocalizing, and the mother will rush in, retrieve her baby, and leave with it. At least during the first 6 months, it seems that the mothers are almost always aware of their offspring's location. On a number of occasions, I have seen a mother rush into a group of 5 to 10 infants and go straight to her infant, retrieve it, and leave.

As the infants grow older they are separated from the mother for increasing periods of time in their play-forage groups. There is some indication that other mothers and even colony males (at least subadults) may behave protectively toward these partially separated infants. On one occasion, a subadult male came over from 10 ft away to retrieve a baby that was alone and which I was menacing mildly. A few moments later he gently pushed the baby off but remained near. As I stared intently at the baby, he retrieved it again much as a mother would and left with it riding on his back.

In another observation, a group of six to seven infants were fascinated by a large rat snake that was resting in a small tree and were watching intently while making alarm chirps. Suddenly a mother came running over, and while eyeing the snake warily, went to her infant, gave the purr call and retrieved it. As she left, the other infants also left. This incident occurred, when most of the young were from 4½ to 5½ months old and were generally independent. It appears that maternal interest is still maintained when suitably stressful conditions arise, even though quite dissipated by this age under normal circumstances.

Under current conditions, early in December, i.e., when they are between 4 and 5 months old, mothers begin gently pushing their young away and somewhat later they may repel them even more roughly. As they increase their separations from their infant, the mothers begin spending more and more time on the ground foraging. The males, which are by that time in the fatted state and acting more self-assured, are again permitted into the female group and frequently interact sexually with the females. Nonetheless, even during this period a mother sporadically will go into a play group and a juvenile one will run to her and start nursing. These nursing episodes may also occur at the juvenile's initiation. In that case, the juvenile runs after the mother, making the purr call which usually results in her stopping. A number of mothers during this period are observed to have what appears to be milk-enlarged breasts. This perhaps explains the episodes of maternal initiation of nursing which probably continue until cessation of lactation.

It is during the period of the mating season that the adult females exhibit the most varied and active social behaviors we have observed among squirrel monkeys. Sexual interactions with the males become more and more prominent as the males who were aggressed as outsiders again become integral members of the colony. Some females begin to follow the fatted male group or will follow an individual male making the same purr calls which several months earlier were given to the young exclusively. Nonestrous females, however, continue exhibiting considerable antagonism toward the adult males throughout the mating season.

5. Infant and Juvenile Behavior

From birth the infant clings to the dorsal surface of the mother and, in a sense, during much of this period probably contributes as much to its own survival as does the mother. The infant does not seem to raise its head off the mother's back much during the first week and then during the following 2 weeks, the only direct contact with its environment is from its mother's back, looking around briefly while riding, and grasping twigs and leaves within reach while the mother rests. The infant, incidentally, occasionally has been observed to raise its hips out and away from the mother while still clinging with the forelimbs during elimination thus keeping from soiling the mother.

At between 8 and 10 weeks the infants are in definite play groups much of the time, though still riding on the mother when locations in the Rainforest are changed. As the mothers arrive at the feeding station, the riding juvenile one quickly hops off and takes some food.

Infants, as we have seen, show penile displays and copulatory motor actions at a very early age and have been seen displaying from the mother's back to a nuzzling female when only a very few weeks old. As soon as ground play develops, the juvenile one seems to reflexively initiate copulatory thrusting and positioning at almost any time its genital area comes in pressure contact with a wrestle partner. Play can be quite active and rough at 8–10 weeks of age and thus such close contacts are quite frequent by this time.

The general play pattern, even in the juvenile two, is usually initiated by one animal hopping bipedally to another monkey and grasping it on the back with its hands. The second monkey then twists around toward his "attacker" and a wrestle pair forms which usually ends a few seconds later with one pulling away and scampering off, being chased by the partner. Among juveniles 3 months or older, one animal frequently gets too rough or a threesome forms with two against one, and on these occasions, the one getting the worst of it will start vocalizing in pain or fight back very violently. As mentioned earlier, during the first 6 — 7 months, mothers frequently rescue their offspring on these occasions.

Juveniles have been observed executing a sort of play-inviting posture which consists of turning away from the prospective play partner, bending over so as to look at the play partner from between their legs, and sometimes reaching through with the hands at the partner. The play partner usually jumps on the initiator and a play-wrestle pair develops. Ploog *et al.* (1963) describe this as a form of sexual play, however, observations of this in the seminatural environment seem to indicate a more general play invitation is involved.

By the end of the first year, the juvenile ones are almost completely independent of the mothers who by this age are not even sleeping in contact with them in all likelihood. At the approach of the next mating season, the now 1½-year-olds are still in the same peer play groups though now this play is considerably rougher. As a general rule, the animals comprising any play group are similar in age and size. The juvenile twos may occasionally play with one of the juvenile ones but are frequently chased away quite roughly by the mothers. The juvenile two males are frequently involved in penile displays and fights that most often develop out of play groups. The penile displays are not identical to those typical of the mature fatted male which usually only flexes one thigh: the juvenile often flexes both thighs, "peeping" loudly and shows little concern as to what animals he may display to or the other animals' reaction to it. Juvenile males also show interest in the estrus females but in this are also different from the fatted males. There is no ritualized pattern, just a simple following and an attempt to sniff the genital area as the female walks away. Neither the females nor even the fatted males sometimes displayed to normally respond to these juvenile advances, although occasionally a fatted male may return a display.

Juveniles from 6 months to 2 years show more interest in inanimate objects than at any other age although even at this age sustained object manipulation is not regularly observed. One animal may pick up an object only to be surrounded by a host of 8 to 10 animals and lose the object. It seems likely that by 2 years the developing animal has become quite familiar with most objects to be found in the area and loses interest in objects that cannot be eaten.

At about 36 months the female enters the reproducing female group, probably going through an initial aunt phase during which she may or may not be pregnant. It appears reasonable to hypothesize that the female learns some of her subsequent adult maternal roles during the aunt stage.

The juvenile males apparently must develop another 2 years before entering the fatted male group and it is during this immediately prepuberal period that separation of some from the main colony to form the bachelor male group must occur. As a male becomes fatted for the first time, he apparently must contest with the established males for his position in the display groups. Indeed, it was during this stage that several first-time fatted males were probably killed in the dominance fights of December, 1966.

6. The Bachelor Male Group

For the past several years, groups of young adult or just preadult males have been observed living separately from the colony outside the Rainforest boundaries. The bachelor group customarily ranged from the park area adjacent to the Rainforest where they could beg food from the public and over the remainder of the 15-acre jungle premises. They were observed to sleep habitually in the same cluster of royal palms some 200 yards from the Rainforest night after night for a period of 4 months.

As the mating season started to develop, the group suddenly ceased sleeping in the royal palms, began entering the Rainforest, and seemed to be attempting to reintegrate with the colony. Several were observed making sexual approaches to the females and at least two were becoming fatted. At first Scar harassed them, then other males took up the harassment. The adult females did not seem as much disturbed by their presence as were the males.

The bachelor male group remained inside during the entire mating season and was not observed once in the royal palm area; however, they have been observed sleeping at the extreme Northwest edge of the Rainforest, on the opposite side from that in which the colony was observed sleeping. The bachelor male group by no means became fully accepted and when at the feeding station were continuously alert for the approach of the fatted males.

Toward the end of the mating season there were several incidents of adult females associated with juvenile ones, chasing the bachelor male group amid a wave of chucks. At another time, however, bachelors were observed in a group on the ground near the main colony as it moved with no noticeable antagonism. Several days later, apparently signaling the conclusion of the mating season, (on April 3) the bachelor group along with two new young males from the colony was observed outside the enclosure in the same palm trees habituated before the mating season. They resumed their former pattern and were not seen inside the area again that year.

One of the bachelor males that had become fatted, however, did not move out with the group. He had been observed somewhat separated from his fellows earlier and during April attempted to join the colony male group. He successfully displayed to Charlie and Scar but was violently chased by Silver and Pink, who were then Alpha and Beta. During this unsuccessful attempt to join the colony he was usually seen hiding close to the male group, watching intently, and would frequently kick. Whenever

Charlie and Scar were alone he would come in and display to them; any-
time Silver and Pink moved toward him he would disappear.

On April 27 he was seen outside with the bachelor group, was no longer
fatted, and was not seen inside again. It is possible that had the experimental males not been present this male would have successfully joined the
colony.*

B. Vocal Communications†

The squirrel monkey is one of the most vocal of all primates, presenting
a multiplicity of vocalizations, many high pitched and almost birdlike, that
are given in a variety of social and individual situations. The actual sound
elements are limited and many calls are made up of differing combinations
of tone, length, overtone quality, and rapidity of elements. Many of the
calls have a continuum of intensity that appears to convey varying shades
of meaning. To further complicate analysis, as the animals move through
various phases of the yearly cycle the vocalization patterns of the various
subgroups change markedly. For example, during the birth season the affectionate purr is heard only from females in association with infants but
during the mating season a similar sound is also heard from fatted
males and estrus females in sexual interactions and from juveniles soliciting nursing.

Calls uttered by animals in a relatively low arousal state seem somewhat
variable; for example, while foraging or resting, when most animals are in
fairly continuous contact, some vocalizations such as the contact chirps
and peeps each occur intermittently. Calls made by animals in a high state
of arousal are more specific and the conditions under which they are given
can be described with some certainty.

Since much of the squirrel monkey's time is spent in individual foraging
activity, contact calls may be quite important in preventing separation
from its group. During very windy weather when visual or auditory contact
is more difficult, contact chirps are more frequent.

The systematic analysis in quantitative terms such as that undertaken
by Winter and his colleagues (Chapter 10) represent a vital step in the understanding of the vocal behavior of *Saimiri* which seems to be a major
area of this primate's total behavior. However, Winter's work was with
Saimiri of Brazilian origin, while the Monkey Jungle colony is of the Peru-

---

*This male, along with another bachelor male which became fatted during the 1967-1968
mating season successfully joined the colony male group and appear to be totally integrated.
The remainder of the bachelor group moved out of the Rainforest March 25. It was noted
that the bachelor group was not harassed nearly as violently as in the previous year, further
supporting the belief that the experimental males disrupted the relationship between the
bachelor group and the colony.

†See Chapter 10.

vian variety, and his studies were carried out in the laboratory with its una-voidable spatial and social limitations. It is then of use to describe some of the sounds heard frequently enough in our semifree-ranging setting to be tentatively associated with particular social contexts or sets of conditions and which in many cases repeatedly have elicited responses from other animals hearing it (Table III).

TABLE III

SIGNIFICANT VOCALIZATION OF *Saimiri* IN A SEMINATURAL STATE

Major group	Call and phonetic approximation[a]	Description of situations and behavior in which call is heard
Clear note "eeee" continuum Single calls	Distressed isolation "eeeeeee". Long whistle note approximately 1 second long (isolation peep)	Heard when a major predator or a trapping incident disperses colony. May be answered in kind by other displaced animals. When a trapped member was released and gave the call, it was answered by "contact chirps." Probably indicating lower arousal of the colony animals and/or the "I am here" function of the contact chirp.
	Mild isolation "eeee". Shorter and less intense than above, approximately $\frac{1}{2}$ second (variation of isolation peep)	Apparently given when an animal has lost contact with its group and wishes to rejoin or reestablish contact. May be answered in kind or by contact chirps.
	Very low arousal "eee." Shorter and less intense than above (peeps)	Heard in a variety of mild attention situations; apparently almost anything occurring that may slightly raise the state of attention or arousal higher than before the call
	Startle "eee" Very short, very high note (alarm peep)	Heard when an animal is startled or surprised. Subject and other animals rush upward or away from stimulus, then look back; may be repeated by other animals. Frequently heard during ground forage activity
Multiple calls	Infant or juvenile isolation "eee-eee-eee" rhythmically repeated	Heard from distressed infants or young juveniles separated from mother; a shorter call than adult isolation
	Moderate arousal peep "ee-ee-ee" rapidly repeated. Can become more intense with overtones: "eh-eh-eh"	Heard from juvenile animals; frequently accompanied by an erection in the following situations: (1) Social conflict such as being chastised by an adult, i.e., hair-pulling aggression. (2) Getting the worst of a play situation. (3) Juvenile penile display

TABLE III (Continued)

Major group	Call and phonetic approximation[a]	Description of situations and behavior in which call is heard
	Play peep "eee--- eee." Clear short note randomly repeated (play peep)	Heard from primarily younger juveniles while playing. If play becomes rough or one animal is getting hurt "moderate arousal peeps" occur
Chirp "che" continuum Single calls	Alarm chirp "cheun." Ends with a nasal sound; contagious to others (yap)	Heard from animals frightened by an identified threat such as a snake, cat, or human. Juveniles give call to fatted males. Other animals usually approach to watch object and repeat calls. Young juveniles may give call to object neutral to adults which then ignore the call
	Aggressive chirp "chuck." Repeated single calls, contagious (cackling)	Heard in noncontact aggressive behavior such as: (1) From a group chasing noncolony males from colony area. (2) From females chasing colony males from immediate area. (3) From fatted males during displays. During birth season given mostly by females. During mating season given mostly by fatted males. A similar call seems to be a warning. It is heard when a hawk flies close to monkeys in a group
	Single chirp "che." Sounds like single element of contact chirp	Heard in nonspecific, low arousal situations with no obvious meaning, at times seems to be an answer to other calls
Multiple calls	Mild aggressive chirp "chu chu." Harsh, almost staccato (chuck)	Seems a mechanism for maintaining spatial separation. Given primarily by adult females to older juveniles and adult males when they approach a mother — infant group; receiver maintains distance or avoids caller. May give way to aggressive chucking if receiver does not respond
	Contact chirp "che che." Less harsh than above. On a higher pitch (twittering or chirp)	Given by animals mildly attempting to establish contact with others in a group. Usually short range. May be given as answers to isolation calls possibly as a directional aid to seeking animals; may be given and answered in kind with no observed behavior change
	Feed chirp "eeche-che" or "che che che," etc. A softer and higher tone than above and frequently has an "eee" element included (trill)	Heard at feeding time by animals about to eat

TABLE IV (Continued)

Major group	Call and phonetic approximation[a]	Description of situations and behavior in which call is heard
Squawks and raucous purrs	Male raucous squawk "rdddt" (err)	Heard very frequently during mating season from fatted males during displays; in male—male confrontations, when a male is chased by a female, or when an outside disturbance such as a low-flying airplane disturbs the males. Seems to indicate arousal, tension or annoyance; on five occasions a male hearing a squawk looked in direction of call and executed an arousal kick, which may suggest the arousal this call causes in hearing males. It has been heard in branch-shaking rage and aggression. Similar but less strong call is heard also from females
	Raucous purr "d-d-d-d-d-d." Distinguished from squawk in that each "d" element is equal (churr)	Heard frequently during penile displays, particularly when dominance positions are stable and well accepted by participating males, also from males in rest huddles. Females emit call at a negative object or during a female genital display
	Short purr "d-d-d." Shorter, softer than above	Heard when animals meet and there is apparently some tension; also if human closely approaches an animal. Caller may straighten torso and spread shoulders while making call
Soft purr	Affectional purr "rrrt." A true purr or humming sound; does not have well-separated elements (purr)	Has a continuum of tone and intensity at times almost a scrape sound which seems to be associated with a more solicitous attitude. During birth season given by mothers and aunts toward any infant; frequently associated with nuzzling the infant; or may be given to induce infant to climb on. During mating season, given by mothers or juveniles soliciting nursing episodes; by mothers while nursing, or in a rescue situation. Given by adult males to females or females to males during sexual interactions but not during copulation
Solicitous male twit	Male to female call "se-se-se-se." Very soft, rapidly repeated high note	Only observed from fatted males directed to a specific adult female during the mating season. The caller looks at the female and flutters his ears by pressing them to head in rapid sequence; usually results in female approaching
Rough aggressive call	Bark "awr-awr-awr" (spit?)	Heard when a single animal directs aggression toward a particular monkey. The caller is usually in close contact with the object which usually attempts flight; heard frequently from mothers to older juveniles playing too roughly with juvenile ones

TABLE III (Continued)

Major group	Call and phonetic approximation[a]	Description of situations and behavior in which call is heard
Relationship to above call uncertain	"Ah-ah-ah" with overtones; rough sounding low tone repeated	Heard from juvenile animals apparently socially disturbed or excited
Scream	Shriek — scream. Rough sounding very loud scream (shriek)	Given by animals being hurt or beaten as in a fight. Seems to be primarily a pain call

[a]Whenever possible these calls were related through behavioral situations or sound to the calls spectrographically identified by Winter (Chapter 9). When there has been a tentative correlation Winter's name for the call appears in parentheses.

IX. Experimental Projects

As noted above, the day-to-day social behavior of the squirrel monkey social unit involves some rather subtle relationships, and two experimental projects were worked out with Mr. Baldwin and Mr. Mazur who were conducting behavioral studies of their own in the Rainforest at that time. The purpose was to exert some unusual stresses on the social organization and thus further reveal the actual dynamics of the social structure. It was also hoped that we might learn something of the colony's reactions to outside groups and thus the degree to which our squirrel monkey colony represented a closed social unit. These first studies would also provide another look at the seasonal shift from the Iquitos environment to the local environment.

A. PROJECT ONE: SINGLE FATTED MALE INTRODUCTION

On July 14, 1966, 12 (6 males and 6 females) squirrel monkeys were purchased from a local importer. These animals had arrived in Miami the previous day from Iquitos, Peru and presumably had not been out of the jungle very long. Healthy mature monkeys were selected from a large group. They had arrived from the field, presumably during the early stages of the Iquitos mating season. The males were all in the fatted state. The animals were tagged with different colored belts for the males and neck collars for the females. Collars are used with the females so that if they become integrated into the colony and subsequently pregnant, the tag will not interfere with delivery of young.

The first project involved introduction of a single mature male into the colony. A single female had been introduced in April, 1965 and had apparently experienced no problems in becoming integrated into the colony, but it seemed likely from our observations that reactions to a strange male might well be different.

The remainder of the newly purchased group was kept in a cage completely separated from the colony for about 4 weeks to permit them to develop some group cohesiveness prior to their introduction into the colony in the second project.

The single male, which we named Charlie, was large and rather aggressive. He was placed in a small wire cage near the afternoon feeding station and kept there for 48 hours to permit us to observe preliminary colony reactions and to permit him to become aware of the immediate jungle area and the feeding schedule.

As Charlie was being carried into the jungle toward the feeding station area, he vocalized the alarm chirp which attracted the attention of Scar and the three males usually with him. The colony males came over, looked, and after having seen Charlie, apparently lost interest and left.

For about an hour after he was set out in the cage, there was very little colony reaction to him. Charlie answered several of the female "contact-chirp" vocalizations. Several subadult males came to the cage and made penile displays to him to which he did not respond. As we have seen, this is not at all an unusual pattern.

About 2 hours after he was placed in the Rainforest in the cage (6:15 P.M., during a peak social activity period of the colony) a large wave of aggressive chucks was heard from the colony, mainly from females all of whom were looking in the direction of Charlie. At this point, Scar and his group of males came toward the cage. As Scar reached the cage, he attempted to huddle. Charlie acted very submissive to Scar, avoided his direct glance, and assumed the submissive crouch position. The occurrence of the female threats directed at Charlie was, up to that time, the most prominent collective behavior that had been observed in the colony.

On the second and third day of exposure, very little attention was given to Charlie by the colony other than by a few subadult males that approached and made penile displays toward him to which he gave no response.

On July 16 at 5:15 P.M. Charlie was released. Within 5 minutes he was spotted and chased by several females toward the north and west. He then was approached by three subadult males who displayed to him; this time, Charlie submissively received their displays. Later Scar and his group approached him. Two simultaneously displayed to Charlie who in this case was most submissive, crouching very low and very still as Scar held the display position for 30 seconds.

After the initial displays were completed, the adult males seemed to express little interest in Charlie. Occasionally, subadult males would still approach him and display. Several nights later, two subadult males were observed following him and apparently at least one huddled with him as he began bedding down for the night.

The females continued to harass Charlie and seemed very uneasy about his presence. Once, at dusk, a large group of 15 to 20 violently chased him after he had spent some time climbing around in the favored lodge tree of the females.

Charlie was observed to vocalize more than the colony males did at that time. It was later learned that as the mating season approaches, the males vocalize more and become more aggressive in approaching the females. Probably much of Charlie's early troubles were related to his fatted state and increased boldness toward the females, who were not themselves in breeding condition.

For the next several days Charlie made a more or less continuous effort to enter into the large female group. When he got too close, the females would chase him 15 to 20 ft away and return to their group.

On July 21, Charlie was observed making a slow and cautious approach to the feeding station but did not venture near when females were present. The next several weeks were characterized by increasing tolerance of Charlie and his consistent efforts to join the colony. The major aggression directed at him was by the females though Scar was observed to chase him on several occasions. The young juveniles seemed afraid of him and would at times give alarm chirps if he happened to be moving toward them.

After 3 weeks had elapsed, Charlie was well tolerated but although he was no longer considered the threat that he was earlier, he still could not move within the female group. However, it is important to remember that at this time of year the colony males of the Rainforest do not move in the female group either. This leads to speculation that had Charlie been in the nonfatted state, when the males make no effort to interact with the females, he might have become integrated into the colony far more easily, as his continued efforts to enter into the female group apparently were contributing to the females' aggressive responses.

B. PROJECT TWO: GROUP INTRODUCTION

The second phase of these experimental projects involved the group that had been kept together in the community cage for 4 weeks. Several observations of the caged group detected some genital sniffs of the females by the males and several of the arousal state kicks. Some fighting was noted but their great fear of humans prevented close observation.

On August 7, 1966, this group, like the individual male, was taken out into the Rainforest in a wire cage for orientation. Two males had died and one female was dying from an ulcerated neck caused by a reaction to the collar so that the group now consisted of five females and three males, Silver, Pink, and Gordon.

Several differences from the single male Charlie were observed during caged orientation. The new females were quite active in reaching out and grabbing at juveniles that climbed on the cage. Scar and other colony males branch-shook at the cage of new animals and seemed highly aroused. The females were not as much in evidence as a month earlier with Charlie. In the late evening after the colony bedded down, the caged animals occasionally would alarm chirp and this would trigger several alarm chirps from the colony after which the colony seemed uneasy. Charlie did not make an appearance near the cage. On August 8 the group was released. Prior to release, a large group was around the cage, some making aggressive chuck sounds. On release, all seemed to scatter; the males went to the periphery and acted very timid. The new females did not seem to cause any disturbance in the colony and separated from the experimental males. The colony was evidently somewhat uneasy at the strange animals in their midst as they did not bed down until about 7:30, rather later than usual.

On the morning of August 9, the colony was apparently still disturbed over the presence of the new animals. The new males seemed to be primarily responsible as the females seemed to move through the group without any interactions from the colony. The colony was late in arriving for the morning feeding and had been on the northwest edge where a little later the experimental males were observed. As they saw me, the new males moved inward, at which time aggressive chucking was heard from the colony.

Observations over the next several days indicated that at least three (later all) of the new females were moving as a group, had come to the feeding station, and were able to move with complete freedom through the main colony. The new males were very actively aggressed and kept on the extreme periphery of the jungle. They were much more persistently aggressed than was the single male Charlie. On August 16, Scar and several colony males were observed violently chasing the three new males to the outside of the jungle and onto the surrounding grass. That same evening, all five new females joined in a sleep group not far from the center of the jungle. At 7:30 P.M. just at late dusk, Charlie approached the experimental female group and was observed through field glasses nuzzling several of the females very much like the sexual interactions observed during the mating season. The females did not react in any observable way, and 20 seconds later Charlie left the group. Several times after that, Charlie was observed in close association with the experimental females but it was not possible to determine if there had been any further sexual interactions.

A month of observations were lost due to other projects and when we were able to resume observations Silver and Pink had made their entry into the colony while Gordon, the third male, was no longer seen. Gordon was tentatively sighted once, badly cut up and lame, and he presumably died of wounds inflicted by the colony males.

By mid-January 1967, the three males, Charlie, Silver, and Pink were all integrated into the colony and had participated in the premating season establishment of a male hierarchy as described earlier.

At the beginning of the 1967 birth season the three experimental males and Scar were no longer fatted and comprised a fairly close group of colony males that were usually seen together.

It is probable that the presence of the new animals was responsible for the 1967 birth season starting 1 month to 6 weeks earlier than usual. Two of the collared females gave birth in late April and several colony females gave birth at this time also.* These conceptions must have occurred in November, at a time when no copulations had been observed, which is an indication that the fertile copulations may be the more "private" ones not easily observed.

With regard to the earlier birth season onset, it is noteworthy that the experimental males maintained their fatted state from their importation on through the local mating season, a period of 9 months; they thus may have stimulated an earlier onset of mating in colony females, while they accommodated to the local environment reproductive cycle in less than 1 year. The usual discreteness of the mating seasons in *Saimiri* probably is influenced by the synchronous occurrence of reproductive peaks in both sexes.

There is still some indication that the experimental females have not completely integrated with the colony, although they apparently have no problems with any of its members. Their nonparticipation seems at this time more a function of their own close association among themselves rather than any rejection by the other animals. It may well be that as they become mothers, in phase with the other colony mothers, further integration may occur.

Two fundamental differences were observed between the single male, Charlie, and the group of three males. Although Charlie made consistent efforts to integrate into the colony, there was less violent and persistent aggression directed toward him. The group of three males did not seem to

*The 1968 mating and birth seasons were closer to those previously recorded and the first infant was observed May 15, 1968.

make the persistent efforts to integrate yet were much more violently aggressed by the colony and were even observed attempting to leave the area but had not yet learned to scale the retaining fence. Consideration must be given to the possibilities either of different individual personalities, or that the colony might have progressed into a different behavioral phase of the annual cycle and thus reacted differently to the introductions 4 weeks later. It seems more probable, however, that Charlie, because he was alone, was more motivated to join the group and also apparently posed less of a threat to the colony than the group of experimental males. The three males had some group cohesiveness and were not as motivated to become integrated. The group entered the colony after Gordon's disappearance when it contained only two males, and this reduction from three to two may have been a factor that accelerated their integration.

This project was of interest in that it provided comparisons of colony reaction to strange males and females and demonstrated that new animals, particularly females, can be introduced into a stable colony even though the *Saimiri* social unit, particularly the subgroups, may appear rather tightly knit. Evidence of colony male reactions to outside males during the mating season, for example, to the bachelor male group, as opposed to reactions during the birth season suggests that the introduction of new adult males might be more successful during the birth season when the colony males are less aggressive. It would be expected that the females would aggress such strange males but not as violently as the colony males would later when they become fatted.

X. Notes on Husbandry and Possible Application from This Study

A. The Seminatural Environment

The care, maintenance, and feeding of a semifree-ranging colony of squirrel monkeys such as the one described above involves minimal personnel and expense, other than the necessary land space. As noted above, the highly varied diet, the frequency of feedings, the tropical enrichment of the environment, and the irrigation system probably would not be necessary as far as husbandry of the squirrel monkey is concerned. The basic requirements for such a social unit are a suitable tract of jungle (several acres or more), either fenced or in some way confining such as an island might be, and situated in a climate warm enough to permit year round outdoor living. One or more permanent feeding stations with regular feedings of probably twice a day would be adequate. This would depend on the ratio of population to cubic area of environment. If a fairly low population density was anticipated, the monkeys could probably forage a moderate amount of diet specialties from the environment, while a high-density population might require more frequent feedings of a more complete diet. A constant supply of fresh water also should be provided. A fairly large group of recent imports containing at least 25% adult females and no more than 10% adult males all in the same reproductive phase would probably foster the development of a normal social unit.

B. The Laboratory Environment

1. The Physical Environment

While the above-described facility would be ideal and would present a minimum of basic problems, it is realized that this kind of environment is impractical or impossible to duplicate in less suitable climates or where there might be space limitations. The minimum criteria or threshold conditions for the establishment of a self-perpetuating, normally reproducing social unit of *Saimiri* were not known at the time of the formation of the Monkey Jungle environment. What was attempted was the elimination of as many negative variables as possible and inclusion of as many features of the field environment as possible to insure the successful formation of the unit. How far this threshold was overshot is not yet known; however, certain suggested criteria and minimum environmental standards might now be postulated from the behavioral information so far obtained. The area for 8 to 10 animals should be probably no less than 15 by 8 by 6 ft high; an even larger area would be preferable and would prove to be necessary as group size is increased.

Another important feature would be to permit the separation of the subgroups during times when this seems important. This might be provided for by either adjoining several cages with fairly small connecting openings or, if a single larger cage were planned, partial partitions might be installed which could allow some degree of separation or isolation. Since visual separation might be as important as the spatial separation, the partitions might best be opaque.

2. The Social Environment

The social environment would have to meet certain criteria also. If successful breeding is to begin rapidly, a group of animals all in the same reproductive phase would be a fundamental requirement. Continuity of group membership should also be maintained, at least among the adult subgroups. The adult male to female ratio should be maintained at no more than one male to four females and in larger groups, 1 to 10 might be optimal. It probably would also help if some maturing females were permitted to remain in the group to replenish the reproductive female group and to obtain "maternal" experience as they mature. Occasionally, a maturing male should also be permitted to integrate into the adult male group as the reproductive female group increased or for replacement of losses should they occur.

The inclusion of these key dimensions in this environment would permit rather permanent in-phase subgroups to form naturally and allow for the natural seasonal behavior dynamics.

XI. Perspectives

The description of squirrel monkey behavior presented in this chapter of course has its limitations. However, it was felt in keeping with the goals of this volume, that present research might be directed more purposefully at more meaningful goals if suggestions and hypotheses based on still-developing information were presented. Thus postulations, conclusions, and generalizations based on samples smaller than ideal were arrived at, at the risk and with the expectation that future adjustments might prove necessary when a broader base of observations is assembled.

It was pointed out earlier for example, that not until 1966 did the young colony develop a full spectrum of age groups for both sexes and that each phase of the annual reproductive and behavior cycle is transitory and continually in a state of dynamic progression to the next phase. It follows that only short glimpses of each phase were possible.

A further limitation on the normative material was added with the introduction into the colony of the experimental animals. These undoubtedly had some effects on the development of the fatted male subgroup of the 1966—1967 mating season. It will be another year before the full effect can be evaluated. This experimental project did, however, provide a wealth of information that otherwise could not have been obtained and has also provided a group of tagged animals that will be of great value during the following year's observations.

Some broad but speculative comparisons between the squirrel monkey and some of the better known Old World monkeys, particularly the macaques, baboons and langurs, might be presented for consideration at this point. By comparison, squirrel monkeys seem relatively primitive with a smaller repertoire of behavioral expressions. Their life seems, to a greater extent, controlled by seasonal physiological changes.

This smaller repertoire of available behavioral responses is evident in a number of areas of the squirrel monkey's behavior. It was noted that grooming is seldom observed; that maternal care is more passively expressed than in the observed Old World monkeys; that the males during the birth season, when not involved with the colony for mating are virtually excluded from the central sphere of the Rainforest colony; that dominance hierarchies seem variable and impermanent and that collective colony defense is minimal; that colony organization and direction is not so much a function of direct social interactions or leadership as it is a function of simultaneous individual reactions to some stimulus; that gestures and facial expression play a minor role in communicative behavior; that possessiveness is poorly developed, and that investigative behavior so characteristic of Old World primates seems poorly developed in juveniles and almost nonexistent in adults.

ACKNOWLEDGMENT

I wish to acknowledge the great help Mr. John Baldwin of the Department of Social Relations at The Johns Hopkins University was to me in the preparation of this chapter. Mr. Baldwin was, at the time of my observations, making a parallel study of squirrel monkey behavior at the Monkey Jungle. Although some of his observations were coincident with mine, many were made at different hours or days. Not only were the mutual discussions with him invaluable but also the fact that his observations were made at different times had the effect of enlarging the observational base sample when we concurred on interpretations and tentative conclusions, each from our own individual observational samples and when we did not concur, the inadequacy of our samples were readily recognized and clearly pointed to areas that need more observations.

REFERENCES

Altmann, S. A. (1959). Field observations on a howling monkey society. *J. Mammal.* **40**, 317-330.

Beischer, D. E., and Furry, D. E. (1964). *Saimiri sciureus* as an experimental animal. *Anat. Record* **148**, No. 4, 615-624.

Castell, R. and Maurus, M. (1967). Das sogenannte Urinmarkieren von Totenkopfaffen *(Saimiri sciureus)* in Abhängigkeit von umweltbedingten und emotionalen Faktoren. *Folia Primatol.* **6**, 170-176.

Carpenter, C. R. (1934). A field study of the behavior and social relations of howling monkeys. *Comp. Psychol. Monographs* **10**, No. 48, 1-168.

DeVore, I., and Hall, K. R. L. (1965). Baboon ecology. In "Primate Behavior: Field Studies of Monkeys and Apes" (I. DeVore, ed.), pp. 20-52. Holt, New York.

Kendrew, W. G. (1953). "Climate of the Continents." Oxford Univ. Press (Clarendon), London and New York.

Lancaster, S. B., and Lee, R. B. (1965). The annual reproductive cycle in monkeys and apes. In "Primate Behavior: Field Studies of Monkeys and Apes" (I. DeVore, ed.), pp. 486-513. Holt, New York.

MacLean, P. D. (1964). Mirror display in the squirrel monkey, *Saimiri sciureus. Science* **146**, 950-952.

Mazur, A., and Baldwin, J. (1966). Huddle and sprawl behavior of semi-free ranging squirrel monkeys. *Lab. Primate Newsletter* **5**, No. 4, 5-8.

Ploog, D. W., Blitz, J., and Ploog, F. (1963). Studies on social and sexual behavior of the squirrel monkey (*Saimiri sciureus*). *Folia Primatol.* **1**, 29-66.

U. S. Department of Commerce (1941-1950). "World Weather Records 1941-1950." Weather Bureau, Washington, D.C.

U. S. Department of Commerce (1951-1960). "World Weather Records 1951-1960," Vol. 1, North America. Weather Bureau, Washington, D.C.

CHAPTER **5** _____

Some Aspects of Female Reproductive Physiology in the Squirrel Monkey*

Leonard A. Rosenblum

I. Introduction

It is critical to the establishment of any species as a useful laboratory animal that basic characteristics of its reproductive functioning be ascertained. Maximum utilization of a species in those research areas that require subjects of known age, condition, and experience and thus necessitate laboratory breeding colonies, demands information regarding a wide variety of topics. This chapter will attempt to present some of the basic material, still quite fragmentary, regarding reproductive cyclicity in female squirrel monkeys and the successful maintenance of pregnancy in this species.

Despite the obvious need for basic information and notwithstanding the widespread use of squirrel monkeys in laboratories around the world, data regarding many facets of their reproductive physiology are still lacking. The fact that the production of viable young in squirrel monkeys bred in captivity is still not a consistent occurrence, with neither successes nor failures well understood, attests to this paucity of essential information.

*The original research reported here was supported in part by U.S.P.H.S. grant #HD-00840 and N.I.M.H. Research Career Development Award #K3-MH-23685.

II. Reproductive Cyclicity

A. THE ESTRUS CYCLE

That periodic variations in the reproductive status of squirrel monkey females regularly occur in the wild state first became evident from reports by commercial animal dealers. Their information strongly suggested a well-delineated reproductive season. In both major *Saimiri* supply areas, Iquitos, Peru and Leticia, Colombia (see Chapter 1), pregnant females were usually observable in the collecting compounds from October to January and newborn infants with their mothers from about January to March. In addition, independent young infants became available from these dealers during April through June, further suggesting the existence of a restricted January to March birth period. The likelihood of reproductive seasonality in the laboratory was suggested by Wiswell *et al.* (1963) who, in a brief early report on research involving autologous transplantation of ovarian fragments to anterior eye chambers in *Saimiri*, indicated the strong suggestion of "... seasonal gonadotropic receptivity" (p. 434) in his data. However, to lay a more substantial base of biological knowledge and before more specific and controlled delineation of reproductive seasonality could be undertaken, it was necessary to gather data on the nature of subseasonal changes to determine, for example, whether or not these animals were seasonally polyestrus and, if so, the duration of each estrus cycle. Although Wiswell (1963) mentioned assessment of estrus cycles in his animals, the data are not presented. The first formal data on estrus cyclicity in the squirrel monkey were published in 1964 by Denniston, who estimated the cycle at about 24 days. In 1963, our laboratory undertook a fairly extensive study of reproductive cyclicity in a group of female squirrel monkeys over an extended period (Rosenblum *et al.*, 1967). For this purpose, 15 squirrel monkeys, all of the Iquitos Peruvian variety, were studied for varying periods of time over a 2-year period, the median period of study being 16 months (range: 1 − 20 months). These subjects were housed either individually, in all-female groups or in small groups with one or two males. During the entire study, the subjects were maintained under constant conditions of 11 hours of light and 13 hours of relative darkness. The feeding schedule was kept quite constant throughout this period and the diet consisted almost entirely of standard Ralston Purina monkey chow.

Assessment of changes in reproductive state was based primarily on the degree of epithelial cell cornification observed in vaginal smears. Smear material was taken by means of a platinum wire loop, then fixed in 96% alcohol for 1 − 2 minutes, stained with Harris hematoxylin for 2 − 3 minutes, and counterstained with eosin for approximately 1 minute more. Samples were generally taken daily, 5 days per week, and a total of over 3200 smears was obtained and analyzed.

Each slide was studied microscopically and scored for the relative number of cornified epithelial cells, young epithelial cells, leukocytes, and red blood cells (RBC's). In addition, when females were housed with males, the presence or absence of spermatozoa was tabulated. A female was judged as manifesting an estrus smear when cornified epithelial cells were at a relative maximum number and both young epithelial cells and leucocytes were entirely absent or present as only a few scattered cells. Since both RBC's and spermatozoa did not seem to vary greatly in number when present, only their presence or absence was noted.

Analysis of the data obtained and scored in this fashion seemed quite consistent and conclusive. As may be seen in Fig. 1, both the interval between estrus scores on the one hand and the presence of RBC's on the other, point to a modal interval of 7 days. The median interestrus interval across all subjects ranged from 6.0 to 9.5 days with 12 of the 15 subjects showing modal intervals of 7 days. Since red blood cells were less frequently detected, intervals between their appearance could only be assessed in 11 of the subjects, although 9 showed modal intervals of 6 or 7 days. In 11 instances, sperm appeared more than once in the smears of given females so that intervals between appearances could be tabulated. In 9 of the 11 cases, the intervals were 7, 8, or 9 days; the median of the distribution was 8 days. Thus, at least for the subjects of the Peruvian race of *Saimiri* that we studied, each of the three measures obtained, interestrus interval, the appearance of red blood cells and of spermatozoa, all agreed in pointing to a 7- to 8-day estrus cycle in these animals.

It must be pointed out that these and any other data based on peripheral material such as changes in vaginal cornification or the presence of spermatozoa cannot be taken as direct proof of actual ovulation. Thus, although these data suggest that the squirrel monkey may well have the shortest primate estrus cycle (Asdell, 1964) studied to date, the above caveat must be retained until material from repeated laparotomies and histological examinations is obtained. Indeed, even on the peripheral indications of estrus, all observers do not agree on the length of the estrus interval. Although Goss (see Chapter 6) presents data which seem confirmatory for a 6- to 8-day cycle by means of observations of copulatory plugs and some subtle weight changes apparently associated with ovulation, both the published material of Denniston (1964) and a recent study by Lang (1967) do not support this figure.

Based on estimates of 14 periods of high cornification observed in five females over a 3-month period, Denniston calculated a mean cycle length of approximately 25 days. Calculation was based partially on the assumption that several long cycles were probably in reality two or three cycles combined, and the results of dividing these "cycles" were also included. It seems possible that inferences drawn from so small a sample may well be subject to the distorting influence of brief estrus periods which occurred far more frequently than observed. Much as Denniston suggests, the duration of the estrus state itself is extremely brief (12−36 hours) being detected in the great majority of cases in our own study on only single days;

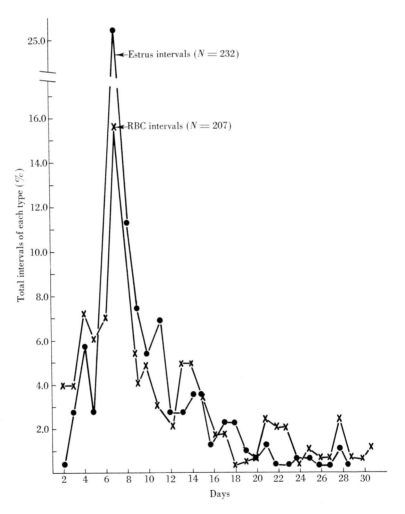

FIG. 1. The distribution of intervals between estrus-criterion days and between appearances of RBC's in the vaginal smears of all subjects.

thus, if some of the brief estrus states were missed, the "shorter" cycles observed by Denniston may actually have been multiples of the 7- to 8-day cycle obtained by Rosenblum *et al.* Indeed, as will be noticed in Fig. 1, in our own data, secondary peaks occur in the 13- to 14-day range, 21- to 23-day range and at 28 days, all rough multiples of the 7- to 8-day period.

Lang (1967), however, utilizing much more substantial data than Denniston, obtained from 25 Leticia, Colombian squirrel monkey females for periods of 8—12 months, presents a strong case for a cycle with a mean length of 12.54 ± 2.01 days. Lang utilized a vaginal lavage technique which involved insertion of approximately 1 ml of distilled water into the vagina and then aspiration of the fluid. One drop of the wash, diluted with two drops of distilled water, was air-dried on a slide, then fixed and stained. The smears obtained showed several consistent characteristics: the complete absence of red blood cells throughout; no systematic relationship between the presumed cycle and the ratio of basophilic to acidophilic cells; and most importantly, a decrease in the percentage of nucleated acidophilic cells on the sixth through eighth days of the suggested 12- to 13-day cycle. The difference in the sampling techniques used, distilled water lavage versus loop, and the varieties of squirrel monkey observed, Western Brazilian versus Central Peruvian, may in some manner be involved in the differing estrus cycles suggested by Lang and by Rosenblum *et al.* The use of distilled water by Lang for vaginal lavage obviated the possibility of observing RBC's due to lysis in this hypotonic solution; in the subjects of our study, the RBC's seemed significant since their appearance followed a similar cyclicity to that of the remaining cellular material. It may be noted in this regard that in the Rosenblum *et al.* material, the presence of red blood cells was usually quite out of phase with the judged estrus smears and probably represented the low estrogenic phase of the cycle. It seems likely as regards the epithelial tissue that both sets of data agree on a substantial drop in young nucleated cells as an indication of estrus, but it is not at all clear how the Rosenblum *et al.* data could have shown clear signs of a repetition of this decrease after 7 days when Lang's data fails to show any signs of the same. Although, as in the case of Denniston's material, it is possible to interpret longer cycles as the result of missed shorter ones, the reverse is of course not reasonable. Just as was true of our own data, however, Lang does indicate a wide range of cycle length, from 6 to 18 days. Thus, there is clear overlap between the two sets of data and possibly the judgment and differentiation of middle and end points of the cycle represents the area of confusion. Regarding these observed variations in cycle length, Rosenblum *et al.* examined consecutive cycles within females across the year plus month-by-month analyses across all subjects and found no systematic or gradual changes in the length of those cycles that did occur.

There is in addition some indirect behavioral data on estrus cycle length derived from the intervals between the appearance of spermatozoa in the vagina of mated females. Contrary to the indications of Goss' observations and our own (both made on Peruvian squirrel monkeys), Lang reports primary evidence of copulation only on or about the seventh day of the 12- to 13-day cycle that he observed. Lang points out that vulvar plugs of desquamated vaginal epithelial cells often appear right after estrus and are easily confused with copulatory plugs upon gross inspection and, conceivably, some plugs observed by Goss without microscopic examination might have been of this type. This is unlikely, however, and would not explain either the 6- to 8-day cyclicity of the plugs noted by Goss or his or our own data on the cyclic presence of spermatozoa in the vaginal smear. Clewe (1966) also reports 5- to 6-day peaks of mounting receptivity in females during the mating season. Finally, of practical relevance to all of this material, Lang indicates that of 20 of his females whose ovaries were examined histologically, only one showed signs of true ovulation despite the fact that the subjects were sacrificed in August which, as we shall see later, might well have been expected to be part of the breeding season.

In summary then, we cannot at present state what the precise length of the estrus cycle of squirrel monkeys is or if it is identical for all races, although it seems likely to fall between 7 and 13 days. This cycle range is still quite short compared with Old World primates studied to date, virtually all of which show approximately lunar cycles. The several New World forms for which some data exist are *Cebus* with a suggested cycle of 16−20 days and *Ateles* and *Alouatta* with 24- to 27-day cycles (Asdell, 1964). More precise resolution of this critical characteristic in *Saimiri* must await further study of large numbers of acclimatized specimens of both Peruvian and Brazilian forms under controlled conditions of maintenance and with the use of repeated gross and histological examination of ovarian tissue.

1. Influences of Exogenous Hormones and Superovulation

Before leaving the general area of estrus cyclicity, it should be noted that several pieces of data have also been obtained on the influence of exogenous hormones on vaginal cornification and on ovarian function. With a view partially toward validating the indications of the vaginal smear pictures obtained as indicative of differing hormonal balances, a pilot study was carried out in our laboratory to determine the influence of exogenous hormone treatment upon the vaginal smear picture. Beginning in late August (1964), a month, as we shall see below, in which many females in our laboratory have begun to pass into an anestrus phase while others remain sexually active, 13 females were chosen from the colony. Seven of these showed consistently low cornification levels and the remaining six, relatively high degrees of vaginal cornification and indications of estrus. Vaginal smears taken during a 15-day preadministration period showed an average of only 21% of the low-cornification group showing estrus criterion smears on any given day whereas an average of approximately 80—90% of the high-cornification group showed estrus smears on these days. Beginning on the sixteenth day of the study, the low group received 2 mg daily of urestrin (estrogen) for 5 days and the high group received daily injections of 5 mg of progesterone for the same period. For days 17—22 the percent of the low group in estrus jumped to 46% while the previously high group fell to 43%. Within 5 days however, the low-cornification group fell to preadministration levels of 19% and the high group rose again to approximately 63% in estrus, the seasonal shift toward anestrus probably having grown more pronounced by this time.

Further preliminary efforts at manipulation of squirrel monkey ovarian function by means of exogenous hormones have included attempts at superovulation in our own laboratory and by Bennett (1967a), and induction of ovulation in conjunction with artificial insemination (Bennett, 1967b). Induction of ovulation in rhesus monkeys had been achieved for many years using a variety of compounds (e.g., Simpson and VanWagenen, 1963). Considering this related data and utilizing rough extrapolations of hormone levels used in mice on the one hand and humans on the other, in 1965 we successfully induced superovulation in three squirrel monkeys in the following manner: two i.m. injections of 50 IU of pregnant mare's serum were administered in 1 ml of water at a 3-day interval; 2 days later, 75 IU of human chorionic gonadotropin was injected. Two days later, laparotomies were performed on two subjects and 3 days after that the third subject was examined. Gross and histological examination indicated that considerable enlargement of the ovaries of all subjects had occurred with numerous large follicles in each. The first two subjects had not actually ovulated at the time of laparotomy whereas the ovaries of the third showed numerous sites at which ovulation had occurred. Bennett (1967b), in more recent and considerably more substantial work, has successfully used the following regimen to induce ovulation in squirrel monkeys: two injections daily of 20 IU PMS (Pabryn: Paines & Byrne, Ltd.) for 9 days; during the last 4 days, the subject also received two injections of 250 IU of HCG (Pregnyl: Organon). Other work by Bennett (1967a) suggests that the critical dose of PMS required to induce ovulation lies between 5 and 10 mg injected twice daily. A number of females have been superovulated in this fashion and when semen electroejaculated from males has been introduced 1 or 2 days after completion of the hormone series, fertilized ovum have been recovered from both the fallopian tubes and uterus (Bennett, 1967b). The production of viable offspring by means of artificial ovulation and insemination has not as yet been reported; this seems a likely next step, albeit a potentially difficult one although artificial insemination alone following natural ovulation might prove much less difficult. It also seems reasonable to speculate that the relatively short estrus cycle normally occurring in this species and the growing ability of investigators to manipulate *Saimiri* reproductive functions should greatly expand the use of squirrel monkeys in studies of basic primate reproductive physiology in the near future.

B. SEASONAL CYCLICITY

Although some disagreement existed in the early literature reported by Hill (1960), there seems to be general accord among most current observers that a fairly well-defined "birth peak" as defined by Lancaster and Lee (1965) exists in the wild for most squirrel monkey varieties studied to date. In our own study of vaginal cornification cycles (Rosenblum *et al.*, 1967), within several months of the beginning of our research it became apparent that general changes were occurring in the appearance of the vaginal smears that were characteristic of many of our subjects. As shown in Fig. 2, there appeared a sharp tendency for most of these Peruvian subjects to show some degree of estrus during our late spring and early summer months during the first year of captivity. Far fewer subjects on the other hand came into the designated estrus condition during autumn. Accompanying the increased tendency to manifest full estrus according to our criteria, there appeared a generally sustained level of heightened cornification reaching a peak in July. For quantitative purposes, both cornified epithelial cells and young epithelial cells were each scored in all our slides on a half-point scale from 0 to 3 depending on the quantity of each cell present in relation to the total amount of cellular material in the field. By subtracting the noncornified tissue scores from those for cornified cells on each day, a simple index ranging potentially from -3 (completely noncornified smear) to $+3$ (completely cornified smear) was obtained. Figure 3 presents the mean monthly index value obtained in this way from the various subjects tested during the 21 months of study as well as the range and standard deviation of the scores across the months. After a rather variable period at the beginning of the study, characterized by widely ranging scores (perhaps reflecting differential adaptive reactions to capture, shipment, etc.), the mean monthly index was observed to be increasing toward a sharp peak in July. Given the presence of suitably active males (see DuMond, Chapter 4), this peak season of estrus in July would be associated with a subsequent birth season beginning late in December and January. Although there are some indications that the actual birth season in the collection areas of Iquitos and Leticia in South America (i.e., ca. 4–6° S. latitude) continues on into February and possibly March, the quantitative distribution of births throughout this season is not as yet available and the current data obtained under laboratory conditions suggest the possibility of a peak in January, given a $5\frac{1}{2}$-month pregnancy (see p. 162).

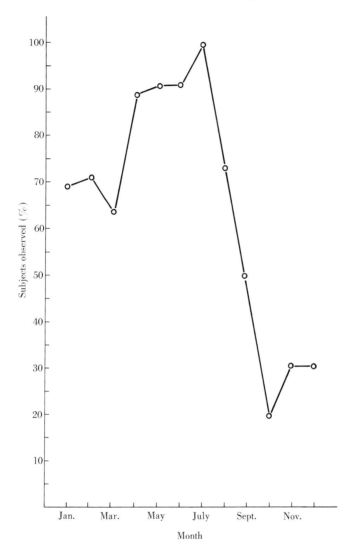

FIG. 2. The percentage of subjects showing estrus-criterion smears in each calendar month.

The seasonality in reproductive performance that characterizes this species in the wild state and which may be maintained at least initially in captivity has important implications for investigators who wish to achieve rapid breeding in this species in captivity. Obviously, acquisition of subjects during the period when estrogenic activity is in the decline may well result in a number of months of nonproductivity. It seems reasonable to suspect that acquisition of females, and in all likelihood males as well, in the late spring and possibly early summer of the northern hemisphere

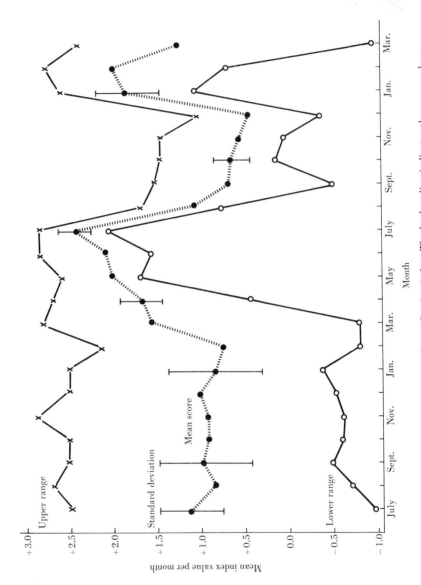

FIG. 3. Annual changes in the vaginal cornification index. The broken line indicates the mean values.

might maximize breeding potential during the first year in captivity. The restricted breeding season of this species in the wild and the potential alteration of this seasonality in captivity indicate that the study of the environmental factors that regulate squirrel monkey reproduction is vital to any general understanding of behavioral and physiological response systems in these animals and obviously to goals of efficient reproduction under laboratory conditions.

C. FACTORS INFLUENCING SEASONALITY

The primary environmental factor implicated to date in other animals that show breeding seasonality is some influence of changes in illumination (Bullough, 1951). Beginning with Rowan's classic study on birds (1925) and including more recent work on members of almost all orders of the animal kingdom, the effect of light on reproductive processes seems well established. The precise influence of changes in light differs from species to species, some responding to increases, some to decreases, either abrupt or gradual, and others to changes in the composition of light or its intensity when length does not vary or changes little. In a recent survey of annual reproduction cycles in monkeys and apes (Lancaster and Lee, 1965) covering a variety of primate forms, it was concluded that "in general, the timing of conceptions in the annual cycle of all populations shows some association with decreasing day length, favorable diet and high levels of precipitation (p. 509)." Similarly, MacRoberts and MacRoberts (1966) present evidence indicating that the annual reproductive cycles of both the Barbary ape and Japanese macaque are regulated by decreasing day length which triggers the onset of the mating period.

1. The Possible Role of Precipitation Cycles

DuMond (see Chapter 4), however, suggests that because most squirrel monkeys studied to date derive from areas so close to the equator the variation in total daylight from one part of the year to another is likely to be far too minimal to be the prime regulator of breeding cyclicity. He suggests that although both in South America and in his Florida jungle breeding occurs following a decrease in total length of daylight (minimal in South America, substantial in Florida), the correlation with the onset and termination of the rainy period seems of more likely significance. Mating, it is suggested, seems more closely associated with dry periods than with any particular change in illumination and results in birth coincident with the height of the rainy season and expanding plant growth and food sources. The evident correlations of the reproductive cycle and precipitation periods presented by DuMond cannot be denied and are of obvious adaptive value in terms of food availability for the late-pregnant and postparturent female and her infant. However, the systematic reversal in birth periods to the North American summer seen by DuMond in Florida, by Goss in New Orleans, and more recently by Lehner *et al.* (1967) in Winston-Salem, North Carolina under conditions of sustained high-level food supplementation requires further investigation of the environment at mating time as a means of establishing the basic regulatory mechanisms. We must avoid the pitfall of allowing the "birth tail" to wag the "mating dog" in elucidating this possibly complex cause and effect relationship.

2. *The Possible Role of Changes in Illumination*

It certainly is true that total length of illumination varies little in equatorial areas from season to season; however, as part of the growing precision of meteorological measurement, Gates (1966) and others (e.g., Johnson *et al.*, 1967) have made increasingly precise measurements of the variations in the spectral composition of sunlight as a function of a number of factors. Thus, for example, changes in the total air mass through which the light passes (as occurs with seasonal shifts in the position of the sun) and the relative amount of dust particles and water vapor in the air (likely to shift inversely in dry and rainy seasons) all influence total intensity of illumination and have differential filtering effects throughout the visual, infrared, and ultraviolet spectra. Since the red end of the spectrum seems considerably influenced by each of these factors (Gates, 1966), and squirrel monkey sensitivity in this region is relatively low (Jacobs, 1963), changes in the intensity of the reds might place this portion of the light suddenly below visual threshold or back above it and thus *Saimiri* might show more discrete, differential responses to shifts in sunlight than would be evident to human observers. It may be noted in this connection that Lockard (1963) reports that in 1937, Watanabe found that red light regulated irregular sexual cycles of female rats whereas blue light upset the sexual cycle.

Several years ago in our laboratory as a first approach to the question of the influence of illumination on female squirrel monkey reproductive states, the following study was undertaken: three Peruvian squirrel monkey females, each in the laboratory from 5 to 10 months prior to the onset of the study, were used. The subjects were placed into a light-tight box 18 inches wide, 36 inches long, and 22 inches high. A light-baffle blowing system provided appropriate ventilation and dry-bulb temperature readings (27°C) and wet-bulb readings (18.6°C) remained quite constant throughout the study. A single fluorescent fixture containing a Ken-rad 20-W daylight fluorescent bulb provided illumination within the chamber. The light—dark cycle was regulated with an automatic 24-hour timer and feeding, watering, and handling always took place during the light period of the day. Vaginal smears were taken and prepared 4—5 days each week in a fashion identical to that described previously (Rosenblum *et al.*, 1967). Each slide was assessed for attainment of estrus criteria and cornification index scores were tabulated.

In order to assess the influence of illumination during the period of dynamic change in cornification levels, the study was begun in mid-July and run through the middle of November. Five separate conditions were imposed: (a) *Darkness:* For the first 3 weeks of this study, the subjects were placed on a regimen of 20 hours of darkness and 4 hours of light. (b) *Increasing light:* One hour of light was added during each of the next 16 days until the subjects were receiving 20 hours of illumination each day. (c) *Full light:* During the next 5 weeks, subjects were maintained on the 20-hour light/4-hour darkness schedule. (d) *Decreasing light:* For the next 16 days, the light period was decreased by 1 hour per day until all subjects were once again obtaining only 4 hours of light each day. (e) *Darkness:* For the last 3 weeks of the study, subjects were maintained under 20 hours of darkness and 4 hours of light, the same conditions under which the study had begun. As indicated in Fig. 4, one subject, no. 23, failed to show any discriminable reaction to the changing light conditions that could not be interpreted in terms of a normal seasonal shift toward anestrus and low cornification values. Comparison of the cornification values for subjects SA and SB when compared with those for seven normative control subjects observed continuously throughout this period indicated a marked reversal toward increasing cornification with the decreasing and low-level illumination instituted during October and November. Scores for SA and SB during July, August, and September were not grossly different from those of the control subjects. However, the scores obtained in October and November for SA and SB during the period of decreasing light and almost complete darkness were higher than all of the seven control scores available in October and higher than all but one in November. Even in the previous year of our normative study all subjects who showed positive cornification indexes in September, as did SA and SB, showed drops in the following month. In neither year did any normative subject drop as low in index value in September as did SA and SB (1.0 and 0.86, respectively) or show values even approaching those of SA and SB for the immediately succeeding October and November.

Finally, it may be noted that during the period of increasing and full light SA and SB showed only 5% and 10%, respectively, of smears that could be judged as meeting the estrus criteria. On the other hand, of smears taken during October and November, which as indicated in Fig. 2 above were periods of lowest estrus attainment in normative subjects, 21% and 17% respectively reached the estrus criteria.

Clearly, a preliminary study of this sort, with its few subjects, special housing conditions, and relatively arbitrary manipulations of the light—

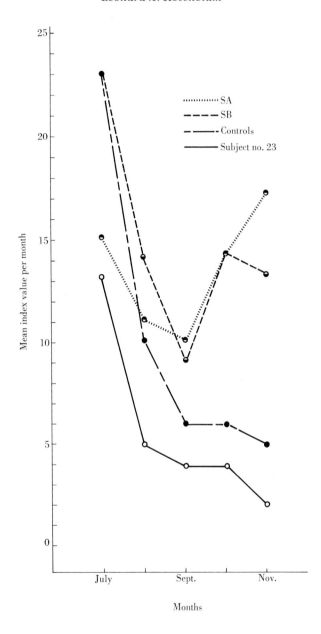

FIG. 4. Monthly changes in mean cornification levels in control subjects under normal laboratory lighting conditions and in experimental subjects following reduction in the light — dark ratio.

dark cycle, can be no more than an initial guide in stimulating the formulation of more exacting investigations in this potentially significant area. At the same time, however, it seems not unreasonable to suggest that the role of illumination change, though only grossly varied here, may not be dismissed out of hand with regards to its potential role in regulating reproductive cyclicity in squirrel monkeys in the wild.

Notwithstanding seasonally restricted seasons of breeding in captivity, most investigators working with stable colonies under adequate conditions of maintenance (see Lang, Chapter 14) report relatively high levels of conceptions in this species. In our laboratory, for example, when the total breeding colony is considered, including new arrivals and older animals, a conception rate of 4 to 5 per 100 animal months (number of subjects times the number of months in the colony) is obtained. Considering the restricted breeding period, this at least approaches the figure of 6 to 7 per 100 animal months which seems characteristic of the less seasonally breeding *Macaca nemestrina* and *Macaca radiata* colonies we have maintained in our laboratory under relatively similar conditions over the past 6 years. The outcomes of these *Saimiri* pregnancies present a considerable problem, however. Although the production of viable infants has apparently improved considerably over recent years (see Goss, Chapter 6; Lehner *et al.*, 1967), the information received informally from various investigators indicates that nonviable terminations of pregnancy and neonatal deaths still present a considerable difficulty in many laboratories.

III. Problems of Reproduction

A. ASSESSMENT OF PREGNANCY

In order to evaluate the pregnancy problems that beset these subjects under most laboratory conditions, it is first necessary to make reliable and systematic assessment of conceptions, such that early abortions will not be missed and credited to nonconception categories. As Goss (Chapter 6) and Beischer and Furry (1964) point out, maintenance of systematic weight charts and continuous visual and palpatory examinations should enable one to detect most pregnancies in the colony. However, with daily weight variations of 20 gm or more possible from the ingestion of food or water or minor health changes, and with both visual and palpatory pregnancy inspections requiring some degree of sophistication and experience, these measures often may not be reliable indicators of pregnancy until about 6 or 8 weeks after conception, i.e., about one-third of the way through the pregnancy. Goss (Chapter 6) indicates strong evidence of gestational length at 170 ± 2 days and this seems a quite precise average, probably more accurate than the estimate of 167 ± 2 days based on weight changes in a single subject by Beischer and Furry (1964). Wiswell (1965), in a similar estimate, though based on more substantial data (eight births), estimated gestation at 165 ± 5 days.

We have found that a method based on the biological assay for chorionic gonadotropin developed by Delfs (1941) has been useful when one wishes relatively early and reliable diagnosis of pregnancy in a squirrel monkey colony (Nathan *et al.*, 1966). This technique is based on the increase in uterine weight of immature rats (21- to 23-days-old) in response to treatment with a substance containing chorionic gonadotropin. In essence, for this method a small amount of dried precipitate of monkey serum is injected into test rats and an equal quantity of fluid containing known amounts of International Standard chorionic gonadotropin is injected into controls. Comparison of the uterine weights of test and control rats allows assessment of chorionic gonadotropins in the monkey's blood and pregnancy evaluation to be made. This approach seems reliable after about 3 weeks gestation and until at least the fifteenth week.

B. DIET AND PREGNANCY OUTCOME

1. Vitamin D₃ Deficiency

The actual outcome of pregnancy has largely been studied with respect to the influence of dietary factors. A recent preliminary report to the *Laboratory Primate Newsletter* by Lehner *et al.* (1967) indicates that vitamin D_3 in the diet may be important for successful reproduction of captive *Saimiri*. In a group of 18 Brazilian females fed a 23% protein diet containing vitamin D_3 instead of D_2, conceptions were obtained in 17 females, resulting in 16 live births after the subjects had been in the laboratory for about 18 months. In striking contrast to the results obtained in many other laboratories, including our own and that of Goss (see Chapter 6), only a single stillbirth was obtained in this sample. A second study indicated that protein content in the diet in the range of 16−28% did not seem to influence the outcome of pregnancy (67% in the low-protein group, 75% in the high group), nor did fat content in the diet. In this second sample, reproduction also began after a captive period of about 14 months but was not nearly as successful as in the first group. Of the total of 53 young, probably nulliparous females, conceptions were detected in only 33 and of these 10 (30%) resulted in apparent stillbirths. This is closer to the results of others including our own laboratory and Goss (Chapter 6) who used a rich and varied diet but had only 42.5% of 40 specifiable conceptions terminate in vigorous infants. Although Lehner *et al.* do not report their means of conception detection, it is possible that some undetected early abortions (none are reported as occurring) may account in part for an exceptionally high reproductive success figure. Furthermore, Cooper (1966) has indicated that in his outdoor colony, in which substantial sunlight is available and thus apparently no need for any artificial vitamin D supplementation is presented, despite high conception rates in multiparous females, only 30−40% of conceptions result in viable infants. Needless to say, in this, as in most other areas of squirrel monkey reproductive biology, many loose ends still persist. Nonetheless, the results of the two studies by Lehner *et al.* seem at present to warrant the conclusion that inclusion in the diet of vitamin D_3 instead of D_2 is worth considering and may play an important role in successful reproduction in some forms of *Saimiri* at least. Hampton *et al.* (1966) have reached the same conclusions regarding the importance of D_3 in the breeding of marmosets. The use of more fully matured though still young adult subjects by Lehner *et al.*, as in their first study, also seems likely to enhance successful outcomes of pregnancy.

2. Folic Acid Deficiency and Megaloblastic Anemia of Pregnancy

Several years ago, Nelson and I became impressed with the similarity of the pregnancy difficulties observed in many captive squirrel monkeys and those reported in human women suffering from megaloblastic anemia of pregnancy. This disease in humans, stemming primarily from folic acid deficiency, has recently aroused considerable attention among obstetricians because of its previously unsuspected prevalence in human pregnancies. Giles (1966), in an extensive study of 335 pregnant women suffering from megaloblastic anemia, presents some important findings potentially quite germane to the problems encountered in squirrel monkeys. Stillbirths, for example, though rather uncommon in women, were more than twice as frequent in women with megaloblastic anemia than in controls. The relevance of human experience with folic acid deficiency is enhanced by the fact reported by Giles that although in every pregnancy the developing fetus makes increasing demands on the maternal stores of folic acid, in the case of multiple pregnancies the depletion is intensified. The excessive fetal demand of twin pregnancies in humans seems likely to correspond to the demand placed on squirrel monkey mothers by a fetus growing to about 15% of her own body weight. In humans, in addition to the normal fetal demands intensified in multiple pregnancies, dietary insufficiency of folic acid and malabsorption play major roles in producing the megaloblastic anemia. Women whose diets were low in meat and eggs and fresh fruits and vegetables represented about one-third of Giles' sample. Selective low rates of absorption of folic acid, apparently of a fairly permanent sort, also characterized a majority of the women in the megaloblastic group.

Since, as Giles reports, sharp increases in mean corpuscular volume

(MCV) are frequently observed in the more pronounced cases of megaloblastic anemia, Nelson and I concentrated our attention heavily on this aspect of the blood indices for a number of squirrel monkey females during various periods of their pregnancies. Blood indices were obtained from a total of 43 squirrel monkeys during pregnancy, including samples taken within 1−2 weeks of the termination of pregnancy. In addition, a series of blood scores were obtained on six nonpregnant control females beginning approximately 6 weeks after arrival at the laboratory. All subjects were maintained on *ad lib* diets of Purina chow, but about half the pregnant subjects received vitamin−iron−folic acid supplementation, 5 days per week for an average of 9 weeks prior to termination of pregnancy. This supplementation, administered in a single eyedropper of milk, included approximately 1 mg of folic acid (Folvite: Lederle), 1.25 mg of iron (Feosol: Smith Kline and French), and a drop of multivitamin mixture (Poly-Roy: Royal). Although a direct relationship appeared between the outcome of pregnancy and the mean corpuscular volume of blood drawn from the ear just prior to termination of pregnancy, no significant correlation existed between the number of weeks of supplementation and the final mean corpuscular volume obtained. Table I presents the mean blood indices for the (1) control females, (2) mothers of live viable infants, (3) mothers of infants born alive who survived less than 10 days, (4) mothers delivering apparent fullterm stillbirths, and (5) females producing early abortions. These scores are based on samples drawn 1−14 days (mean = 7.3 days) prior to the termination of pregnancy. Note the systematic increase in mean corpuscular volume from mothers of viable infants to those having abortions. The placement of the "controls" between groups 2 and 3 suggest that these presumed controls may not have been adequately acclimated when used; Giles (1966) indicates that a variety of stresses other than pregnancy will also produce folic acid depletion in subjects prone to this difficulty. The separation of the outcome groups in terms of MCV is further indicated by the fact that only one mother of the 13 viable infants had a MCV as high as 59.0 μ^3 whereas 43% of both the neonatal death group and the stillbirth group and 71% of the early aborters had scores higher than 59.0. Indeed, only two aborters of the seven were below 63.2μ^3. As indicated in Fig. 5, a sharp sustained rise in MCV early in the last third of pregnancy characterized both the aborter and stillbirth group. A similar peak appears in the neonatal death group several weeks later. As shown in the graphs provided by Goss (Chapter 6), it is approximately at the beginning of the last 8 weeks of pregnancy that weight gain of the female squirrel monkey shows a dramatic rise, reflecting undoubtedly the rapidly increasing size of the fetus.

TABLE I

MEAN BLOOD INDICES FOR FINAL SAMPLES DRAWN 1–14 DAYS (MEAN = 7.3 DAYS)
PRIOR TO TERMINATION OF PREGNANCY

	N	RBC	HGB	PCV	MCV	MCH	MCHC
(1) Nonpregnant	6	7.77	12.3	45.5	58.8	15.8	29.9
(2) Live births	13	7.77	12.5	42.5	54.8	16.3	29.8
(3) Neonatal deaths	7	7.02	10.9	39.0	55.6	15.7	28.7
(4) Stillborn	16	6.63	11.0	38.9	59.7	16.9	29.4
(5) Abortion	7	5.95	11.5	38.9	65.6	19.6	30.0

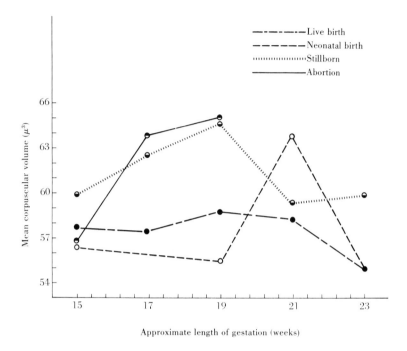

FIG. 5. Changes in mean corpuscular volume during pregnancy in various outcome groups.

Although Giles reported that in women it is generally only in severe cases of megaloblastic anemia of pregnancy that megaloblasts, the large embryonic precursors of mature red blood cells, are found in the peripheral blood, we have observed such cells in a number of peripheral blood smears. More extensive analysis of these peripheral smears and related bone marrow films, the latter representing the most reliable indication of megaloblastic anemia, are now underway. Nonetheless, although a complete discriminating diagnosis is yet to be made, there seems to be a comparable symptomatology of humans with megaloblastic anemia of pregnancy and our own pregnant squirrel monkeys and a parallel relationship of the blood picture and pregnancy outcome. As a result, we feel there is strong presumptive evidence that folic acid deficiency resulting in megaloblastic anemia of pregnancy, perhaps confounded with other hematological problems, accounts at least in part for the inconsistent production of viable young in *Saimiri* in our own colony and perhaps elsewhere in captivity.

The fact is, however, that approximately 1 mg of folic acid per day, 5 days per week for approximately the last 9 weeks of pregnancy did not entirely eliminate the problem, even though on a body weight basis it represents between 20 and 100 times the recommended prophylactic doses for humans discussed by Giles. This outcome suggests that if the problem described is indeed a primary folic acid deficiency, malabsorption may be the basic cause of the difficulty. Despite the failure of folic acid supplementation to produce uniformly successful outcomes of pregnancy, its administration has nonetheless coincided with a vast improvement in the breeding program of our own laboratory. From 1964 to date, a total of 56 pregnancies has been followed in our laboratory. Of these, primarily in the early phases of our work, 29 were followed with the subjects' receiving only the standard Purina diet without supplementation of the folic acid mixture described above. Of this group, 1 viable birth, 3 neonatal deaths, 14 apparent stillbirths, and 11 early abortions were obtained. In the last 18 months, however, 27 pregnant subjects have received 4 weeks or more of the folic acid-enriched supplement; of these pregnancies, 52% resulted in viable young, 19% were born live but died within 10 days, 29% were stillborn, and no early abortions occurred. These findings do not seem dependent upon simply increased periods of time in the laboratory, as a number of successful outcomes occurred within less than 10 months after arrival. As a result of this entire compilation of material, the conclusion that folic acid depletion of the pregnant female, perhaps complicated by related deficiencies, represents a significant source of difficulty in producing viable Peruvian squirrel monkey young in our colony, seems warranted. Thus, it would be our recommendation that prophylactic supplementation of the diet, from early in pregnancy onward, with a mixture very rich in folic acid may greatly enhance successful husbandry in *Saimiri* if any direct signs of megaloblastic anemia are present. Until further clarification of the dietary problems of *Saimiri* are obtained and since the sources of folic acid are quite economical in the dosages suggested here it would perhaps be wise to include this supplementation as a precautionary measure, even when direct diagnosis of megaloblastic anemia cannot be made. If Giles' data on humans are correct, considerable tolerance of high-dosage levels of folic acid may be anticipated without adverse affects and thus, as he recommends, it seems wise to err on the generous side.

ACKNOWLEDGMENTS

The author wishes to acknowledge with thanks the considerable contributions of Dr. I. Charles Kaufman, Dr. James Nelson, Dr. T. Nathan and Miss E. Levy in carrying out the original research.

REFERENCES

Asdell, S. A. (1964). "Patterns of Mammalian Reproduction." Constable, London. 2nd edition.

Beischer, D. E., and Furry, D. E. (1964). *Saimiri sciureus* as an experimental animal. *Anat. Record* **148**, 615-624.

Bennett, J. P. (1967a). The induction of ovulation in the squirrel monkey (*Saimiri sciureus*) with pregnant mares serum (PMS) and human chorionic gonadotropin (HCG). *J. Reprod. Fertility* **13**, 357-359.

Bennett, J. P. (1967b). Artificial insemination of the squirrel monkey. *J. Endocrinol.* **37**, 473-474.

Bullough, W. S. (1951). "Vertebrate Sexual Cycles." Methuen, London.

Clewe, T. H. (1966). Mating of squirrel monkeys (*Saimiri sciureus*) in captivity. *Am. Zool.* **6**, No. 3, 343-344.

Cooper, R. W. (1966). Personal Communication.

Delfs, E. (1941). An assay method for human chorionic gonadotropin. *Endocrinology* **28**, 196-202.

Denniston, R. H. (1964). Notes on the vaginal cornification cycle of captive squirrel monkeys. *J. Mammal.* **45**, No. 3, 471.

Gates, D. M. (1966). Spectral distribution of solar radiation at the earth's surface. *Science* **151**, 523-529.

Giles, C. (1966). An account of 335 cases of megaloblastic anemia of pregnancy and the puerperium. *J. Clin. Pathol.* **19**, No. 1, 1-11.

Hampton, J. K., Hampton, S. H., and Landwehr, B. T. (1966). Observations on a successful breeding colony of the marmoset. *Oedipomidas oedipus. Folia Primatol.* **4**, 265-287.

Hill, W. C. O. (1960). "Primates: Comparative Anatomy and Taxonomy." Vol. IV. p. 297. Edinburgh Univ. Press, Edinburgh.

Jacobs, G. H. (1963). Spectral sensitivity and color vision of the squirrel monkey. *J. Comp. Physiol. Psychol.* **56**, 616-621.

Johnson, T. B., Salisbury, F. B., and Connor, G. I. (1967). Ratio of blue to red light: A brief increase following sunset. *Science* **155**, 1663-1665.

Lancaster, J. B., and Lee, R. B. (1965). The annual reproductive cycle in monkeys and apes. *In* "Primate Behavior" (I. DeVore, ed.), pp. 486-513. Holt, New York.

Lang, C. M. (1967). The estrous cycle of the squirrel monkey (*Saimiri sciureus*). *J. Lab. Animal Care* **17**, 442-451.

Lehner, N. D. M., Bullock, B. C., Feldner, M. A., and Clarkson, T. B. (1967). Observations on reproduction of laboratory-maintained squirrel monkeys. *Lab. Primate Newsletter* **6**, No. 1, 1-3.

Lockard, R. B. (1963). Some effects of light upon the behavior of rodents. *Psychol. Bull.* **60**, No. 6, 509-529.

MacRoberts, M. H., and MacRoberts, B. R. (1966). The annual reproductive cycle of the Barbary ape *(Macaca sylvana)* in Gibraltar. *Am. J. Phys. Anthropol.* [N.S.] **25**, No. 3, 299-304.

Nathan, T. S., Rosenblum, L. A., Limson, G., and Nelson, J. H. (1966). Diagnosis of pregnancy in the squirrel monkey. *Anat. Record* **155**, No. 4, 531-535.

Rosenblum, L. A., Nathan, T., Nelson, J. H., and Kaufman, I. C., (1967). Vaginal cornification cycles in the squirrel monkey (*Saimiri sciureus*). *Folia Primatol.* **6**, 83-91.

Rowan, W. (1925). Relation of light to bird migration and developmental changes. *Nature* **115**, 494-495.

Simpson, M. E., and VanWagenen, G. (1963). Induction of ovulation in *Macaca mulatta* by human chorioniopausal gonadotropin. *In* "Research with Primates" (D. E. Pickering, ed.), p. 67-74. Tektronix Found., Beaverton, Oregon.

Wiswell, O. B. (1963). Some reactions in the squirrel monkey *(Saimiri sciurea)* to autologous transplants and gonadotropins. *Anat. Record.* **145,** No. 2, 369-370.

Wiswell, O. B. (1965). Gestation, parturition and maturation in the *Saimiri sciureus* (squirrel monkey). *Excerpta Med. Intern. Congr. seri.* **99,** E52. (abstract)

Wiswell, O. B., Gibbs, W. E., and Kent, C. R. (1963). Possible seasonal ovarian transplant response in the squirrel monkey, *Saimiri sciureus. Texas J. Sci.* **IX,** No. 4, 434. (abstract)

CHAPTER 6

Observations on the Relationship between Embryological Development, Time of Conception, and Gestation

Charles M. Goss, Lee T. Popejoy II, John L. Fusiler, and Tom M. Smith

I. Introduction

The essentials of the embryology and placentation in the squirrel mon-key are described in the Croonian lecture of Hill (1932) and in *Primatologia* by Starck (1956). The material Hill describes is from the Bluntschli collec-tion and comprises some 9 or 10 stages of development through the entire period of gestation. The specimens were collected in the field; some are well preserved and some not, and no information is available concerning the gestational age.

The purpose of the project that is partially described in this chapter was the continuation of the study of the embryological development of this species. The emphasis in the chapter, however, will be placed on the data acquired concerning the time of ovulation, length of the period of gestation, and the correlation of stage of development with the chronological age of the embryos. The highly specialized nature of the morphological features of the embryos makes it desirable to give only a preliminary account of them, and the detailed description will be reserved for a later communication. The acquisition of a closely timed series of mammalian embryos is a prolonged and difficult undertaking and our series is regrettably short. The background material concerned with conception and gestation, however, is considerably more extensive and is more appropriate for reporting in this chapter.

In 1949 a research grant was awarded by the National Heart Institute to support an attempt to develop a small primate into a convenient laboratory animal with a breeding colony. The squirrel monkey was recommended by its size, ease of handling, and availability. A small colony was started under laboratory conditions. During the next 10 years this species proved to be a good laboratory animal as far as survival and ease in handling was concerned, but the breeding was unsuccessful because the continuity of the colony was interrupted several times by remodelling and new construction of the building. Beginning in 1959, however, the colony was stabilized and breeding became successful, with the result that the time of conception could be established and several embryos obtained for special studies, especially of the earliest development of the heart.

II. Method

A. Breeding Colony

The breeding colony regularly consisted of 20 to 24 adult squirrel monkeys, *Saimiri sciureus,* housed in cages with 1 male and 3 females in each cage. The animals were obtained from various dealers who could not furnish their exact geographic source but it is likely that most were of Peruvian origin (see Chapter 1). As individual monkeys were removed from the colony for use in experiments or other reasons, they were replaced by new members recruited from dealers.

Each cage consisted of an indoor portion 36 inches long, 36 inches high, and 18 inches wide with an access through a 4 × 6 inch opening and chute to an outdoor portion on the roof of the medical school building. The outdoor cages, 72 inches long, 48 inches high, and 24 inches wide, were suspended from metal beams with the wire mesh floor of the cage 18 inches above the cement-covered roof.

1. Feeding

The routine of feeding consisted of the following, the amounts given being the basic daily ration for each cage, and the sequence being followed except on weekends:

First morning feeding, right after weighing the animals and cleaning the cages: 1 or 2 slices of bread, diced, and mixed with a liquid polyvitamin mixture (Polyvisol, Mead Johnson Laboratories).

Midmorning: 2 sliced, hard-boiled eggs or, on alternate days, approximately 100 gm of ground lean beef. In preparation of the latter, 5.5 kg of beef were mixed with 10 gm of dried skim milk and 20 gm of raw wheat germ, made into a flat cake, and then roasted just long enough to make the ingredients hold together. The cake was diced into 1-cm cubes for the feeding trays. Wheat germ had been stored in airtight plastic bags in a deep freezer. Also on alternate days, approximately 25 gm of string beans (canned) or separate kernel, yellow corn (canned) was given at midmorning.

Later morning: 1 orange, sliced, and 2 or 3 bananas, sliced.

Late afternoon: approximately 24 roasted peanuts in the shell. Peanuts were purchased in 100-lb bags, received hot from the roaster, and immediately stored in small airtight plastic bags. They remained quite fresh to the taste and were not contaminated with insect larvae.

Water was available at all times from water bottles with stainless steel tubes.

At irregular times during the day, each animal was offered 6 or 8 live crickets.* This popular item of diet was used to tame and hasten the adaptation of newly acquired monkeys as well as for nutrition. Miniature marshmallows were used to coax monkeys in and out of cages and to reward them for accepting the handling required for weighing and other procedures. Medication of various kinds was easily administered by mouth by burying dry material in the center of a marshmallow. Pregnant and lactating females were given supplemental vitamins in this manner using Natabek (Parke-Davis).

The amount of feeding was increased if the cage contained a pregnant female and if the daily weights of the monkeys suggested that they were receiving an inadequate amount.

---

* Live crickets were shipped every 2 weeks by Fluger's Cricket Farm, Baton Rouge, Louisiana.

2. Records

Routinely, the weight of each monkey was recorded in the morning before feeding. The vaginal orifice was inspected for the presence of a copulation plug or a discharge. The condition of the external genitalia was given a rating of 0 to 4 plus in terms of an indication of estrus changes. During a 2-year period, the rectal temperature was taken with a thermistor probe. A few notes on temperatures are available but all daily records and charts of this have been lost.* Also lost were the records of 2 years of daily Papanicolaou smears of two monkeys.

B. REMOVAL OF EMBRYOS, HYSTERECTOMY

When a monkey appeared to be in early pregnancy, the condition of the ovaries and uterus was estimated by palpation through the abdominal wall. If indications were appropriate, an exploratory laparotomy was performed under intraperitoneal sodium pentothal anesthesia. When positive evidence was obtained, a panhysterectomy was performed. After the operation the animal was either killed while still under anesthesia, or the wound closed and the animal allowed to recover. Healing was very prompt and after complete the monkey was used for experimental studies not involving the reproductive system, or traded to a local pet shop as a spayed animal.

A monkey that did not appear to be pregnant at laparotomy had the wound closed and, after a day in a recovery cage, was returned to its accustomed place in the colony. As many as three operations were performed on one monkey (no. 27) over a period of 4 years.

C. PREPARATION OF EMBRYOS

After removal, the uterus, tubes, and ovaries were immediately placed in Bouin's picro—formol fixative. Fifteen minutes later a 23-gauge hypodermic needle with a blunt tip was gently inserted into the lumen of the cervix a distance of 2 or 3 mm and 1 or 2 ml of the fixing fluid injected slowly into the cavity of the uterus. The uterus was returned to the jar for completion of the fixation.

After fixation, the uterine tubes were severed close to the uterus and the uterus was opened by an incision along the cranial border, connecting the openings of the two tubes into the uterus. The incision was carried along the lateral borders from the tubal openings to the external orifice of the cervix and the uterus laid open. The purpose of making the incision in this

---

*The data are incomplete in many places because some of our records were lost during a hurricane that damaged our laboratory in September, 1965.

manner was to avoid cutting into the placenta which was characteristically attached by the two discoidal parts to the ventral and dorsal surfaces of the uterine cavity. The chorionic vesicle was photographed before and after it was opened and the embryo photographed in place before it was embedded in paraffin. Serial paraffin sections of 10-μ thickness were mounted and stained with hematoxylin and eosin.

III. Observations

TIME OF OVULATION AND INSEMINATION

The time of ovulation and successful insemination was determined quite accurately in two instances only, by the observation of copulation and recovery of live sperm from the vaginal orifice. No other completely reliable method of determining ovulation and insemination was discovered, however, and the following criteria were used to estimate the time of conception:

(1) Observation of a copulation plug or live sperm. (2) Evidence of increased hormonal activity within the period of heat, represented by changes in the external genitalia, or by behavioral changes of the animal. (3) A quite characteristic weight change revealed by a chart of the daily weight. (4) Palpation of an enlarged uterus and ovaries. (5) Evidence of pregnancy shown by laparotomy.

1. Vaginal Plugs

The observation of a plug or live sperm was accepted as reliable evidence of effective copulation but not necessarily of ovulation with insemination. During the breeding season as many as eight plugs were found at intervals in the vagina of one female. The plugs were observed both before and after the copulation which was responsible for insemination (Clewe, 1966).

These instances of multiple plugs offer indication that specific periods of acceptance of the male occur within a longer breeding season. The interval between these specific periods was observed frequently to range from 6 to 8 days but was usually rather constant in any one individual. In some monkeys a white discharge appeared at intervals similar to those of plugs, and a discharge a few days after a plug was not unusual. Considerable skill and experience were necessary to identify the plugs.

2. Hormonal Changes

Changes in the external genitalia of the female characteristically occurred during the entire longer breeding period and even on into pregnancy. It was also characteristic, however, to have some variation in the degree of change with increase in intensity at the time of copulation. The changes observed consisted of enlargement of the labia majora with an increase in the length of the introitus, at times in a multipara almost constituting eversion. The color was often a heightened redness. The clitoris exhibited a variable amount of swelling and lengthening beyond the usual protuberance characteristic of this species.

The mammary region underwent change during the breeding period in most monkeys. The nipple in a virgin female is small and unpigmented. In a multipara, the nipple is pigmented, having retained the change in color which took place during a previous pregnancy. In both nullipara and multipara the nipple enlarged during the heat period, from an inactive 2- to 3-mm diameter and 3-mm protrusion to as much as 5- to 6-mm diameter and 8-mm length. The pigmentation of the nipple in some multipara was intensified.

The behavioral changes during the period of heat varied with the character of the female. A usual manifestation was greater activity and aggression, and mounting or being mounted by other females. Accompanying this was an increase in vocal expression. One of the students made tape recordings of the sounds, but was never quite sure that a particular note of invitation could be identified.

The weight changes associated with heat, although significant, are difficult to interpret. They are necessarily superimposed upon many environmental influences, the most obvious of which is the state of nutrition. In this colony, during a period of months in 1963 and 1964, the animals were consistently underfed because of an economy drive on the part of the caretaker. This also became evident in the lower birth weights in 1963 and 1964 (see Table II). The changes during the period of heat were characterized by greater fluctuations within intervals of a few days. These were not easily recognized in daily records, but became quite significant if plotted on a graph. At a time of observation of a copulation plug, a particularly marked change was represented by loss of as much as $20-40$ gm either just before (Fig. 7) or just after the plug (Fig. 6). This change was used to assist in establishing the time of conception in those instances of pregnancy in which a plug was lacking.

3. Temperature Changes

Changes in temperature were not considered to be of significance. Comparisons cannot be given because the daily records are missing (see footnote). A notation available gives the average weekly temperature at a time of insemination of from 102.2°F (39°C) to 102.8°F (39.33°C). One female had an average of 103.1°F (39.5°C), another 101.4° F (38.5°C).

All of the preceding indications of the time of conception must be taken together and weighed as a clinical type of evidence. A few days after conception, more objective evidence became available by palpation through the relaxed lower abdominal wall. During the interval between breeding seasons the uterus and ovaries cannot be palpated with any degree of certainty. In the period of heat, the uterus can be distinguished as a firm mass in the midline just above the pubis and the ovaries as two smaller and somewhat firmer masses on each side. The final and most objective indication that insemination had taken place was obtained in some instances through laparotomy. After 20–25 days, a slightly enlarged (2-cm) and somewhat hyperemic uterus, flanked by an ovary with a corpus luteum of appropriate size, was considered evidence of pregnancy.

It must be emphasized that the validity of the diagnosis of pregnancy was not always established but it is believed that the acquisition of six closely timed early embryos proved the practical value of the criteria described above.

IV. Results

A. NUMBER OF PREGNANCIES

A total of 62 pregnancies was recorded with accurate data (Table I). Two or three births that occurred during the earlier period of the colony are not included. After a few pregnancies had come to term, the data obtained concerning time of conception seemed sufficient to warrant interruption of others for the purpose of obtaining embryos (Tables II and III). Since the

TABLE I
PREGNANCIES

Births at term	
Vigorous; full survival	17
Live, weak; short survival	5
Caesarean birth; breathed 5 minutes; overanesthetized	1
Stillborn	4
Obstetrical deaths[a]	3
Survival not recorded	1
	31
Abortions	10
Hysterectomy for embryology	21
Total pregnancies	62

[a] One face presentation; two caesarean births.

TABLE II
BIRTHS WITH FULL GESTATION

Animal no.	Birth date	Infant weight	Survival
44	22 Aug. 1960	114 gm	Vigorous; full survival
42	22 Aug. 1960	115 gm	Stillborn
32	9 May 1961	114 gm	Vigorous; full survival
30	1 June 1961	Term	Survived 1 hour; heat stroke
24	12 June 1961	91 gm	Live; survived 2 days
27	14 June 1961	104 gm	Vigorous
22	16 June 1961	104 gm	Dead; face presentation; caesarean birth
21	4 July 1961	74 gm	Stillborn
28	28 July 1961	88 gm	Vigorous
65	30 Dec. 1961	110 gm	Stillborn
66	12 Jan. 1962	104 gm	Vigorous
60	2 Feb. 1962	No record	Weak; survived 2 days
51	4 Feb. 1962	No record	Premature; caesarean birth
63	8 Mar. 1962	104 gm	Vigorous
55	24 Sept. 1962	87 gm	Stillborn
27	20 Feb. 1963	105 gm	Caesarean; survived 5 minutes; overanesthetized
61	25 Feb. 1963	Term	Dead; caesarean; breech
66	14 May 1963	100 gm	Vigorous
78	15 May 1963	92 gm	Live; survived 6 days
72	30 May 1963	93 gm	Vigorous
89	21 Feb. 1964	90 gm	Vigorous
91	2 Apr. 1964	98 gm	Trypan blue; short survival
27	27 June 1964	85 gm	Vigorous
75	17 June 1964	76 gm	Vigorous
72	10 June 1965	65 gm	Vigorous
55	19 July 1965	85 gm	Vigorous
78	20 July 1965	85 gm	Vigorous
73	31 July 1965	115 gm	Vigorous
85	Aug. 1965	100 gm	Vigorous
96	5 Jan. 1966	90 gm	Vigorous
106	10 Jan. 1966	73 gm	Vigorous

specific project involved primarily the study of the earliest embryology of the heart, it seemed advisable when a pregnancy appeared to have advanced well beyond this stage, to allow the female to continue her pregnancy in order to add to the accumulation of data on reproductive physiology.

1. Survival

Two of the term deliveries with vigorous offspring gave us what appeared to be reliable information that the period of gestation had been 172

TABLE III
PERIOD OF GESTATION

Animal no.	Birth date	Conception date	Copulation evidence	Genital rating	Weight change	Period of gestation (days)
32	9 May 1961	19 Nov. 1960	Live sperm	Not recorded	21–23 Nov.	172
24	12 June 1961	23 Dec. 1960	Plug 13 Jan.	4 plus 23 Dec.	Record missing	171
27	14 June 1961	25 Dec. 1960	Record missing	4 plus 21 Dec. – 3 Jan.	21 Dec. –3 Jan.	171
22	16 June 1961	26 Dec. 1960	Plug 3 Jan.	Record missing	Record missing	172
21	4 July 1961	14 Jan. 1961	Plug 7 and 30 Jan.	4 plus 14 Jan.	16 Jan.	171
28	28 July 1961	9 Feb. 1961	Plug 9 Feb.	4 plus 9 Feb.	6 and 13 Jan.	169
60	2 Feb. 1962	16 Aug. 1961	Blood clot	3 plus 10 Aug.	11 Sept.	170
63	8 Mar. 1962	21 Sept. 1961	Not recorded	2 plus 27 Sept.	Not significant	168
55	24 Sept. 1962	7 Apr. 1962	Blood	4 plus 9 Apr.	10–16 Apr.	170
27	20 Feb. 1963	1 Sept. 1962	Plug 16 Aug.	3 plus 11 Sept.	13 Sept.	172
61	25 Feb. 1963	8 Sept. 1962	Plug 8 Sept.	Not recorded	Not recorded	170
72	30 May 1963	10 Dec. 1962	Plug 2 Nov.	4 plus 10 Dec.	14 Dec.	171
89	21 Feb. 1964	3 Sept. 1963	Not recorded	4 plus 13 Aug. – 11 Sept.	4 and 11 Sept.	171
91	2 Apr. 1964	15 Oct. 1963	Plug 15 Oct.	4 plus 11 and 17 Oct.	3 and 22 Oct.	169
27	27 June 1964	9 Jan. 1964	Not recorded	4 plus 9 Jan.	16 Jan.	171
75	17 June 1964	28 Dec. 1963	Plug 28 Dec.	Not significant	10 and 14 Dec.	171
72	9 June 1965	18 Dec. 1964	Plug 18 Dec.	Not recorded	Not recorded	172
55	19 July 1965	29 Jan. 1965	Plug 10 Jan.	2 plus 22 Jan.	25 Jan. and 1 Feb.	171
73	31 July 1965	13 Feb. 1965	Plug 13 Feb.	Not significant	Not significant	168

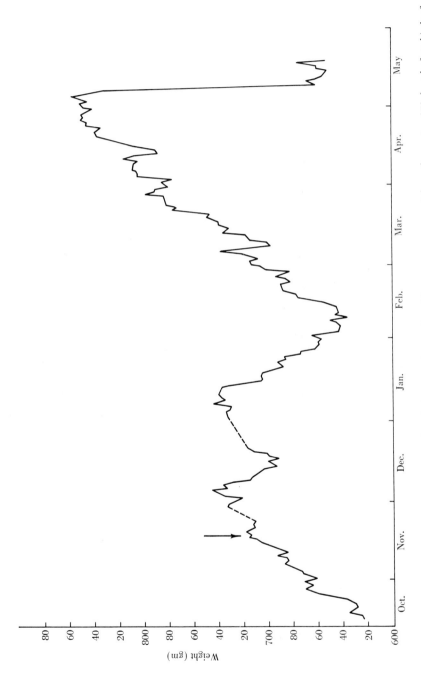

FIG. 1. Chart of daily weight of monkey no. 32. Copulation was observed and live sperm recovered from the vagina 172 days before birth of a full-term, vigorous offspring. Arrow indicates the time of conception and the sudden drop in weight indicates birth. (see Tables II and III). The animal was explained by clinical observations other than an adverse effect of cold, inclement weather.

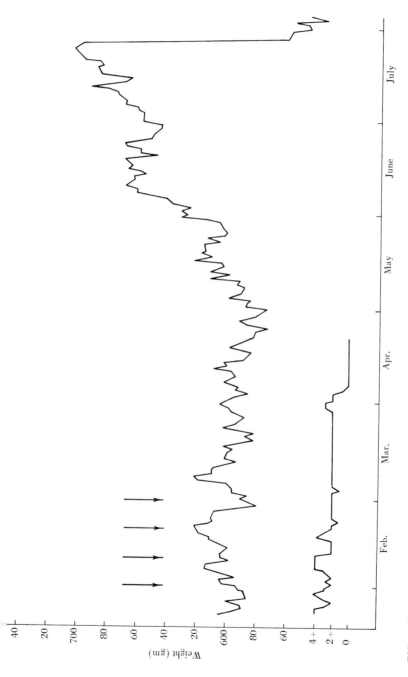

FIG. 2. Chart of daily weight of monkey no. 28. Vaginal plug, condition of external genitalia, and weight variations were used as criteria of probable time of conception. Arrows indicate observed vaginal plugs. Gestation: 169 days

TABLE IV
ABORTIONS

Animal no.	Birth date	Conception date	Criterion of conception	Length of gestation (days)	Weight of fetus	Remarks
25	22 Aug. 1960	No record	No record	No record	No record	—
26	16 July 1962	31 Mar. 1962	3 plus 31 Mar. and 7 Apr.	106?	40 gm	—
31	13 April 1961	8 Dec. 1960	Sperm 8 Dec.	122	No record	Partly eaten
55	14 Jan. 1964	18 Sept. 1963	3 plus 18 Sept. and weight drop	124	No record	Macerated
68	25 Oct. 1961	No record	No record	?	No record	—
77	12 April 1963	7 Jan. 1963?	2 plus and weight change 7 Jan.	95	27 gm	—
84	31 Oct. 1963	26 July 1963?	4 plus 26 July	98	No record	Hard uterus and purulent exudate
87	9 Dec. 1963	30 Aug. 1963	Uterus palpation	100	40 gm	—
73	28 Mar. 1963	21 Nov. 1962	Plug 21 Nov.	145	No record	—
78	25 Mar. 1964	27 Jan. 1964	Plug 27 Jan.	55	No record	Trypan blue 2 days previous

and 169 days (Figs. 1 and 2). Other term pregnancies seemed to corroborate this time period, 170 ± 2 days, and none failed to fit into this schedule, (Table III). The average weight of the mature newborns was 96 gm, the variation between 73 and 115 gm, but one should expect the offspring of well-nourished females to be at least $100-110$ gm.

2. Obstetrical Problems

The size of the head of the fetus, especially in the occipital region, and the size of the fetus as a whole compared with that of the female might be expected to cause dystocia and obstetrical problems (Table IV). The weight of the term fetus is about one-fifth that of the mother, a surprising ratio, which would correspond to a 25-pound human newborn. This weight of approximately 110 gm and the period of gestation of 172 days does not seem to fit into the schedule advanced by Carmichael (1967) for primates, showing that the heavier the adult, the longer is the period of gestation. Four caesarean sections were performed. One (monkey no. 22) was for a face presentation; the fully-formed fetus was dead because an embryotomy had been attempted. A second had been delayed too long to save either female or fetus. A third, also a face presentation, successfully delivered what was apparently a vigorous offspring, but it breathed for 5 minutes only, probably because the mother had accidentally been given a double dose of anesthesia. A fourth was for a breech presentation in which the fetus did not survive. In one instance of dystocia with foot presentation, an emergency maneuver with chloroform anesthesia was successful, but the animal caretaker, an untrained anesthetist, became so interested in the proceedings that he forgot to watch the breathing, and the monkey died.

B. Embryos Recovered by Hysterectomy

The first embryo obtained by hysterectomy was removed on what was diagnosed as the thirty-fifth day of gestation. It was fixed for histological study and prepared in serial sections. It had 18 somites and a corresponding development throughout the other systems of the body (Table V and Figs. 3,4, and 5).

The next embryo was removed on the scheduled thirty-first day, fixed, and mounted in serial sections. The result was a very fine specimen of seven somites which corresponded in general with the famous Payne (1925) human embryo (Table V and Fig. 6).

Seven other embryos were removed successfully and made into serial sections with gestational ages of $23-27$ days. They range in development

TABLE V

ANIMALS HYSTERECTOMIZED FOR EMBRYO

Animal no.	Sacrifice date	Conception date	Copulation evidence	Age of embryos (days)	State of development
29	28 Jan. 1961	4 Jan. 1961	Plug 4 Jan.	24	Live embryo crushed
25	1 Apr. 1961	25 Feb. 1961	Plug 25 Feb.	35	18 somites, serial sections
23	19 May 1961	18 Apr. 1961	Plug and sperm 18 Apr.	31	7 somites, serial sections
54	14 Aug. 1961	24 July 1961	4 plus; weight drop 27 July	21	Live embryo crushed
65	9 Feb. 1962	6 Jan. 1962	2 plus 6 Jan. 1962?	?	Specimen missing
67	12 Feb. 1962	Records missing	Records missing	?	Specimen missing
24	26 Feb. 1962	30 Jan. 1962	Copulation and live sperm	27	Primitive streak, serial sections
32	20 Apr. 1962	17 Mar. 1962	Enlarged uterus and ovaries palpated	34	Placenta, embryo not found in serial sections
22	29 May 1962	6 May 1962	4 plus 6 May; weight drop 5 and 9 May	23	Early embryonic shield, serial sections
31	5 July 1962	8–10 June 1962	Enlarged uterus and ovaries	25–27	Head process embryo, serial sections
21	4 June 1962	11 May 1962	4 plus 11 May; weight drop 3 and 14 May	24	Embryonic shield, serial sections
62	21 Oct. 1962	24–26 Sept. 1962	3 plus 25 Sept.	24–26	Chordal canal embryo, serial sections
28	2 Nov. 1962	25 Sept. 1962	Plug 25 Sept.	36	"Large embryo" missing
71	15 Nov. 1962	15 Oct. 1962	1 plus; weight drop	30	Specimen missing
74	24 Nov. 1962	3 Nov. 1962	Plug 3 Nov. '62	21	Specimen missing
60	8 Dec. 1962	14 Nov. 1962	Plug 14 Nov.	25	Specimen missing
68	3 Apr. 1963	14 Feb. 1963	Plug 14 Feb.	48	Advanced but abnormal embryo
63	11 May 1963	3 Apr. 1963	Plug 3 Apr.	38	Embryo large, missing
86	9 Sept. 1963	9 Aug. 1963	Copulation 9 Aug.	30	Specimen missing
82	15 Jan. 1964	13 Dec. 1963	Plug 2 Dec.	34	Embryo missing
88	15 Jan. 1964	4 Oct. 1963	Plug 4 Oct.	104	5-cm embryo

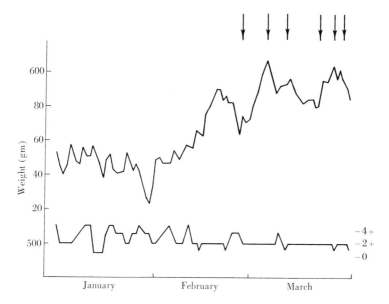

FIG. 3. Chart of daily weight of monkey no. 25. Conception was diagnosed by observation of a vaginal plug 35 days before hysterectomy when an 18-somite embryo was recovered. The first arrow indicates time of plug; subsequent arrows show days when a white or creamy discharge was observed. The weight drop after the vaginal plug was considered significant.

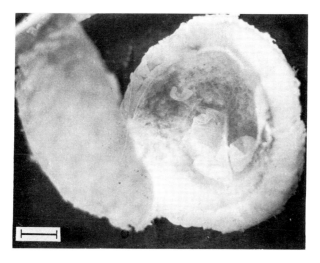

FIG. 4. Photograph after histological fixation of endometrium peeled out of myometrium and cut open to show embryo in place. Marker indicates 2 mm.

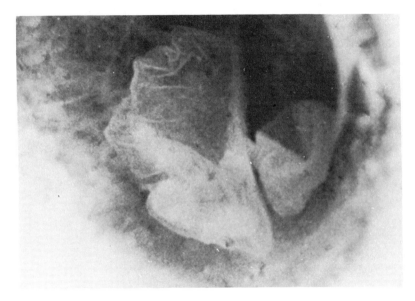

FIG. 5. Photograph of embryo shown in Fig. 4 with greater magnification. The amnion is collapsed; placental area is at bottom of figure.

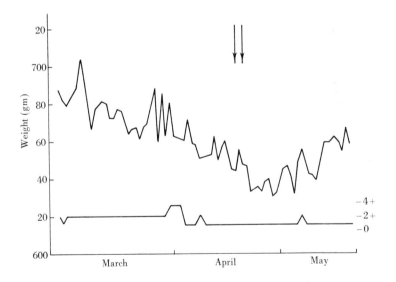

FIG. 6. Chart of daily weight of monkey no. 23. Arrows indicate observations of vaginal plugs, the second accompanied by recovery of sperm. Weight drop followed plug and helped to diagnose conception. Seven-somite embryo was recovered by hysterectomy on the 31st day of pregnancy.

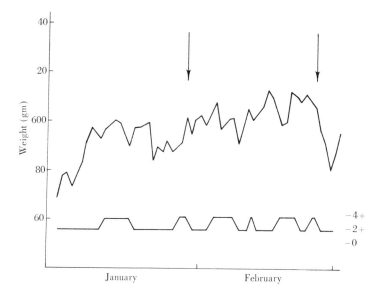

FIG. 7. Chart of daily weight of monkey no. 24. First arrow indicates date of observation of copulation with live sperm recovered. Second arrow indicates hysterectomy on the 27th day of gestation when an embryo with a primitive streak was recovered. The weight chart continues after operation because the animal recovered and was given away as a pet.

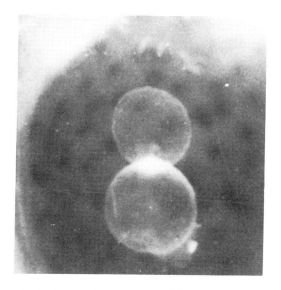

FIG. 8. Photograph of embryo and uterus recovered from monkey no. 21 on the 24th day of gestation (see Table V). The two vesicles are the amnion and yolk sac. The white area between is the embryonic shield with an early primitive streak.

from a bilaminar blastocyst to a well-formed primitive streak (Figs. 7 and 8). Other embryos at this stage of development and somewhat older were removed and photographed, but the specimens and photographs are missing (see Table V and footnote on p. 174).

V. Discussion

A. FEEDING

The various aspects of feeding squirrel monkeys are ably discussed by Rosenblum (Chapter 5) and Lang (Chapter 14) in this volume. It is encouraging to find that Lehner *et al.* (1967) have been able to document the necessity for certain vitamins in bringing pregnancies to a satisfactory termination with vigorous offspring. In a report during the *Saimiri* reproduction conference organized by the editors of this volume and hosted by the above investigators (Cooper, 1965), the senior author (C.M.G.) pointed out that the single most important factor that appeared to underlie his success, unusual at the time, in breeding experiments with this species was the addition of the vitamin complex Natabek (Parke Davis) commonly given to pregnant women.

The monkeys were fed a natural diet instead of prepared chow for two reasons. First, a reliable monkey chow was not readily available at the time the colony was started, and it was desirable not to delay for experimental feeding. Prepared chow was not adopted later because it was found that monkeys already adapted to their environment did not respond favorably to this change. The vitamin content of prepared chows is not always reliable because of the lapse of time between preparation and receipt from the distributor (see Chapter 14). Also, the manufacturers may, without informing the user, find it advantageous to make substitutions that may or may not have been adequately tested in their laboratory for special conditions such as breeding. Second, it seemed reasonable to suppose that animals brought in from the field would adapt more quickly to a diet of familiar foods and be more likely to breed and raise their young than with prepared or experimental diet. Also, the monkeys seemed to enjoy the freedom of choosing favorite foods. The recent results of many other investigators have shown that this species thrives on a prepared food, but it is interesting that these monkeys have unrestrained foraging habits in their native forests (Thorington, 1967). The sequence of feeding the individual ingredients was established in order to present items that the animals are likely to neglect, namely vitamins and protein, before they could dull their appetites with bananas and other fruit. Intake of vitamins was assured by giving an amount of bread soaked with liquid polyvitamin to each cage which resulted in some of the pieces being left in the feeding tray at the end of the day. This seemed to allow the less aggressive monkeys to have access to the vitamins. In the New Orleans climate the animals could go outside for sunshine during a large part of the year, even on individual days in winter. The enclosure on the roof contained green shrubs and banana trees planted in tubs.

B. BREEDING

The breeding period during the first 2 years occurred within the late autumn and winter months, indicating that this is the usual season for breeding in this species. During later years, however, the evidence indicated that the time of occurrence was influenced by the degree of adaptation to the local climate. Most of the examples of breeding at other seasons occurred when animals had not been brought into the colony recently.

The recent progress in defining the breeding season and periods of estrus is also discussed by Rosenblum in Chapter 5. It is quite obvious that the method of determining the time of conception and the period of gestation described above was a preliminary attempt and will have to be revised by comparisons with the results obtained by other investigators and in other laboratories. This is particularly evident because of the smallness of numbers and the loss of important data (see footnote on p. 174). The practical value of the method would seem to be established, however, by the success in obtaining a series of quite closely timed, young embryos.

The charts of weights were selected as more or less usual types (Figs. 1,2,3,6, and 7). The ones with the greatest variations are not illustrated, partly because an environmental reason for the differences could be found. A typical pattern could not be established other than the abrupt rise in later pregnancy and greater daily variations during the periods of heat. Many of the longer variations such as that in Fig. 1 were not explained.

C. UNUSUAL HISTORIES

One or two notes concerning unusual experiences in the colony may be of interest and worth recording because they show the response of the species to laboratory conditions and surgical operations.

Monkey no. 22 appeared on June 16, 1961, to be in severe dystocia. An embryotomy was attempted, but was unsuccessful, and diagnosis by means of a speculum proved not to be feasible. A caesarean section was performed which disclosed the cause of dystocia to be a face presentation, and the attempts at embryotomy had killed what must have been a viable fetus. A year later, May 29, 1962, early pregnancy was diagnosed and a hysterectomy performed. An apparently normal embryonic shield was obtained and prepared histologically (Table V).

Monkey no. 27 gave birth to a vigorous offspring on June 14, 1961 (Table II). Abdominal laparotomies were performed on April 20, 1962, and August 16, 1962, but the wound was closed in both instances because pregnancy was not diagnosed. She was obviously pregnant again on February 20, 1963, but was in severe dystocia. A caesarean section was scheduled. One of our team of students who could not be present at the operation administered a surgical dose of nembutal without warning the operator. The latter added a light dose of nembutal and a few whiffs of ether were administered to hasten the anesthesia. The well-developed fetus had a sturdy heart beat on removal but could not be made to breath and survived only 5 minutes. The female recovered uneventfully and gave birth to an 85-gm vigorous infant on June 27, 1964 (Table II).

Monkey no. 33, not before mentioned in this chapter, was born in the colony in June, 1959. A month later she was found lying in the bottom of the cage. Pneumonia was diagnosed, and after a few days' treatment with antibiotics, recovery seemed assured. The mother would not nurse her, however, and a technician nursed her with a medicine dropper and brought her up to a state of vigorous health. She lived 6 years, but at the age of 2 began to have epileptic seizures, both grand and petit mal, very similar to those observed in man but quite different from experimentally induced seizures (Miminoshvili, 1960). An electroencephalogram was made and diagnosed by the Department of Neurology as of a type not associated with organic lesion, and apparently not previously seen in a subhuman primate. Experimental studies were planned but unfortunately were never carried out. The personality of this monkey, with her identification of herself with human beings rather than with the other monkeys, makes an interesting, even entertaining, story.

The results of two preliminary observations following injection with trypan blue are not recorded in detail because the results were negative. The infant born at term by monkey no. 91 (Tables II and III) was autopsied with especial care but no congenital abnormalities were found. The fetus aborted by monkey no. 78 (Table IV) was in a severely macerated condition when found and could not be autopsied. These observations indicate, however, that experiments with trypan blue will require considerable background information related to this species.

D. SUMMARY

In a breeding colony averaging 20 to 24 squirrel monkeys (*Saimiri*, sp.), males and 18 females, over a period of 6 years, 62 pregnancies were recorded. Of these, 17 were full survival, 5 survived several days, 4 were still-born, 3 had obstetrical deaths (caesarean birth, etc.), 1 survival not record-ed, 10 abortions, and 21 underwent hysterectomy for recovery of embryos. Time of conception was diagnosed by observation of copulation, recovery of sperm from vagina, vaginal copulation plugs, weight changes, and hor-monal changes. Period of gestation was recorded as 170 ± 2 days. Embryos obtained were 18 somite, 7 somite, and 7 blastocysts. Embryo with 18 som-ites from 35 days of pregnancy, 7 somites from 31 days, and blastocysts from 21 to 27 days of pregnancy. Feeding was composed of natural ingre-dients, not prepared chow: meat or eggs, bread and vitamins, fruits, pea-nuts, and live crickets. Animals were in cages with indoor part with con-trolled temperature and outdoor part on roof of medical school building in New Orleans.

REFERENCES

Carmichael, L. (1967). The relationship of gestation-duration and birth weight in primates. *In* "Progress in Primatology" (D. Starck, R. Schneider, and H. J. Kuhn, eds.), pp. 55-58. Fish-er, Stuttgart.

Clewe, T. H. (1966). Observations on frequency of ejaculation of squirrel monkeys, *Saimiri sciureus*. *Am. Zoologist* **6**, 411.

Cooper, R. W. (1965). Squirrel monkey reproduction conference. *In* "Experimental Breeding of Subhuman Primates," 3rd Ann. Rept. Contract PH 43-63-56, p. 18. NIH Cancer Inst.

Hill, J. P. (1932). The developmental history of the primates. (Croonian Lecture.) *Phil. Trans. Roy. Soc. London* **B221**, 45-176 and Plates 1-21.

Lehner, N. D. M., Bullock, B. C., Feldner, M. A., and Clarkson, T. B. (1967). Observations on reproduction of laboratory-maintained squirrel monkeys *Lab. Primate Newsletter* **6**, No. 1, 1-3.

Miminoshvili, D. I. (1960). Experimental neurosis in monkeys. *In* "Theoretical and Practical Problems of Medicine and Biology in Experiments on Monkeys" (I. A. Utkin, ed., trans-lated from the Russian by R. Schachter), pp. 53-67. Pergamon Press, Oxford.

Payne, F. (1925). General description of a 7-somite human embryo. *Contr. Embryol. Carneg. Instn.* **16**, 115-124 and Plates 1-3.

Starck, D. (1956). Primitiventwicklung und Plazentation in Primaten. *In* "Primatologia" (H. Hofer, A. H. Schultz, and D. Starck, eds.), Vol. 1, pp. 723-886. Karger, Basel.

Thorington, R. W., Jr. (1967). Feeding and activity of *Cebus* and *Saimiri* in a Columbian forest. *In* "Progress in Primatology" (D. Starck, R. Schneider, and H. J. Kuhn, eds.), pp. 180-184. Fisher, Stuttgart.

CHAPTER 7

Physical Growth and Dental Eruption in Captive-Bred Squirrel Monkeys, *Saimiri sciureus* (Leticia, Columbia)*

James O. Long and Robert W. Cooper

I. Introduction

Despite the growing popularity of squirrel monkeys as laboratory animals and as pets, little information has become available regarding their developmental biology (see Chapters 4, 6, and 8). Although large numbers are captured in the wild and exported each year (see Chapter 1) and increasing numbers are being bred in captivity, no data has appeared until the present on physical growth and age of dental eruption in *Saimiri*. Many immature animals, from infants to juveniles and subadults, are among the thousands of wild-caught squirrel monkeys that are sold by animal dealers and pet shops in the United States each year. Accurate information on growth rate and dental eruption age and sequence should permit close estimation of chronological age in such specimens. Since squirrel monkeys have a strictly seasonal annual reproductive cycle in the wild (see Chapters 1 and 4), it should not be difficult to separate imported immature *Samiri* into relatively homogenous age groups corresponding to their particular years of birth. Until now, using body weight alone, such age based selection has not been possible.

*This study was supported by Contract PH 43-63-56 with the Program Resources and Logistics Section, Viral Oncology, National Cancer Institute, National Institutes of Health.

II. Materials and Methods

The present study has been conducted on 10 male and 11 female captive-bred squirrel monkeys born over a period of 4 years (1963—1967) to animals captured near Leticia, Colombia and supplied by the Tarpon Zoo of Tarpon Springs, Florida. Our colony has been maintained at the Institute for Comparative Biology of the Zoological Society of San Diego in a Primate Research Colony previously described by Cooper (1964).

The *Saimiri* were caged out of doors in adult groups of one male and three to six females in units measuring $1.8 \times 1.8 \times 1.5$ meters. All captive-bred animals used in this study were born from 1963 to 1967 in the months from August to November. Infants generally remained with their mothers in the group cage until removal for weaning at about 4 months of age. At that age infants were moved, usually in pairs or trios, to nearby cage units measuring $1.8 \times 0.9 \times 1.5$ meters. In the new cages their diet was the same as that fed to the adults, namely, commercial monkey biscuits softened by soaking in warm water. *Saimiri* infants have been observed to nibble soaked biscuits as early as 1 month of age and by 4 months eat quantities sufficient to allow weaning to be accomplished without apparent interruption of growth and development.

A total of 333 combined physical growth and dental eruption examinations have been made on 21 colony-bred monkeys to accumulate the data presented here. Five males and six females were examined at birth and were examined at monthly intervals thereafter. The remaining five males and five females included in the study were examined at biweekly intervals from birth until deciduous dental eruption was complete and were examined subsequently at monthly intervals. Examinations were continued for all animals on or about their monthly birth date until 24 months of age. By that age dental eruption is complete but since physical growth continues, measurements were made thereafter during the second week of each month. Since viable female infants were not produced in the colony until 1966 and 1967, growth chronology and dental eruption data from *Saimiri* beyond the age of 14 months were collected only from males.

At all examinations the teeth were checked carefully for eruption status and individual dental charts updated; notations of loose teeth and eruption status were also made. (A tooth was not considered erupted until the *entire* crown was clearly visible above the gingiva.) The following body measurements were made: overall length from the brow to the fleshy tip of the tail, tail length from the right angle of the back to the fleshy tail tip, and length of the right foot from the heel to the tip of the longest digit. Because many individuals suffered a loss of some portion of the tail during the study, overall length and tail length could not be used to measure physical growth. As a result, tail length has been subtracted from overall length to obtain the "head and body length" as a more accurate index of growth under these circumstances.

III. Results

The deciduous dentition of squirrel monkeys consists of 2 incisors, 1 canine, and 3 premolars on either side of both the maxilla (upper jaw) and mandible (lower jaw) for a total of 24 teeth. Most *Saimiri* newborns we have examined exhibited upper first incisors and lower first and second incisors which were either barely protruding through the gingiva or were clearly visible immediately beneath it. Eruption of these incisors was usually quite advanced by 2 weeks of age. Observations to date on this and the balance of decidual dental eruption in 10 captive-bred squirrel monkeys have been summarized in Table I. All eruptions tended to proceed in order from the front to the rear of the jaw with the appearance of individual mandibular teeth usually preceding that of their maxillary counterparts. The eruption of deciduous dentition was generally complete by 9 weeks of age, and by 12 weeks the last deciduous tooth (maxillary third premolar) reached complete occlusion.

From the third to the fifth month postpartum dentition remained unchanged. During the fifth month the mandibular first molar was the initial permanent tooth to erupt. Usually during the ninth month the mandibular

TABLE I

ERUPTION SEQUENCE OF THE DECIDUOUS DENTITION
IN *Saimiri sciureus* (LETICIA, COLOMBIA)

Tooth	Observations	Range (weeks)	Mean (weeks)
Maxillary			
I1	10	0−3	1.3
I2	10	1−3	2.2
C	10	2−4	3.4
P1	10	4−6	4.9
P2	10	5−7	6.1
P3	10	8−11	8.9
Mandibular			
I1	10	1−3	1.3
I2	10	1−3	1.4
C	10	3−4	3.4
P1	10	4−6	4.8
P2	10	5−7	5.7
P3	10	7−9	8.3

first incisor was the first deciduous tooth to be replaced by a permanent tooth. Our complete observations to date on the sequence and age of dental eruption of permanent maxillary and mandibular teeth are summarized in Table II. All mandibular teeth preceded their maxillary counterparts in mean eruption time from as little as 1 week (mandibular third premolar) to as much as 7 months (mandibular third molar) with the single exception of the mandibular second premolar which has *followed* its counterpart by an average of 2 months. *Saimiri* have a total of 36 permanent teeth composed of the permanent replacements for all 24 deciduous teeth plus 3 molars on either side of both the maxilla and mandible. No apparent sex-related differences appeared in the dental eruption data for either deciduous or permanent teeth. However, as mentioned previously, females were studied only to an age of 14 months and the total sample size is still quite small. It is known that considerable sexual dimorphism exists in the size and length of canines in adult *Saimiri*, those of males being much larger. We observed that the canines in two mature captive-bred males did not reach full adult proportions until about 30 months of age.

TABLE II

ERUPTION SEQUENCE OF THE PERMANENT DENTITION
IN *Saimiri sciureus* (LETICIA, COLOMBIA)

Tooth	Observations	Range (months)	Mean (months)
Maxillary			
M1	8	5–6	5.5
M2	8	7–9	8.4
I1	8	8–12	9.7
I2	8	10–14	12.0
P2	5	12–15	13.0
P3	7	12–15	13.0
P1	3	14–15	14.7
M3	3	19–22	20.0
C	4	21–22	21.5
Mandibular			
M1	8	5–6	5.1
M2	8	7	7.0
I1	8	8–11	9.2
I2	8	8–11	9.6
M3	3	11–14	12.3
P3	6	12–15	12.8
P1	3	12–16	14.3
P2	2	15	15.0
C	4	19–21	20.5

Our observations on the physical growth of squirrel monkeys are summarized and charted for males in Tables III and IV and Figs. 1 and 2, and for females in Table V and Figs. 3 and 4. The limitations of the sample noted just above with regard to dental eruption data exist for growth data as well. *Saimiri* infants are extremely large at birth relative to the size of their mothers, representing 12 – 16% of maternal nonpregnant body weight (see also Chapter 4). No obvious sex-related difference in birth weight was observed and a large normal range exists for both sexes. Until 3 months of age, body weight seems to increase at about the same rate in both males and females (Table III and Table V). Our limited data show that from 3 to 14 months of age males have gained weight more rapidly than females. Not until 10 months of age do males show a significant increase over females in head and body and right foot measurements, however. Little, if any, longitudinal growth has occurred in males after 36 months of age.

IV. Discussion

A probable sequence of dental eruption in *Saimiri* was first reported by Schultz (1935). His data was obtained from 23 skulls of squirrel monkeys from various localities in various stages of incomplete permanent dental eruption. Schultz considered *Saimiri* the most primitive platyrrhine with regard to the eruption sequence of permanent dentition. His conclusion was based upon the hypothesis that early eruption of molars and late eruption of canines (in relation to the eruption of premolars) represent phylogenetically primitive characteristics. One subsequent report on the permanent dental eruption sequence of squirrel monkeys was provided by Serra (1952). He studied the eruption status of 36 nonadult *Saimiri* skulls, using both direct observation and roentgenography. He concluded that no sexual or interspecific (sic) dimorphism in eruption sequence existed for squirrel monkeys and, erroneously, that the sequence of eruption was identical for the various categories of teeth in both jaws. The permanent dental eruption sequence data of Schultz and Serra compares with that of Long and Cooper as shown in the following tabulation:

Schultz	Max.	M1	M2	I1	I2	P2	P3	P1	C	M3
	Mand.	M1	M2	I1	I2	M3	P2	P3	P1	C
Serra	Max.	M1	M2	I1	I2	P3	P1	P2	M3	C
Long and	Max.	M1	M2	I1	I2	P2	P3	P1	M3	C
Cooper	Mand.	M1	M2	I1	I2	M3	P3	P1	P2	C

TABLE III

MALE *Saimiri sciureus* (LETICIA, COLOMBIA)

GROWTH AND DEVELOPMENT FROM BIRTH TO 18 MONTHS

Age	Sample size	Weight (gm) Mean	Range	Head and body length (cm) Mean	Range	Right foot length (cm) Mean	Range
Birth	10	112	92–129	14.6	13.5–15.3	4.6	4.3–4.9
1 mo.	10	200	161–232	17.6	16.2–18.9	5.9	5.4–6.6
2 mos.	10	272	234–311	19.7	17.0–21.4	6.5	6.0–7.1
3 mos.	8	343	309–391	21.0	18.5–22.5	7.0	6.8–7.4
4 mos.	4	398	364–422	22.5	21.7–23.5	7.2	7.0–7.5
5 mos.	3	451	445–455	23.2	21.7–24.3	7.4	7.2–7.5
6 mos.	3	467	441–496	23.2	21.7–24.3	7.6	7.5–7.7
7 mos.	3	502	480–520	24.1	21.8–26.3	7.7	7.6–7.9
8 mos.	3	546	528–564	24.5	23.5–26.3	7.8	7.7–7.9
9 mos.	3	556	531–582	24.7	23.5–26.3	7.8	7.7–7.9
10 mos.	3	600	562–624	25.4	24.6–26.7	7.9	7.8–7.9
11 mos.	3	624	588–653	26.7	25.4–28.2	8.1	7.9–8.3
12 mos.	3	640	621–662	27.3	26.8–28.2	8.2	8.0–8.3
13 mos.	2	654	611–698	27.6	27.3–27.8	8.2	8.0–8.4
14 mos.	3	680	663–701	27.6	27.0–28.4	8.3	8.0–8.5
15 mos.	4	703	665–770	27.4	26.5–28.5	8.3	8.0–8.7
16 mos.	4	709	677–756	27.4	26.5–28.5	8.4	8.0–8.7
17 mos.	4	729	694–788	27.5	26.5–28.5	8.4	8.0–8.7
18 mos.	4	731	660–797	28.0	26.8–28.5	8.4	8.1–8.9

TABLE IV
MALE *Saimiri sciureus* (LETICIA, COLOMBIA)
GROWTH AND DEVELOPMENT FROM 19 TO 36 MONTHS

Age (months)	Sample size	Weight (gm)		Head and body length (cm)		Right foot length (cm)	
		Mean	Range	Mean	Range	Mean	Range
19	4	751	698 – 808	28.3	27.3 – 29.0	8.4	8.1 – 8.9
20	4	758	713 – 814	28.4	27.3 – 29.3	8.4	8.1 – 8.9
21	4	758	716 – 829	28.6	27.8 – 29.3	8.5	8.2 – 8.9
22	4	779	730 – 827	28.6	27.8 – 29.4	8.5	8.3 – 9.0
23	4	792	760 – 822	28.7	28.0 – 29.4	8.6	8.3 – 9.0
24	4	817	765 – 868	29.0	28.0 – 29.7	8.6	8.4 – 9.0
25	4	853	816 – 885	29.2	28.7 – 29.7	8.6	8.4 – 9.0
26	4	862	843 – 894	29.2	28.7 – 29.7	8.6	8.4 – 9.0
27	3	867	839 – 895	29.2	28.7 – 29.7	8.7	8.4 – 9.0
28	3	905	863 – 966	29.3	28.8 – 29.8	8.8	8.5 – 9.0
29	3	911	866 – 964	29.3	28.8 – 29.8	8.8	8.5 – 9.0
30	3	900	849 – 965	29.3	28.8 – 29.8	8.8	8.5 – 9.0
31	3	906	835 – 973	29.4	28.8 – 29.8	8.8	8.5 – 9.0
32	3	913	837 – 978	29.6	28.9 – 30.1	8.8	8.5 – 9.1
33	3	921	854 – 985	29.6	28.9 – 30.1	9.0	8.8 – 9.1
34	3	916	867 – 962	29.7	28.9 – 30.4	9.0	8.9 – 9.1
35	3	931	907 – 959	29.7	28.9 – 30.4	9.0	8.9 – 9.1
36	3	942	918 – 962	29.8	29.1 – 30.4	9.0	8.9 – 9.1

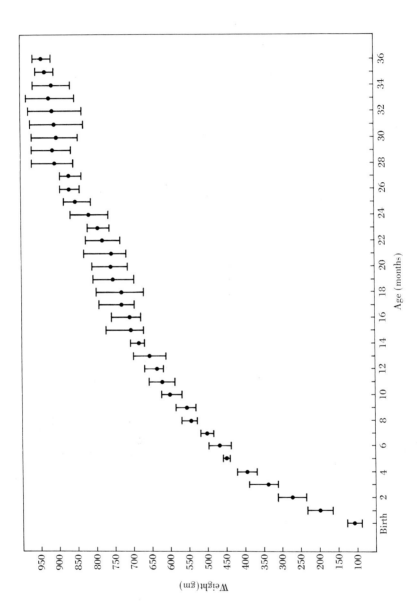

FIG. 1. Body weight of male *Saimiri sciureus* (Leticia, Colombia).

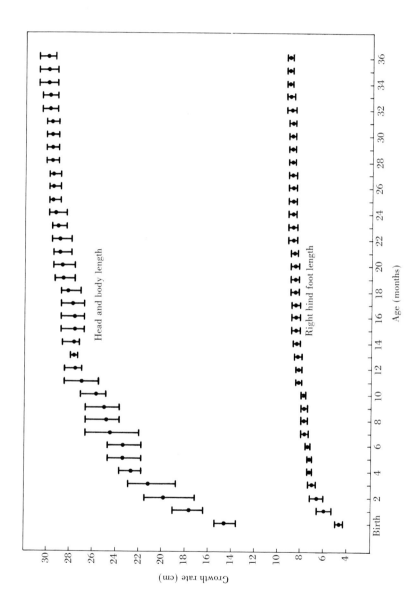

FIG. 2. Growth rate of head and body and right hind foot in male *Saimiri sciureus* (Leticia, Colombia).

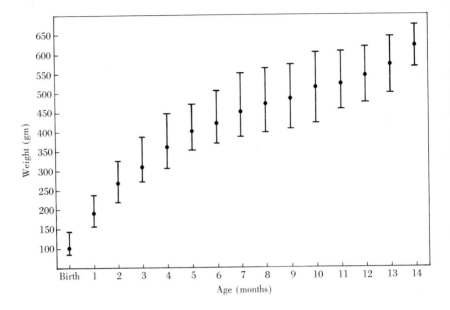

FIG. 3. Body weight of female *Saimiri sciureus* (Leticia, Colombia).

The variation in the eruption sequence of the premolars reported by Schultz (1935) and Serra (1952) as compared to the findings of Long and Cooper probably results from the rapid succession of premolar eruption and also from the fact that their observations were based upon only a very limited number of static or museum specimens. The variance of Schultz with the findings of Long and Cooper on the maxillary third molar, which he indicated follows rather than precedes the canine in eruption sequence, may be attributable also to the limitations posed by working with too few static specimens. However, careful evaluation of Schultz' descriptions of his specimens provides more support for our findings than for the conclusion which he drew. The advantages of studying dental eruption sequence in live animals of known age are exemplified in the present study of *Saimiri*, which to our knowledge is the first such investigation to be reported on any new world primate. With relatively few specimens it has been possible to determine both the sequence of dental eruption and the ages at which these eruptions occur.

The ontogeny of behavior in squirrel monkeys has been the focus of recent study (see Chapter 8) but previously published observations of physical growth in *Saimiri* or other platyrrhines are unknown to the present authors. As opposed to the lack of sexual or subspecific dimorphism reported for dental eruption sequence, physical growth characteristics in squirrel

TABLE V

FEMALE *Saimiri sciureus* (LETICIA, COLOMBIA)
GROWTH AND DEVELOPMENT

Age	Sample size	Weight (gm)		Head and body length (cm)		Right foot length (cm)	
		Mean	Range	Mean	Range	Mean	Range
Birth	11	106	84–144	14.2	12.9–15.5	4.6	4.1–5.0
1 mo.	10	191	156–235	17.4	14.4–19.0	5.7	5.2–6.4
2 mos.	9	269	222–324	19.8	18.0–21.5	6.5	5.8–7.3
3 mos.	6	316	271–389	21.1	19.7–22.7	6.8	6.3–7.3
4 mos.	6	359	307–447	22.4	21.6–24.0	7.2	6.7–8.0
5 mos.	6	397	353–465	22.7	21.6–25.1	7.3	6.8–7.8
6 mos.	6	425	368–507	23.4	22.3–25.4	7.3	6.9–8.1
7 mos.	6	452	389–552	24.4	23.2–25.5	7.4	7.0–8.0
8 mos.	6	471	395–563	24.4	23.5–26.4	7.6	7.2–8.1
9 mos.	5	487	415–577	25.2	23.6–26.6	7.7	7.5–8.0
10 mos.	5	507	427–607	25.4	23.8–27.0	7.8	7.6–8.2
11 mos.	5	522	460–610	25.5	23.9–27.0	7.8	7.7–8.2
12 mos.	5	548	475–618	25.8	24.6–27.6	7.9	7.7–8.2
13 mos.	3	570	503–647	26.6	26.0–27.8	7.9	7.7–8.2
14 mos.	2	620	567–673	26.6	24.9–28.2	8.0	7.7–8.2

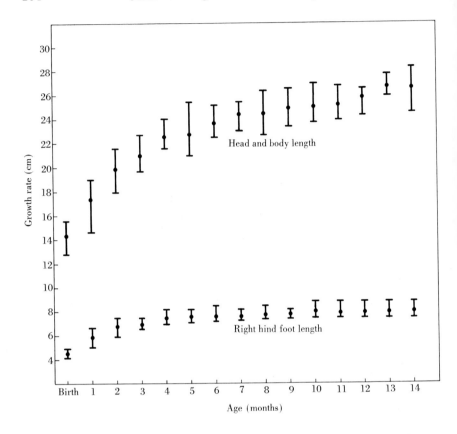

FIG. 4. Growth rate of head and body and right hind foot in female *Saimiri sciureus* (Leticia, Colombia).

monkeys are probably affected by both factors. Our own data on subjects born to parents shipped from Leticia suggest several differences in growth rate between male and female *Saimiri*. Since in addition the average *Saimiri sciureus* (Leticia, Colombia) is considerably heavier as an adult than *S. sciureus* (Iquitos, Peru), and *S. sciureus* (Georgetown, Guyana) is considerably more lanky than either of the other two (see Chapter 1), it seems unlikely that physical growth characteristics will be identical for all such *Saimiri* populations.

References

Cooper, R. W. (1964). A description of a unique outdoor primate colony. *Lab. Animal Care,* **14** No. 6, 474-482.

Serra, O. D. (1952). A sequencia eruptiva dos dentes definitivos nos Simios Platyrrhina e sua Interpretacao Filogenetica. *Anais Facu. Farm. Odontol. Univ. Sao Paulo* **10,** 215-296.

Schultz, A. H. (1935). Eruption and decay of the permanent teeth in primates. *Am. J. Phys. Anthropol.* **19** No. 4, 489-588.

CHAPTER **8**

Mother—Infant Relations and Early Behavioral Development in the Squirrel Monkey*

Leonard A. Rosenblum

I. Introduction

Along with the rapid growth of interest in the general behavior and physiology of the squirrel monkey, the occasional births that have occurred in captivity have resulted in the recording of some preliminary observations of mother—infant relations and infant behavioral development in this species (Takeshita, 1961-1962; Hill, 1962; Bowden *et al.*, 1967; Welker, 1965; Wiswell and Gibbs, 1964; Ploog *et al.*, 1967; DuMond, see Chapter 4). In

*The original research reported here was supported in part by U.S.P.H.S. grant #HD-00840 and #MH-04670.

light of the differences recorded elsewhere in this volume between adult *Saimiri* patterns of behavior and those of the more commonly studied Old World primates, it is clear that the study of the ontogeny of squirrel monkey behavior is of great importance. In addition to considering the pertinent published literature, this paper will focus in some quantitative detail on a description of the first 10 months of development of several laboratory-born squirrel monkey infants of the Peruvian type (see Chapter 2). An attempt will also be made to compare the squirrel monkey's development with that of the infants of bonnet and pigtail macaques (*Macaca radiata* and *Macaca nemestrina*), which we have also studied under similar conditions (Rosenblum and Kaufman, 1967; Kaufman and Rosenblum, 1966).

II. Subjects

The squirrel monkey subjects of our normative developmental study were six infants, of which five were females, all conceived and born in the laboratory to wild-born females. The females, about midway through pregnancy, were removed from a large breeding colony and placed in three or four-member, all-female groups. Each group was housed and observed in a 7-ft-high wooden pen measuring 2 × 2½ ft. At the rear of each pen there were three shelves across the width arranged in staircase fashion, and a ladder from the lowest shelf to the floor. The ceiling was wire mesh, the floor covered with San-i-cel bedding, and all observations were made through a one-way vision mirror in the front door. The lighting schedule was set at 12 hours light, 12 hours darkness, the light period beginning at 7 A.M. Feeding of standard Purina monkey chow occurred once a day at about 4 P.M.; water was available *ad lib.*

III. Methodology

Systematic observations were made between 8:30 A.M. and 11 A.M., usually four times each week, using a check sheet procedure. These quantitative data were supplemented by written protocols made both at testing times and at other times of day when possible. For the check sheet procedure, each mother—infant dyad was observed for 20 minutes each test day; the 20 minutes were broken into four segments of 5 minutes each. In the first and fourth 5-minute periods, a check sheet containing items relating specifically to mother—infant relations was used and both members of the dyad were observed simultaneously. In the second segment, only the infant's behaviors *not* relating to its mother were included; and in the third segment, only behaviors of the mother *not* relating to her infant were recorded. This segmentation of the observation period allowed the observer to focus attention on a more limited array of behaviors at any given time and still allowed sampling of a wide spectrum of pertinent behaviors over the entire observation period.

Each check sheet, listing a large number of items of possible interest, was divided into 10 columns representing consecutive 30-second intervals; during each 30-second interval, demarcated by an electric timer and light, the occurrence or nonoccurrence of each listed behavior was recorded. Regardless of the frequency of occurrence, only one check was recorded within each 30-second interval. All records reported here have been transformed into scores representing the frequency with which a behavior occurred as a percentage of the total number of 30-second intervals the animal was observed. Since our total knowledge of the general behavior of squirrel monkeys is still quite meager, the various influences of specific environmental and social conditions on behavioral development can barely be estimated. Thus, no attempt will be made at this juncture to examine in detail the range and complexity of individual variations in the patterns to be described. Instead, we will examine the basic trends of development in our own and related data that seem most characteristic of squirrel monkeys as a whole. The reader must continuously bear in mind that as our lack of pertinent knowledge in this area is slowly overcome, many of the details and even the gross features of the early studies of development will be altered and perhaps discarded altogether as lacking in generality.

IV. Mother—Infant Relations in Squirrel Monkeys

A. PARTURITION

As with most primates, squirrel monkey births apparently occur normally during the dark phase of the circadian light cycle. All normal births in our own laboratory have occurred during this period and the births described by Hill and Takeshita took place at approximately midnight and 1:30 A.M., respectively. Bowden *et al.* (1967) report that their normal infants were born during the dark phase and indicate that in one female in protracted labor lasting 3 days uterine contractions disappeared during the day with 99% of observed contractions and the delivery itself occurring at night.

We have not observed the entire parturitional process of a viable infant in our own laboratory and the events of parturition are obviously difficult to describe precisely in light of the limited data available. Takeshita (1961-1962) describes a 1-hour first stage of labor during which a number of con-

FIG. 1. One of the characteristic postures accompanying labor contractions shortly before delivery of a dead infant.

tractions occurred (Fig. 1) accompanied by repeated leaking of fluids from
the vulvar region. Bowden *et al.* indicate first stages of 63 and 42 minutes
in a multiparous and a 99-minute initial stage in a young primaparous female. The infant apparently normally emerges in an occiput posterior, ver-
tex presentation, and the infant's full emergence after first appearance
is apparently rapid, less than 16 minutes in all reported instances (Takeshita, Hill, Bowden *et al.*) The placenta appears shortly thereafter (5 –
25 minutes), although is not generally pulled out, and is usually consumed
rapidly although not always entirely. In several instances, even before birth
was complete, the mother was observed avidly licking the infant's face and
body. This rough outline of parturition is quite in keeping with the essential
details of births observed in our laboratory in macaques and in *Cercopithecus aethiops*. However, wide individual variations in the first phase of maternal functioning, i.e., parturition, have been noted in macaque mothers in
our colony and such features as length of labor, placental ingestion, and
activities during and immediately following labor are apparently related to
previous parity, dominance status, and species. Bowden *et al.* in their excellent description of several births of *Saimiri*, apparently of Brazilian origin, and review of related data on other primates, consider some of these
problems; however, with such limited available data on squirrel monkeys
they are unable to draw any firm conclusions. Unfortunately, neither Takeshita nor Hill indicate either the previous parity of their subjects or the
geographic origin of the squirrel monkeys observed.

FIG. 2. Characteristic position of a young squirrel monkey clinging tightly to the mother's dorsal surface.

B. Initial Filial and Maternal Patterns

With respect to the infant's initial behavior, certain features appear consistent. Takeshita, Hill, Bowden *et al.*, and Welker (1965) all agree that the infant is active during the birth; their eyes may be open during delivery and Takeshita reports repeated "chi-chi" vocalizations during this phase; the infant may grasp the mother's fur before completely emerging; within moments of emergence the infant apparently climbs unaided to the mother's back (Fig. 2). It is the assumption and subsequent maintenance of this position at the mother's back immediately after birth that most dramatically distinguishes the squirrel monkey neonate from his Old World simian counterparts. In the macaques, for example, the newborn assumes a close ventral – ventral orientation on the mother and often achieves and maintains oral contact with the nipple for long periods in that position. With the healthy squirrel monkey neonate in the dorsal position, the mother does not make incidental manual contact with it, or attempt extensive exploration or physical support. On the other hand, even with a normal infant able to support itself by means of clasping reflexes in the first days of life, the mother macaque often manually grasps and holds her infant during rapid movements and occasionally even while at rest. Similarly, the newborn macaque infant continuously at the ventral surface of the mother is explored, handled, and groomed extensively shortly after birth and periodically thereafter.

FIG. 3. A 1-day old (68-gm) infant supporting its entire body weight by flexure of its tail around the finger of a technician.

The squirrel monkey neonate apparently is aided in maintaining his position at the mother's dorsal surface by the use of its tail which is usually wrapped around the mother's lower abdomen, or tail base. Unlike the tail of the adult squirrel monkey, which may be used for balance and limited support (see Chapter 4), the infant's tail is somewhat prehensile and, as seen in Fig. 3, is actually capable of supporting the neonate's entire weight for brief periods although it is of course not normally used for this purpose.

During the early days of life, the infants of our developmental study spent almost the entire observational period clinging tightly to the dorsal surface of their mothers. As indicated above, the mother (except for some accommodations to the infant's nursing) almost never interacted directly with her infant during this first developmental phase. In general, she apparently remains, as Takeshita (1961-1962) described it, " ... thoroughly uninterested in the baby on her back" (p. 63). The contrast with the actively engaged macaque mother with her ventrally located infant is striking indeed.

1. Response to a Debilitated Infant

The fascinating work of Rumbaugh (1965), however, suggests that the apparent indifference of the squirrel monkey mother toward her normal infant, under appropriate conditions of infant need, can change to " ... a very concerted, active pattern ... " (p. 174) which includes manual cradling of the infant and bipedal transport of it (see Figs. 4a,b,c,and d). Briefly, Rumbaugh found that if he restrained the arms of young squirrel mon-

FIG. 4a

FIG. 4b

FIG. 4c

FIG. 4d

FIG. 4. A series of photographs made by Dr. D. Rumbaugh illustrating the adaptive potential of squirrel monkey maternal behavior. The normal ventral-dorsal contact pattern of a 5-month old infant and its mother (a). When the hands and feet of the infant were taped thus preventing it from grasping the mother, the mother showed a variety of compensating reactions including a remarkable one-arm hold and carry of the infant (b), a somewhat awkward two-arm cradle of the infant (c), and a ventral–ventral cradle by the mother (d), strikingly similar to those generally observed in the macaques.

key infants or if they were weakened by illness and were unable to support themselves on the mother's back, the mothers, after repeatedly assuming postures which ordinarily would result in the infant climbing on her (see *retrieve*, Section IV, E) would actually pick up the debilitated infant and, cradling it with both hands or arms, scamper off bipedally (Fig. 4). Similar observations have recently been noted by Ploog *et al.* (1967) and in the reaction to a dead fetus by Bowden *et al.* (1967). Thus, the maternal behavior of squirrel monkeys apparently has a degree of adaptability not often observed under normal circumstances. These adjustments of maternal behavior in some measure at least, are influenced by changes in the stimulus qualities and behavioral characteristics of the infant. Again, one cannot help but speculate on the other systematic changes in "normal" squirrel monkey maternal behavior that might result, for example, when experiments involving gross variations in environmental conditions are carried out.

2. Intradyadic Recognition

In light of the quite circumscribed interaction between the normal infant and its mother in the early postpartum weeks and the usual location of the infant reducing face-to-face visual contact between the dyad members, one might expect poor intradyadic recognition during early infancy. In a study conducted in our laboratory, 12 infants, ranging in age from 1 to 18 months, were each released separately in the center of the floor of a 10-ft-long 2½-ft-wide chamber; at one end, restrained by a waist band was the infant's mother, at the other end, similarly restrained, was another female who was a member of the large group in which all subjects lived. Four trials were given in which the location of the mother was alternated, and four different females were offered as alternative choices. The two youngest infants, 4 and 6 weeks old, respectively, had no difficulty in selecting and moving toward their own mothers on each trial, even though the youngest infant was barely able to cover the distance in the alloted 5 minutes. Although first choice became somewhat more variable in the older infants (the two 18-month olds) except for two subjects 3 and 4 months of age, respectively [who had developed an active "aunt" relationship (cf. DuMond, Chapter 4) with one of the alternative females and remained close to her when she was offered] all other subjects rapidly moved to and stayed with their mothers on each trial. The four subjects just described moved to their mothers on three of the four trials.

When the mothers of these 12 infants were in similar fashion offered two choice trials involving their infant and two alternative infants of similar age, rapid choice of their own infant consistently occurred in the mothers of the youngest and, though somewhat more casually, even the oldest in-

FIG. 5. A squirrel monkey infant in the midst of nursing.

fants. Mothers of oldest infants, however, failed to remain near their restrained infant after a brief contact had been made. Thus, even by rather
crude evaluation the minimal degree of overt interaction and face-to-face
visual contact between a mother and infant squirrel monkey, although they
might prove to be irrelevant to the process, at present seem sufficient to
mediate the establishment of quite adequate and specific recognition and
in Harlow's terms "affectional-bonding."

C. MOTHER–INFANT CONTACT AND NURSING

The long periods of close contact with the dorsal surface of the mother
equal to a mean of 86.8% of the observation period during the first month of
life are broken only by periodic nursing episodes. To nurse, the infant
shifts his body to the resting mother's side, between her flexed leg and
abdomen, retaining hold of the dorsal surface with the hind legs; or else,
less frequently, it shifts entirely into a ventral–ventral orientation beneath
the crouched female (Fig. 5). She in turn, apparently in response to the pok-
ing of the infant's head at her arm, raises that elbow slightly to allow the
infant to slip through and then usually arches her torso, maintaining contact with the ground with all four limbs. Nursing periods seem quite variable in length and any sudden movement of the mother will usually result
in termination of the nursing and reestablishment of the full dorsal contact.

As shown in Fig. 6, the amount of dorsal contact shows a progressive
decline and by the fifth month has virtually disappeared during the daylight hours. Vandenbergh (1966) also indicates the rarity of dorsal contact

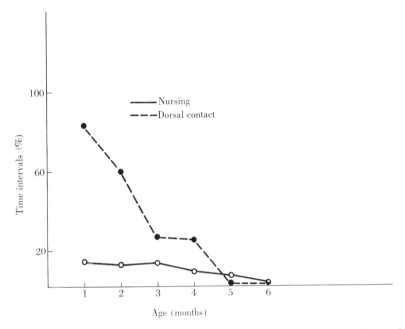

FIG. 6. The decrement with age in the relative amount of time spent by the infants at the mother's dorsal surface and in nursing.

after week 21, with the most rapid period of decline in the first 2 months. Ploog *et al.*, however, also noting the rapid decline of the initial dorsal contact patterns, nonetheless note that in several cases at least, infants were observed to sleep on the mother's back until the fourteenth month. As Fig. 6 also illustrates, nursing behavior, which represented about a quarter of the observation period in the first week, similarly declined although somewhat less sharply than the contacts during the first 6 months and was seen only sporadically thereafter. Vandenbergh's data on nursing is again virtually identical to our own.

By 2 months of life, when longer periods of the day are being spent off the mother, infants often move into a nursing position directly without establishing other contact. After the first 2 months, the mother may also try to prevent the infant's attempts to nurse or even to actively remove an infant from her once nursing has begun. Notwithstanding this weaning behavior of the mother after month 2, nipple contact was sporadically attained throughout the course of both our 10-month and Vandenbergh's 7-month study and Ploog *et al.* report "nursing" episodes in the thirteenth month of life in their subjects. In a more recent study of our own, we observed a brief episode of oral contact with the nipple at 18 months.

1. Comparison to Macaque Patterns

The general decline in the clinging of the squirrel monkey infant to its mother occurs more rapidly than that observed in either of the macaque species we have studied. The bonnet and pigtail mothers and their infants have been studied in heterosexual groups of adults and varying aged infants, housed in pens of approximately 85 — 100 sq ft of floor space. All infants reported on were conceived, born, and raised in these group pens. As indicated in Fig. 7, at 6 months of life, the pigtail and bonnet macaque still spend about 30% of the daylight hours at their mother's ventrum and approximately 15% of their time even at a year of age. Other studies (Rosenblum *et al.*, 1964, 1968) indicate that in these macaques even greater periods of time are spent on the mother during the evening hours. Similarly, our data on nursing (Rosenblum and Kaufman, 1967) indicates that oral contact with the nipple occurs during almost 50% of the observation period during the first half-year of life, more than twice that shown at any age in our squirrel monkey subjects. In macaque infants, during the sixth through fifteenth month, almost all of the time that the infants spend in ventral — ventral contact with the mother, mouth — nipple contact is maintained. To be sure, in most instances oral contact with the nipple does not involve active nursing in macaques whereas it generally appears to do so more fre-

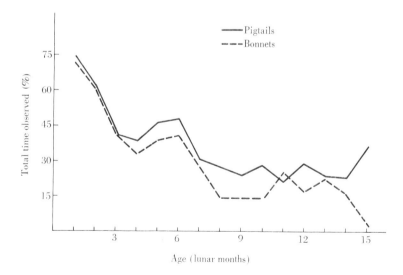

FIG. 7. The decrement with age in the amount of time spent at the ventral surface of the mother in pigtail and bonnet infants.

quently in squirrel monkeys. It is unfortunate that the difficulties of discriminating active nursing from passive oral contact with the nipple make it impossible at this time to determine whether actual sucking duration is more similar in the two genera than it appears from gross observation. In light of the significance that oral behavior holds in theoretical views of human development it is also of interest to speculate upon and eventually systematically to study the pronounced non-nursing oral contact in macaques and the degree to which it differs in squirrel monkeys with respect to its role in the establishment and maintenance of the mother—infant relationship and the subsequent development of infant behaviors in general.

D. Explorations by the Young Infant

After the first several days of life, during which the infant does little else but cling tightly to the mother often dozing or else shifting his body to nurse, the infant begins active visual exploration of the environment. Repeated raising and turning of the head with eyes opened widely becomes prominent toward the end of the first week. The infant shortly afterward begins to raise his entire body off the mother, almost standing on her back while she remains immobile. Beginning at about the third week, while holding the mother's back with its hind legs and tail, the infant begins first to touch tentatively, and then to lean on and actively explore manually, the walls and floor next to the seated mother (Fig. 8). This *manual exploration* while still clasping the mother, as indicated in Fig. 9, rises sharply during the second month and occurs at almost every opportunity at that age. Following rapidly upon the onset of manual exploration in our study, at about

FIG. 8. An early *manual exploration* of the shelving made by an infant while still clinging to the mother's back with its hind legs.

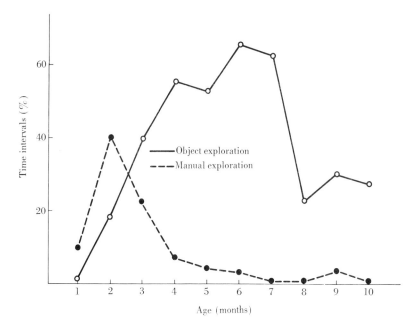

FIG. 9. The development of *manual exploration* while on the mother and *object exploration* made while free of the mother in squirrel monkey infants.

the fourth week, infants briefly begin to release their grasp of the mother to descend to the floor. Vandenbergh indicates his infant was free at 3 weeks, as does Hill (1962), and the infants of Ploog *et al.* descended from the mothers at 3 – 5 weeks.

E. Protective Maternal Behavior

During the initial period of the infant's attempts to descend from the mother, the mother would occasionally prevent the infant's departure. These *prevent departures* took two forms: (1) *bipedal stand*, in which the mother suddenly stands erect on her hind legs and causes the young infant, attempting to crawl down from her, to swing back to a tight four-limb dorsal contact. The mother may stand for only a second or two but will often repeat this movement several times if the infant persists in its attempts to get down; and (2) *prevent-departure arm*, in which the mother rapidly and repeatedly laterally stretches out her arm on the side down which the infant is attempting to climb. Since young infants usually climb down with their forearms first, the movement of the mother's arm effectively thwarts the attempt to descend. Although the prevent departure behaviors are seen at some time in most mothers, it is more frequently the case that if the

FIG. 10. Retrieval of her infant by a squirrel monkey mother.

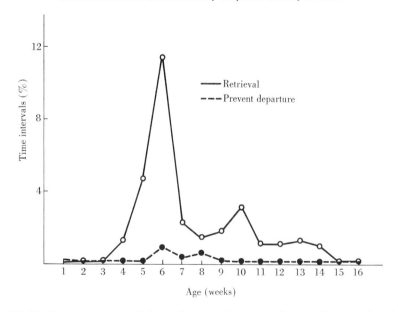

FIG. 11. The development and decay of *prevent departure* and *retrieval* in squirrel monkey dyads.

group is at rest the mother will not interfere with the infant's descent and will allow it to remain off her for brief periods. Usually, in the early days, the infant maintains passive contact with the mother's side and quickly climbs back onto her. As the duration of the descent lengthens or if she becomes agitated, the mother will, however, *retrieve* her infant. In this quite descrete behavior, the mother moves against the infant with her chest pressed close to the floor and her head down, usually nudging the infant with her head and shoulders and gives a characteristic low intensity vocalization until the infant grasps her and climbs onto her back (Fig. 10). As shown in Fig. 11, both prevent departure and retrieve are most prominent in the second month of life and they decrease sharply thereafter, although retrieval continues to appear occasionally afterward when the mother becomes agitated.

1. Comparison to Macaque Patterns

In comparing squirrel monkeys with our macaques, it is of interest to note that the latter also show both departure restraint and retrieval of their young infants. However, the form of the behavior in macaques is markedly different from that in the *Saimiri*. Both behaviors, when performed by macaque females, include direct manual contact with the infant. A macaque restrains her infant by grasping and holding the infant's body or tail and retrieves it by moving to the separated infant and manually pulling the infant to her ventrum. The chronology of appearance and disappearance of these behaviors is similar in macaques and squirrel monkeys, with macaque prevent departure increasing after the end of the first month and disappearing rapidly during month 2, while retrieval increases several weeks later and is sustained at decreasing levels for several months afterward.

The total frequency of protective maternal behaviors is not the same in the two macaques that we have studied, however (Fig. 12). Bonnet mothers spend considerably less time in restraining their young infants or retrieving the slightly older ones than do pigtails. This relative "permissiveness" of the bonnet mothers seems to be an outgrowth of their more affirmatively gregarious quality of adult social patterns, which includes extensive periods of multiple-animal huddling and generally short individual distances (Rosenblum *et al.*, 1964). The squirrel monkey mother, in a stable group in which regular huddling patterns have been established (Rosenblum *et al.*, 1968) although engaging in some protective behaviors as we have seen, seems to behave more in keeping with the permissive pattern of bonnet mothers than the often intense protectiveness of the pigtail females we have observed. We have only just begun to speclate upon the potential influence of these variations in early maternal behavior as it helps shape

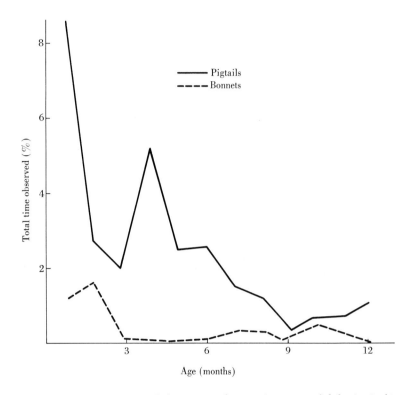

Age (months)

FIG. 12. The development and decrement of *protective maternal behavior* in bonnet and pigtail macaques.

macaque behavioral development (Kaufman and Rosenblum, 1968; Rosenblum and Kaufman, 1968), and as our studies of infant and adult squirrel monkey patterns progress it will be of importance to determine the degree to which similar dynamic factors are relevant in the development of these different genera.

F. Spontaneous Separations between Infant and Mother in Squirrel Monkeys and Macaques

As the restraining and protective gestures of the squirrel monkey mothers wane toward the end of the second month, the time the infant spends off her gradually increases. Initially, as we have described and as indicated in Fig. 13, the infant maintains passive contact with the mother at her side, and rarely moves more than 6 inches from her on the same level of the pen (*proximity*). By the third month, however, the infant and mother increasingly move to other levels of the pen from one another and these *other-level*

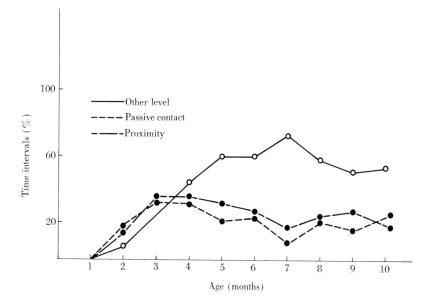

FIG. 13. The development within squirrel monkey dyads of the relative amount of time spent in *passive contact* with one another, in *proximity* (6 inches) to one another and with mother and infant at different levels of the pen.

movements increase to about 25% of the time observed in month 3 and gradually reach an asymptote of about 60% after month 5 (Fig. 13). Although initially both mother and infant readily move to other levels of the pen leaving their dyadic partner behind (*abandon*), by the fourth month, the rapidly increasing locomotor ability of the infant results in most abandon after that age being scored by the infant (Fig. 14).

In our macaque dyads also, movements to other levels of the pen are the last phase of spontaneous separation to develop and it is perhaps not unreasonable that in arboreal species a special significance may be attached, for example, to the descent of one member of the dyad to the ground. It is difficult to compare directly the development of other-level departures in our macaques with the *Saimiri* because of the considerably larger pens utilized for the macaques and the relative distances involved (Rosenblum *et al.*, 1964); however, as with squirrel monkeys, the increase in this behavior in our macaques is most rapid after month 3, although stable levels are not attained in both macaque species until month 8. Similar to the squirrel monkeys, it is the infants of both bonnet and pigtail groups that account for most *abandon* within the dyad.

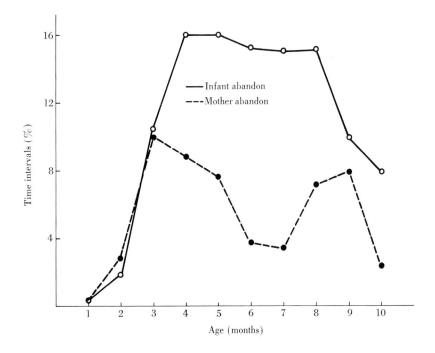

FIG. 14. The relative frequency with which infant and mother squirrel monkeys initiate separation to *other levels* of the pen (*abandon*).

V. Infant Independent Behavioral Development

A. OBJECT EXPLORATIONS AND MANIPULATION

As we look back now on the developing individual behavior of the increasingly independent infant, as indicated in Fig. 9, *object explore*, the more vigorous manual and oral manipulation of inanimate features of the environment while out of contact with the mother, increases rapidly during the second through seventh month. Vandenbergh indicates the appearance of "wood chewing" in the third week; Ploog *et al.* saw it first in the third to fifth week and this age range is similar to the time when our own infants began this form of activity with inanimate objects.

B. EATING OF SOLID FOOD AND DRINKING OF WATER

As indicated in Fig. 15, the interest in and manipulation of various aspects of the inanimate environment eventuates at the beginning of the third month of life in our study in the nibbling of solid food and the onset of

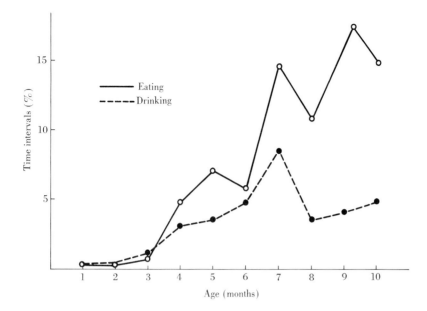

FIG. 15. The development of the *eating* of solid foods and the *drinking* of water in squirrel monkey infants.

drinking. (A pan of fresh water was always available on the lower shelf of the pen.) Again our own data are in general agreement with the data of Vandenbergh, Ploog *et al.*, and Hill, although the first appearance of eating solids was observed a week or two sooner in their subjects than ours.

C. Genital Display in Infants

Interest in the newborn is often manifested by group members immediately following birth and results in sporadic exploration of the infant on its mother's back. However, this early experience of the infant is not overtly interactive. It is during the second month of life as the infant moves away from the mother that obvious social interactions develop. Among the early behaviors is the genital display pattern. This behavior which involves the spreading of the thighs and abduction of one leg while orienting the genital region toward a partner and which is usually involved in dominance and greeting behaviors in older subjects, has received considerable attention in the literature (e.g., Ploog, 1967). Although Ploog *et al.* (1967) indicate that this pattern first may be seen on day 1, we did not detect it until considerably later (about 3 months). Even later in life the genital display pattern was not observed particularly often. Sex differences between their subjects and ours seem not to be the problem, since Ploog *et al.* saw this pattern quite early even in female young. It may be that the early displays, made while on the back of the mother, are rather difficult to observe and since we did not maintain particular focus on this pattern as did the Ploog *et al.* study, they were simply missed by our observers.

D. Social Explorations

In the second month of life, tentative approaches toward and visual and olfactory exploration of social partners appears. These social explorations, *"socex-initiates"* (Fig. 16) occur increasingly while both on and off the mother and are directed at both adults and peers alike.

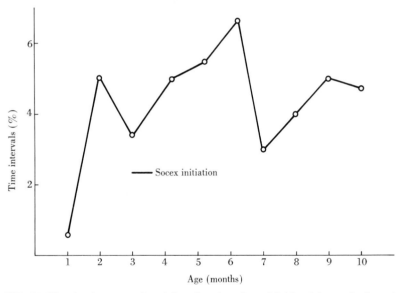

FIG. 16. The development of *social explorations (socex)* initiated by squirrel monkey infants.

E. Aunt — Infant Relationships

Before considering further the development of peer social patterns, however, it is necessary to consider at this point the significant relationships that squirrel monkey infants often develop with so-called "aunts." General interest in young infants is seen in many group members within most primate species. In some cases, fairly sustained involvement of a semimaternal quality can develop between one or more group members and a given infant (e.g., in rhesus, Hinde, 1965; in langurs, Jay, 1963). Under appropriate conditions, this aunt — infant relationship in squirrel

monkeys can be of considerable importance. Ploog *et al.* (1967) indicate that relationships between the infant and an aunt begin usually in the fifth to seventh week of life. The aunt, often a nulliparous female and one who need not have been a particular associate of the infant's mother previously, spends considerable time sitting near the mother and infant. Often, while the infant is clinging to its mother, the aunt makes a repeated, somewhat guttural vocalization not unlike the sound associated with retrieval; the aunt may also make this same retrieval-variant sound when trying to establish contact with a separated infant.

As the infant leaves its mother the aunt will attempt to retrieve it and, if successful, will carry it on her back for extended periods. Some infants will respond to the "retrieval" attempts of the aunt by climbing directly from the mother's back onto the aunt. In general, the aunt's reactions to the infant are not distinctly different from those of the mother during the same age period, although they appear on occasion to be somewhat more excited and intense. Ploog *et al.* report that it is at about the fifth month of life when, as we have seen, close contact with the mother virtually disappears, that the close relationship with the aunt also diminishes.

Our own normative study began before the phenomenon of aunt – infant relationships and its potential significance in squirrel monkey development had been described. As a consequence, with study groups composed entirely of pregnant females and mothers, aunt behavior was at a minimum and as a result no clear aunt – infant relationships were recorded in that study. However, in a more recent observational study involving a large group that contained a number of mothers and their infants (ranging in age from 1 to 18 months) as well as several other adult males and females, pronounced aunt – infant behavior has been recorded. Each of the six subjects from 6 weeks to 4 months of age were observed riding the back of at least one female other than the mother. Neither the single 1-month old nor any of the infants of 6 months of age or older engaged in any aunt – infant relationships. Thus, if this data is representative, it agrees reasonably well with the chronology of aunt – infant involvement described by Ploog *et al.* as beginning at about week 5 and dissipating in the fifth month. It is of interest, however, that the aunt – infant relationships we have seen have not been particularly exclusive with regard to the females or the infants. One female acted in an auntlike fashion toward three of the infants and two other females behaved as aunts toward two of the infants; similarly, one infant was seen repeatedly with three different aunts and two infants showed some involvement with two aunts each.

1. Infant Relations with Other Adults in Macaques

There is a considerable difference between our macaques in the degree to which other adult monkeys of the group became involved with the in-

fants in a manner that might resemble the aunt—infant relationship of squirrel monkeys. Pigtail mothers, as we have seen, in most instances are extremely protective of their infants and will withdraw from or threaten others who attempt to make contact with their young infant. We have occasionally seen pigtail females explore, handle, and even briefly carry ventrally an infant not their own, but in our own experience, despite apparent curiosity regarding newborns, overt interaction with them is the exception rather than the rule in pigtails. In bonnets, on the other hand, newborn infants are the focus of considerable behavior by a number of other group members, often including the adult male. Although even in bonnets it is rare to observe another female carrying an infant whose mother is present, the young infant has ample opportunity to "interact" for long periods with other members of the group, often quite soon after birth. The potential strength of such relationships with adults other than the mother and the difference between the two macaque species is demonstrated most dramatically when mothers are experimentally removed from their infants (Rosenblum and Kaufman, 1968). In pigtails, such infants, separated at about 6 months of age, are generally ingnored or actually rejected by the group, and after a period of initial agitation often show a pronounced depression (Kaufman and Rosenblum, 1967). Return of the mother results in enormous intensification of previous mother—infant relationships which may last for several months following reunion. In bonnets, on the other hand, separated infants of the same age range almost immediately elicit the pronounced solicitude of the other adults of the group. In fact, bonnet infants will usually be "adopted" by another female, occasionally by a female who already has an infant of her own. These adoptions involve prolonged periods spent at the ventrum of the adopted female, usually quite equivalent to that spent at the ventrum of the mother prior to separation. In addition, active nursing behavior and passive mouth-nipple contact is generally recorded. In our most striking case, a bonnet female, the mother of a 5 month old, successively adopted two other infants of comparable age that had been experimentally separated from their own mothers, (Fig. 17). She carried all three, albeit with some difficulty, sustained contact with all of them, and each nursed from her, usually two at a time.

The return of the mothers of these adopted bonnet infants does not immediately result in reassertion of the previous tie between mother and infant. The switch back to the mother is gradual in most cases, often taking a week or more of alternating between adopted and biological mother and in one case at least, an adopted bonnet infant failed to return to its mother at all. Although we have not as yet had the opportunity to separate squirrel monkey infants that have developed active involvements with an aunt, it is our suspicion that complete adoptions by the aunt might well occur with lit-

FIG. 17. A bonnet mother who adopted two experimentally separated bonnet infants of her group while maintaining maternal interest in her own comparably aged infant.

tle sustained disruption of the behavior of the infant and minimal alteration of the normal course of development.

F. PLAY BEHAVIOR

1. Activity Play

In the squirrel monkey infant, it is during the same period that the aunt—infant relationship appears, i.e., the second month of life, when movement off the mother increases and locomotor capacity and coordination progress most rapidly, that play behavior emerges. The rapid growth of tentative exploration and interest in the inanimate and social environment (Fig. 9 and Fig. 16) merges into *activity play* and *social play*, respectively

(Fig.18). Activity play, which includes running, jumping, and swinging from fore or hind limbs, actually develops somewhat more rapidly and reflects the frequent bursts of activity that characterize the squirrel monkey infant during much of the first year of life. Ploog *et al.* also comment that the activity level of the infant squirrel monkey is quite high, considerable exceeding that of adults, and both Ploog *et al.* and Vandenbergh set the onset of these playful activities at the beginning of the second month. Hill notes the same behavior in week 8.

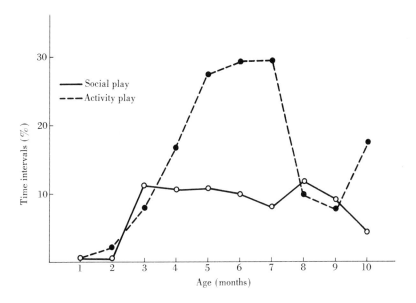

FIG. 18. The development of *social* and *activity play* in squirrel monkey infants.

2. Social Play

Social play, primarily involving infants alternately chasing one another and occasional playful wrestling together, in our own study appeared clearly at the beginning of the third month and remained a rather constant element of the infant's behavior thereafter. We have recently observed it, though at somewhat less frequency, in our two 18-month old juveniles. Ploog *et al.* indicates that social play remains quite high throughout the second year of life although there are pronounced individual differences in the frequency of occurrence. They also note that no clear sex differences in play patterns are evident, although older females tend not to choose males as play partners.

VI. Conclusion

We have seen in this brief outline that the ontogeny of squirrel monkey behavior bears certain parallels and certain contrasts with patterns observed in other primate species (Fig. 19). In comparison to the macaque

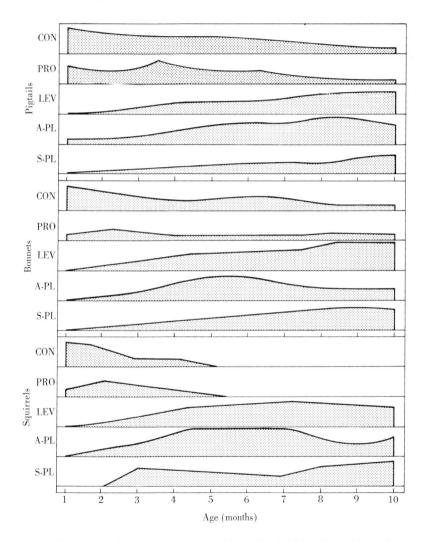

FIG. 19. The relative development and decay of the following behaviors in pigtail, bonnet, and squirrel monkeys: *contact* between mother and infant (CON); *protective maternal behavior* (PRO); time spent by mother and infant at *other levels* of the pen (LEV); *activity play* in infants (A-PL); *social play* in infants (S-PL).

species we have studied, early *Saimiri* infant behavior generally involves less overt interaction with the mother and more obvious elements of attachment including close contacts and nursing behavior appear to dissipate more rapidly. The rather gregagious social behavior within the stable squirrel monkey groups in which development was observed was accompanied by a rather permissive maternal attitute, which allowed for rapid movement of the infant into engagement with the nonmaternal environment. In this regard, the squirrel monkey development occurs in a social setting that parallels in certain respects that of the bonnet infants we have studied and contrasts rather sharply with that of our pigtail groups. As with our bonnet mothers, squirrel monkey females, though possessing a repertoire of restraining and protective behaviors with respect to their infant, employ these with relatively minimal frequency in contrast to the pigtails. It is also true in squirrel monkeys, as in bonnets, that though the mother sporadically engages in rejecting behaviors with their older infants, maternal rejection does not play a critical role in the growing independence of the infant. Indeed, of the three species we have studied, it is the pigtail infant whose mother is ultimately most rejecting, that maintains the greatest dependence on the mother, and the most slowly developing autonomous function. The general hypotheses that has emerged from the macaque and now *Saimiri* normative development and experimental mother—infant studies is that the growth of independent functioning is most readily fostered when the mother allows but does not coerce or continuously interfere with the progressive changes in the behavior of their infants. The striking differences between the intensity and mode of interaction between squirrel monkey mothers and their infants and the dyadic relationships studied in most other primate forms offer great potential for future understanding of the dynamic role played by the mother in influencing and shaping development in complex organisms.

ACKNOWLEDGMENT

The author wants to express his appreciation to Miss E. Levy for her invaluable contributions to all phases of our squirrel monkey research program.

REFERENCES

Bowden, D., Winter, P., and Ploog, D. (1967). Pregnancy and delivery behavior in the squirrel monkey (*Saimiri sciureus*) and other primates. *Folia Primatol.* **5,** 1-42.
Hill, W. C. (1962). Reproduction in the squirrel monkey (*Saimiri sciurea*). *Proc. Zool. Soc. London* **138,** 671-672.
Hinde, R. A. (1965). Rhesus monkey aunts. *In* "Determinants of Infant Behavior" (B. M. Foss, ed.). Vol. III, pp. 67-71, Wiley, New York.

Jay, P. (1963). Mother-infant relations in langurs. *In* "Maternal Behavior in Mammals" (H. L. Rheingold, ed.) pp. 282-304. Wiley, New York.

Kaufman, I. C., and Rosenblum, L. A. (1966). A behavioral taxonomy for *Macaca nemestrina* and *Macaca radiata:* Based on longitudinal observation of family groups in the laboratory. *Primates* **7,** No. 2, 207-258.

Kaufman, I. C., and Rosenblum, L. A., (1967). Depression in infant monkeys separated from their mothers. *Science* **155,** 1030-1031.

Kaufman, I. C., and Rosenblum, L. A., (1968). The reaction to separation in infant monkeys: Anaclitic depression and conservation withdrawal. *Psychosomat. Med.* **29,** No. 6, 648-675.

Ploog, D. W. (1967). The behavior of squirrel monkeys (*Saimiri sciureus*) as revealed by sociometry, bioacoustics, and brain stimulation. *In* "Social Communication among Primates" (S. A. Altmann, ed.), pp. 149-184. Univ. of Chicago Press, Chicago, Illinois.

Ploog, D., Hopf, S., and Winter, P. (1967). Ontogenese des Sozialverhaltens von Totenkopfaffen (*Saimiri sciureus*). *Psychol. Forsch.* **31,** 1-41.

Rosenblum, L. A. and Kaufman, I. C. (1967). Laboratory observations of early mother-infant relations in pigtail and bonnet Macaques. *In* "Social Communication Among Primates" (S. A. Altmann, ed.), pp. 33-41. Univ. of Chicago Press, Chicago, Illinois.

Rosenblum, L. A., and Kaufman, I. C. (1968). Variations in infant development and response to maternal loss in monkeys. *Am. J. Orthopsychiat.* **38,** No. 3, 418-426.

Rosenblum, L. A., Kaufman, I. C., and Stynes, A. J. (1964). Individual distance in two species of macaques. *Animal Behaviour* **12,** Nos. 2 and 3, 338-342.

Rosenblum, L. A., Levy, E. J., and Kaufman, I. C. (1968). Social behavior of squirrel monkeys and the reaction to strangers. *Animal Behaviour* (in press).

Rumbaugh, D. M. (1965). Maternal care in relation to infant behavior in the squirrel monkey. *Psychol. Rept.* **16,** 171-176.

Takeshita, H. (1961-1962). On the delivery behavior of squirrel monkeys (*Saimiri sciurea*) and a mona monkey (*Ceropithecus mona*). *Primates* **3,** No. 1, 59-72.

Vandenbergh, J. G. (1966). Behavioral observations of an infant squirrel monkey. *Psychol. Rept.* **18,** No. 3, 683-688.

Welker, W. (1965). Personal communication.

Wiswell, O. B., and Gibbs, W. E. (1964). "T.L.C." nurtures the infant *Saimiri sciureus. Am. Zoologist* **4,** No 3, p. 64.

CHAPTER 9

Social Communication in the Squirrel Monkey

Peter Winter

I. Introduction

The monkeys of the genus *Saimiri* are largely arboreal animals which inhabit large parts of the tropical forests in South America. They live together in troops the size of which varies to a considerable degree, sometimes comprising more than a hundred individuals (see Chapter 3).

Several species and subspecies of *Saimiri* have been described (Fiedler, 1956; Hill, 1960) but, as noted elsewhere in this volume (Chapter 1), the problem of taxonomy is not yet settled. This particular chapter presents data on the Brazilian type of *Saimiri sciureus*. It differs from the Peruvian type both anatomically and behaviorally (MacLean, 1964).

Behavioral investigations of small groups of squirrel monkeys in captivity have revealed a highly developed repertoire of different behavior patterns and a complicated system of social behavior (Ploog *et al.*, 1963). Generally speaking, the behavior an animal exhibits may be directed to objects, parts of its own body, or to a partner. In the latter case we are dealing with social behavior. A specific behavior pattern directed toward a partner having the function of modifying the latter's behavior may be considered a social signal.

Social signals can be classified according to physical qualities into: visual, auditory, tactile, and olfactory stimuli (Marler, 1965). In squirrel monkeys the most important social communications are auditory and visual signals derived from vocal and motor patterns of behavior.

The function of the social signal (i.e., the way it modifies the partner's behavior) can only be established by observing the behavioral reaction of the receiver animal (Wappler, 1958) and not merely from the inferred intent of the sender. This reaction may be simple or complex. In the first case there is a clear-cut stimulus — response relationship that determines the function. In the latter case, no obvious immediate reaction can be observed. Nevertheless there is a change of complex behavior patterns. Generally this type of complex reaction is true for most types of social signals in squirrel monkeys. Therefore, in order to assess the more subtle shifts in behavior it is necessary to quantify observational data.

II. Method

Groups of monkeys varying in size (2 to 13 animals) and composition were observed over a period of 3 years. The type of cages varied from small ones about 0.3 m³ in volume to large compounds consisting of an indoor and an outdoor compartment. In two cases a group of four to six monkeys was continuously observed for more than 1 year.

The observation followed the scheme: "which animal does what, when and for how long to which." The data were protocolled by a multichannel recording system, and transferred to punch cards for further statistical evaluation.

In addition, vocalization and qualitative observational data were recorded with a stereo tape recorder. The different types of calls were subjected to spectrographic analysis.

III. Results

A. AUDITORY SIGNALS

According to physical parameters — frequency and time course — 26 different calls can be classified into 6 groups of calls (Winter *et al.*, 1966). We shall concentrate here only on those calls that are considered to be of major social importance.

1. Group of Peep Calls

These calls are characterized by a uniform frequency pattern, changes in frequency being less than one octave. The fundamental for the majority of these sounds lies above 6 kc. The duration varies from 0.03 second in some play peeps, up to 1 second in the isolation peep. Harmonics may be detected up to 45 kc.

a. Isolation Peep (Fig. 1a). Animals being separated from the group or babies taken away from their mothers' backs will start to utter this stereo-

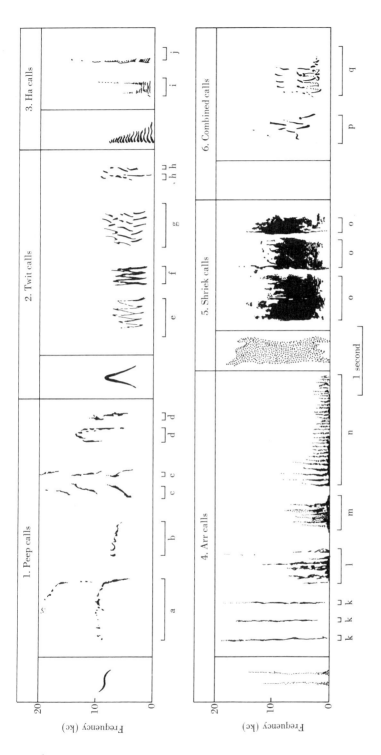

FIG. 1. Sound spectrograms of 17 different calls grouped according to physical characteristics symbolized by drawings at the beginning of each group. a, Isolation peep; b, peep; c, play peeps; d, alarm peeps; e, trill; f, location trill; g, twitter; h, chuck; i, cackle; j, yap; k, spitting; l, err; m, churr; n, purr; o, shrieking; p, chirp; q, kecker.

237

typed peep of high intensity. The fundamental frequency is within the range of 9–12 kc. Its duration may be up to 1 second. The frequency course is characterized by a plateau in its central section and a final steep descent. This pattern is the same in adult and in young animals. Hearing this sound, members of the same or even other groups will answer in the same manner, the result being an exchange of isolation peeps. Instead of using an isolated animal, this call may be played back by a tape recorder, eliciting the same reaction. Evidently the isolation peep has a seeking function, as it is always emitted as soon as visual contact between one animal and its group is interrupted. The physical properties of the call, i.e., its good directionality as well as the continuous exchange between the isolated animal and group members, undoubtedly help the former to find its way back to the group. This call may be regarded as having particular value for arboreal animals as, for instance, *Saimiri* inhabiting tropical forests and foraging within dense foliage.

b. Peeps (Fig. 1b). Peeps are rather frequent calls. They are a relatively constant component of the total vocalization repertoire even within widely varying situations. They differ from the isolation peep by their shorter duration (0.08–0.69 second), weaker intensity, and lower fundamental (7–10.5 kc). Furthermore, they exhibit greater variability in tonal structure. Usually there is no pronounced tone plateau. The peep can take either an upward or downward frequency course.

Exploring animals peep regularly and frequently. They are answered irregularly with the same vocalization by the rest of the group. Persons with neutral or slightly positive valuation elicit peeps when they appear. This is also the case when other types of neutral stimuli attract the attention of the animals. In general, any change of the surrounding stimulus structure, in so far as it does not possess a pronounced positively or negatively conditioned feature, elicits peeping. Thus peeping is associated with vocal contact and attention. It can be compared with contact calls emitted by some songbirds.

c. Play Peeps (Fig. 1c). In contrast to peeping, play peeps are characterized by a rapid change in frequency and rather low variation in duration. Most play interactions, especially those in which only immature animals are involved, are accompanied by play peeping. These play patterns in older infants often include aggressive as well as sexual components (Fig. 2). As soon as grasping, playful nipping, or copulation attempts occur, the frequency of occurrence and the intensity of play peeps are increased.

In addition, especially in the case of young animals, play peeps may accompany genital display. Play peeps can be elicited by placing a mirror in front of an immature animal. The animal will peep while displaying to its own image (Ploog *et al.*, 1963).

FIG. 2. Group of three monkeys involved in playing accompanied by play peeping.

In spite of aggressive elements during play interactions, play never develops into serious aggression. Genital display combined with play peeps does not precede actual fighting. This fact suggests that peeping may convey a nonaggressive intention on the part of the emitter.

d. Alarm Peep (Fig. 1d). The upper frequency of these very short calls (0.05 − 0.13 second) varies between 11 and 16 kc. When a bird flies across the glass dome of the observation cage an alarm reaction is released. It starts with alarm peeping of one animal which may be followed by several others. Immediately following the alarm peep, the whole group flees to the highest points of the cage, remaining there for at least 5 seconds in a state of complete motor and vocal inactivity. It may be noted that in addition to birds, a variety of other stimuli are capable of eliciting the alarm reaction. The reaction can be evoked experimentally by a black disk moved across the top of the cage with an angular velocity of 5 msec per 10°. The alarm reaction characterized by alarm peep, flight, and motor as well as vocal inactivity could be elicited by this stimulus from either side, floor, or ceiling of the cage. Related observations show clearly that the alarm peep triggers an alarm reaction, as the latter may be produced by playing back the alarm peeps with a tape recorder in the absence of the visual stimulus.

2. Group of Twit Calls

The pitch of these calls alternates periodically within the range of 3 − 9.5 kc. The frequency change is more than one octave. For the purpose of describing the various calls that fall within this group a single element of increasing and decreasing frequency will be called a twit element.

a. Trill (Fig. 1e). Trills are made up of two or more elements joined to one another, with the overall pitch of each remaining constant. They may be divided into short (three periods) or long (more than three periods) trills. The duration of one period is about 0.1 second. Trilling as well as twittering (see Section III, A, 2, c) is a very characteristic call regularly emitted during feeding. External stimuli that may be associated with food also elicit these calls. When two animals are observed in a cage during feeding situations, sequences of alternating trilling and twittering calls often are heard.

b. Location Trill (Fig. 1f). This call differs physically from trilling in its higher amplitude of frequency change and in its more steeply ascending and descending wave form.

An animal, settling down on a favorite resting place, may utter the location trill. A young animal that has temporarily left its mother's back and flees back after being frightened vocalizes in the same manner as soon as it has gained its normal riding position.

c. Twittering (Fig. 1g). Twittering is distinguished from trilling by a decrease or sometimes by an increase in pitch. The maximum frequency (9.5 kc) is generally higher than that of the average trill. As in trills, short as well as long twitters may be distinguished. Sometimes trilling and twittering resemble each other to such an extent that, in order to distinguish one from the other, spectrographic analysis is necessary. A functional relationship probably corresponds to this formal similarity. Both calls are heard during similar behavioral situations but with a different likelihood of occurrence. In addition to the situations in which twittering is heard simultaneously with trilling, the former is also observed in the following situation: an animal that has temporarily been separated from the group will, when put back, be welcomed by twittering calls. The animals react similarly toward familiar persons entering and leaving the room. This call is therefore not restricted to feeding; it has a greeting and announcing function as well.

Regarding trills and twitters, one other function has to be taken into consideration. Although squirrel monkeys huddle frequently, they refrain from doing so as long as one of these calls is emitted. This is especially true in the case of twittering. During feeding this behavior is very apparent. This situation is characterized by a large number of twitters and by the maintenance of a fixed distance between the animals which varies according to the size of the cage. As soon as this distance is transgressed, aggressive vocalization is elicited.

d. Chuck (Fig. 1h). A short trill (two to three twit elements) or a single twit element containing only part of the upward or downward sweep of the fundamental frequency, but with a steeper descending slope, is designated a chuck. Unlike most other calls, a chuck is not likely to be repeated. Instead, it tends to appear together with churrs, arrs, and less often with trills. Huddling animals, when becoming restless or trying to change the huddling order, are prone to use this call. It presumably has a significance in maintaining distance between given animals of a group.

3. Group of Ha Calls

The group of ha calls includes all calls of low pitch in the squirrel monkey. The fundamental is much lower than that of all other calls. In addition these calls show a large number of overtones. The frequency course and the duration of the individual calls are irregular.

a. Cackling (Fig. 1i). The fundamental of this call is below 500 cps. Spectrograms reveal a large number of overtones which can be registered up to 16 kc. Duration as well as intensity is variable. Sometimes at the beginning of the call a small band of noise can be distinguished. This type of cackling is called "rough cackling." Cackling is one of those calls that occur in rather varied situations. It occurs regularly in a group of monkeys when a strong animal is put into the group. An increasingly aggressive mood due to food competition or intragroup rivalry is accompanied by cackling calls with increasing intensity and roughness until another type of vocalization appears immediately before the outbreak of an actual fight for dominance.

Cackling is coupled with the initiation of predominantly aggressive behavior. The range of cackling covers expressions varying from slight uneasiness to threatening behavior.

b. Yap (Fig. 1j). Yapping is distinguished by a noiselike initial component. The duration of the whole call varies between 0.1 and 0.25 second. There are even more overtones than in cackling. Yapping may be elicited simply by presenting a snake or a snakelike moving object to the group (see Chapter 10). Presentation of other vertebrate species may have the same effect. In general, the animals always react in the same way. As soon as a monkey detects a potentially dangerous moving stimulus, he flees upward. Simultaneously, he alarms all members of the group by yapping; they move to a higher location orienting themselves toward the suspicious stimulus and begin yapping.

The intensity and elaboration of this reaction, which appears somewhat comparable to the mobbing response of songbirds, depend on the kind of stimulus presented. A strong effect can often be produced by certain fur-bearing animals. Yapping can be distinguished from the alarm peep in two respects. First, with regard to the eliciting stimulus, yapping occurs when the arousing objects do not appear suddenly and unexpectedly within the visual field of the monkey. The stimuli have to move rather slowly, whereas objects causing the alarm peep must have a more rapid minimum angle velocity. Second, following the onset of the yapping, a continuous and increasing sequence of vocalizations starts, which may lead to aggression directed toward the arousing object. In this context, yapping is to be understood as a warning call which at the same time shows an aggressive potential. This is not the case with the alarm peep.

Common to all ha calls is a general aggressive arousal which spreads from one animal to another. Thus these calls may be designated a group of general aggressive calls.

4. Group of Arr Calls

Unlike the calls found in groups 1 to 3, which possess a tonal structure, the sounds of groups 4 and 5 are noiselike in character. The elements making up the arr group consist of single clicklike impulses of 0.02 second duration. One of the characteristics by which the arr calls can be distinguished from each other is the temporal arrangement of successive signals.

a. Spit (Fig. 1k). Spitting is made up of two to three clicklike impulses covering a broad frequency range (>15 kc). Spitting occurs mostly when one subject grasps the head of another with the active participant vocalizing (Fig. 7). It also occurs in other situations including food stealing and genital display. Body contact by means of grasping accompanies the first two of these situations. Head grasping combined with spitting is, however, limited to the dominant partner. It would appear then that we are dealing here with an aggressive call directed toward a specific animal, unlike the ha calls which seem to provide information to the group as a whole.

b. Err (Fig. 1l). When the arr elements are grouped into short irregular and blurred sequences of impulses they are designated err calls. During an increasingly aggressive motivation, cackling is replaced by err calls. Transitions exist between both types and are made apparent by the noise component of the cackling call. This change indicates that a general aggressive disposition will gradually shift into a directed one.

c. Churr (Fig. 1m). In contrast to err calls, the single impulses of which the churr is composed are regularly arranged. Churrs appear together with other aggressive calls, for instance, when a strange monkey is placed in a group. In addition it occurs together with the chuck during huddling and genital display.

d. Purr (Fig. 1n). The number of impulses following in sequence is much greater in purr calls than in churrs. They may exceed 20 in number. The upper limit of frequency of the single impulse is very constant within one call. The impulses are shorter and have lower limits of frequency than churr calls. The volume is also substantially lower. Sucking and purring occur together in infants, beginning with the first hours of life. In addition to the purring of infants, which is called milk-purring, purrs are also uttered by adult animals in connection with body contact and genital display. The low intensity of this call stresses the fact that it is directed toward an animal close by. Up to now the function of adult purring is still obscure.

5. Group of Shriek Calls

These calls are distinguished from the calls of the arr group by their longer duration of 0.1—0.8 second. The frequency is distributed over a wide frequency range (>10 kc). In general, a certain frequency is accentuated in each call.

Shriek (Fig. 1o). Only shrieking will be mentioned here. The intensity of the frequency spectrum below 1 kc is low compared with that between 5 and 7 kc. The range of frequency may vary greatly within one signal. The duration fluctuates between 0.3 and 0.8 second. Several shrieks usually follow one another separated by short pauses.

Shrieking is regularly elicited in the following situations: when an animal is hurt, when a baby is removed from the back of its mother, when a juvenile animal is released into a strange group, when an animal is pursued and attacked by another one, or when two groups of monkeys are put together. In this last case pure "shrieking fights" develop which can lead to fights with severe biting. Shrieking expresses a high degree of excitement which is communicated to other animals and affects their behavior in the same way.

6. Group of Combined Calls

This group comprises calls made up of elements of all five previous groups. They form a category of transitional calls.

a. Chirp (Fig. 1p). This common call consists of a combination of a peep and one or two twit elements. The duration of the signal is essentially determined by the peep component, the frequency of which ranges between 7 and 9 kc. This call is usually uttered together with pure peeps during exploratory behavior and during moderate separation of group members. Together with peep calls, chirping belongs to the most common vocalizations of squirrel monkeys, the occurrence of which does not vary as much as other call types. Apparently this call serves the function of providing vocal contact for short to medium distances.

b. Kecker (Fig. 1q). Twittering and cackling elements are mixed together in this call. If aggression, expressed by cackling, increases a great deal, the vocalization changes from cackling into keckering. In the highest stage of excitation shrieking occurs. Decrease in excitation is expressed by the inverse order of these vocalizations. Like cackling, yapping, and shrieking, keckering has a tendency to produce similar reactions in other group members. This causes a high degree of synchronization of behavior patterns that would be advantageous during aggressive interaction involving the group.

7. Notes on the Ontogeny of Calls

The birth process as well as the ontogeny of squirrel monkeys was observed systematically (Bowden *et al.*, 1967; Ploog *et al.*, 1967). All observations including vocalizations during birth and the postpartum period were tape recorded. Additional recordings were made up to 4 weeks after birth. In one case a baby was brought into our laboratory at the age of 19 days. It was reared separately but auditory and visual contact was maintained with other animals.

Takeshita (1962) describes vocalizations of a neonate that were emitted before it had completely left the birth canal. The author describes this sound as "chee." It probably corresponds to shrieking.

We observed the first sound 5 minutes after birth (Bowden *et al.*, 1967). The baby shrieked three times. Before the end of 24 hours, peeps, twitters, shrieks, and the typical purring sound, emitted during nursing, could be heard.

The catalog of vocalizations in a 4-week-old infant (Fig. 3) consists of: isolation peeps, peeps, tucks (see below), twitters, chucks, location trills, cackles, yaps, errs, purrs, shrieks, screams (see below), oinks (see below), keckers, and grumbles (see below).

Tuck is a special type of peep which descends rather steeply. It occurs regularly together with peeps. The transitional probability for tuck leading to a peep as well as to grumbling, is almost the same. The occurrence is limited to juvenile animals up to 3 months of age. Tuck seems to have an intensified searching function.

Screaming may gradually develop into shrieking if excitement is intensified. In a comparison of sonagrams of screaming, the characteristic criterion is a high (ca. 10 kc) wavering and sometimes interrupted peep to which elements of noise are added at the maximum intensity of the call.

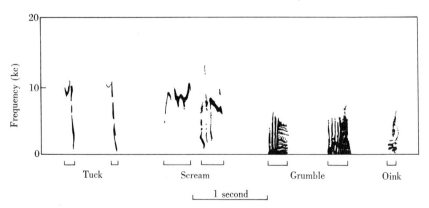

FIG. 3. Vocalizations of juvenile animals.

Grumble is a combination of an err and a cackling component. A hungry infant will frequently vocalize in this way while searching for the nipple.

Oink is a combined call composed of cackling with a twit element following. Although it is characteristic of infants up to 6 months of age, it is still present in the vocalization of adult animals.

As stated earlier, quantitative methods in studying vocal and motor behavior patterns have to be applied in order to determine the function of calls. In the case of a 4-week-old infant, reared artificially in a small cage with a surrogate mother, the prefeeding behavior was recorded on 3 days for about 20 minutes. The infant was able to see the observer.

Figure 4 shows the distribution (diameter of circles) of five types of vocal and two types of motor behavior, exploring and clutching, as a percent of the total behavior.

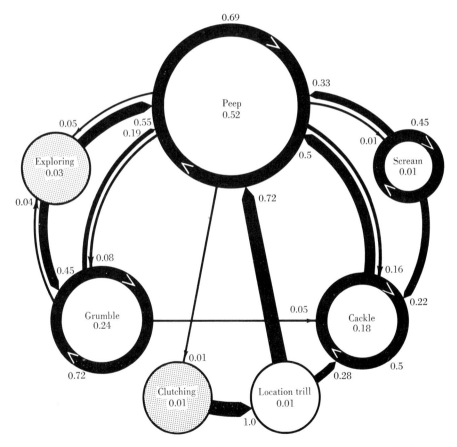

FIG. 4. Diagram showing the frequency of occurrence of five vocal and two motor behavior patterns (circles) and their probabilities of transitions (arrows).

When the baby, while riding on its surrogate mother's back, starts exploring, it first lifts its head, looks around, and orients. It may even leave its surrogate mother and climb around within the cage. When regaining the normal riding position, a baby will clutch tightly with all four limbs, uttering the location trill.

More than 50% of the total amount of vocalization consists of peeping. It is followed by grumbling (24%) and cackling (18%). In addition, Fig. 4 shows the probability of transitions from one behavior pattern to another one (width of arrows).

Peeps are not only the most frequent calls, they also have the highest number of possible transitions. Exploring is almost equally associated with grumbling and peeping. On the other hand grumbling may be followed only by cackling and a rather high possibility of going back to peeping. In contrast to adult animals it is interesting to note that shrieking does not follow cackling.

A clear-cut connection exists between clutching, location trill and peeping. The location trill has to be considered as the vocal signal exclusively combined with clutching (see Fig. 5).

Using this kind of quantitative approach the function of calls can be analyzed further.

FIG. 5. Four-week-old infant clutching and vocalizing on the hand of the observer.

B. VISUAL SIGNALS

Some motor behavior patterns have obvious functions as visual signals. They can be divided grossly into three broad groups: social signals of dominance, social signals of submission, and social signals of cohesion. The most significant examples are the following.

1. Signals of Dominance

a. Genital Display. Figure 6 shows the characteristic features of the genital display. The lateral position of the leg with the hip and knee bent, together with a marked supination of the foot, abduction of the big toe, and the erection of the penis (or clitoris), sometimes with the release of a few drops of urine. Juvenile as well as adult animals of both sexes show this characteristic behavior pattern. It is always directed toward a partner. One can generally distinguish two positions: (1) the open position, whereby the partners maintain a distance of approximately 10 cm to 4 meters from one another, and (2) the closed position, in which the animal displaying maintains body contact with its partner (Ploog and MacLean, 1963; Ploog *et al.*, 1963, 1967; Ploog, 1967).

FIG. 6. Mirror displaying of a 7-week-old infant.

Genital displaying is generally associated with peeping in immature animals, or churr in mature ones. The display pattern is a social signal which helps to determine the formation of the group structure. Generally this behavior can be interpreted as having the function of self-assertion.

b. Head Grasping. The active animal grasps the fur of the head region of another animal with one or both hands (Fig. 7), at the same time pressing the head slightly downward. This behavior is generally accompanied by spitting.

c. Waist Grasping. An animal grasps the waist of the partner with both hands. This behavior may be observed as the last event in a sequence of aggressive interactions. Waist grasping is also an element initiating copulatory behavior.

d. Threatening. A jerking movement, directing the head, neck, and thorax toward the partner, often together with the showing of teeth, is usually accompanied by cackling, err, and churr calls.

Threatening may develop into chasing and physical attack. Generally the attack stops if the subordinate flees for some distance. Sometimes chasing may lead to serious aggression. Often the outbreak of a fight between male rivals is triggered by females through keckering and shrieking.

2. Signals of Submission

Except for the defense position, these signals are generally not evident and therefore difficult to observe. Often mere looking away or the mainte-

FIG. 7. Head-grasping behavior in which one monkey presses down the head of another animal.

nance of a minimum distance from the dominant animal is the only signal of submission.

a. Avoidance Reaction. The animal increases the distance from a partner by moving away.

b. Defense Position. The animal glances toward the partner by looking between its own legs. This behavior has been observed in young animals being threatened by older ones. The assumption of this posture usually stops actual aggression.

3. Signals of Cohesion

This class of signals is composed of behavior patterns in which both partners are almost equally involved. The fact that there exists a certain amount of interaction between the members of the group is characteristic for this type of social signal. Apparently they are important for the cohesion of the group.

a. Contact. All types of short, intended contact by touching are included.

b. Huddling. At least two animals sit together side by side in close contact.

c. Playing. All types of playing with a partner are included. In the case of sexual play, male animals exhibit penile erection. Usually playing is restricted to immature animals but sometimes the playmate can be an adult animal. One type of play between juveniles and adult males can be regarded as a "fighting tournament." The immature animal tries to attack the adult male repeatedly, whereas the adult male just seems to defend itself. In the course of playing an animal may change its role from initiator to recipient (Ploog *et al.*, 1967).

IV. Summary and Conclusion

Vocal and visual signals are probably the most important elements of social communication in squirrel monkeys. Apart from distinctions between auditory and visual stimuli as a result of their physical qualities, an important characteristic of auditory signals is that most of them are directed to more than one partner, whereas visual signals are generally directed to a specific partner. There are various examples in which vocal and visual signals are combined, as for instance in head grasping and in some cases of genital display. For the purpose of this chapter we felt justified in handling both the auditory (Section III, A) and the visual (Section III, B) communication system separately.

From a total of 26 different calls that we have identified, 17 have been selected as representative and described as serving social functions. According to their physical characteristics revealed by sound spectrography, they can be divided into six groups of calls. Within 24 hours after the birth of a monkey, four calls of different groups were heard in highly differentiated form. This leads one to the assumption that much of the basic pattern of vocal communication is innate rather than learned, although more material is obviously needed before the extent to which this assumption applies can be ascertained.

The system of vocalizations also may be subdivided according to the degree of variability of the calls. Peep and twit calls are rather uniform with little intracall variability. Most of these calls function without visual control, and are directed toward more than one partner. In contrast to peep and twit calls, most of the ha and arr calls are rather variable. This is especially the case with cackling in which the spectrum of transitions may range from cackling to err. The calls of the ha and arr groups can be looked upon as being aggressive calls directed against a specific partner. It is likely that this increase of variability is associated with additional visual information. The combination of vocal and visual signals serves to minimize ambiguity in communication.

This hypothesis can be tested by observations on related, nocturnal primate species. From the studies of Moynihan (1964) on the night monkey, *Aotus trivirgatus*, one obtains the impression that the calls of this species are generally more stable than those of the squirrel monkey and the titi monkey (Moynihan, 1966). Instead of variations in pitch and duration, repetition and sequential ordering of different calls allow the transmission of more complex information during social interaction.

It is difficult to compare the vocal repertoire of the squirrel monkey with those that are known in other primate species. This is a result of the fact that there are few papers with accurate physical descriptions, including spectrograms. In trying to compare the variety of vocal utterances found within different species, we looked for the occurrence of calls that may be grouped into one of the five groups established by us (Table I).

According to these criteria the New World monkeys exhibit a generally larger variety of vocal patterns than Old World monkeys. On the other hand, the intracall variability increases in Old World monkeys, being best expressed in the chimpanzee and gorilla. This development is paralleled by the evolution of increasingly variable facial expressions.

Motor behavior includes a variety of different behavior patterns, e.g., locomotion, resting, cleaning, feeding, sexual, and agonistic activities. Furthermore, the total amount of behavior an animal exhibits in different situations is characteristic for its position within the social group (Castell and Ploog, 1968).

In our studies the main task was to determine those patterns of motor behavior that could be characterized as social signals. This means that we had to search for patterns of behavior closely correlated with the establishment and maintenance of a stable position within group hierarchy. Postures appear to be the most prominent type of motor signals, for instance, genital display and the postures of defense and huddling.

According to Lorenz (1966), social signals have been subjected to a process of ritualization during phylogeny. The social significance of a behavior pattern often derives as an epiphenomenon of some more primitive behavioral pattern. For the genital display this process of ritualization can be demonstrated hypothetically (Ploog, 1963; Ploog and MacLean, 1963;

TABLE I

THE OCCURRENCE OF FIVE DIFFERENT VOCAL PATTERNS IN
15 SPECIES OF MONKEYS

Species	Type of call					Reference
	Peep	Twit	Ha	Arr	Shriek	
Lemur fulvus	x		x	x	x	Andrew (1963)[a]
Microcebus minurus	x	x	x	x	x	Andrew (1963)[a]
Galago crassicaudatus	x		x	x		Andrew (1963)[a]
Aotes trivirgatus	x	x	x	x	x	Moynihan (1964)[a]
Callicebus moloch	x	x	x	x		Moynihan (1966)[a]
Alouatta palliata	x		x	x	x	Carpenter (1965)[1]
Saimiri sciureus	x	x	x	x	x	Winter *et al.*, (1966)[a]
Cebus albifrons	x		x	x	x	Andrew (1963)[a]
Ateles belzebuth	x	x	x	x		Andrew (1963)[a]
Cercopithecus aethiops	x		x	x	x	Struhsaker (1967)[a]
Macaca mulatta	x		x		x	Rowell and Hinde (1962)[a]
	x		x		x	Altmann (1962)
Macaca fuscata	x		x		x	Itani (1963)
Papio hamadryas			x	x	x	Hall and DeVore (1965)
Presbytis entellus	x		x		x	Jay (1965)
Pan troglodytes			x		x	Andrew (1963)[a]
	x		x		x	Reynolds and Reynolds (1965)[a]
Gorilla gorilla beringei	x		x		x	Schaller (1965)

[a] According to sonagrams.

Wickler, 1966): the display includes penile erection or clitoral enlargement, elements which originally are part of reproductive behavior. This suggests that simple classification of the social behavior of these animals, e.g., according to sexuality, aggression, and flight, is not adequate because single social signals often have derived from several separate sources. In the process of selective adaptation, the original pattern as well as the original function may have been transformed for specific social purposes. In this way social signals have gained relative independence and have developed into a highly differentiated communication system.

ACKNOWLEDGMENTS

I would like to acknowledge my gratefulness to my colleagues R. Castell, S. Hopf, and D. Ploog for permission to incorporate their findings within this chapter.

REFERENCES

Altmann, S. A. (1962). A field study of the sociobiology of rhesus monkeys, *Macaca mulatta. Ann. N.Y. Acad. Sci.* **102**, 338-435.

Andrew, R. J. (1963). The origin and evolution of the calls and facial expressions of the primates. *Behaviour* **20**, 1-109.

Bowden, D., Winter, P., and Ploog, D. (1967). Pregnancy and delivery behavior in squirrel monkeys (*Saimiri sciureus*) and other primates. *Folia Primatol.* **5**, 1-42.

Carpenter, C. R. (1965). The howlers of Barro Colorado Island. *In* "Primate Behavior" (I. DeVore, ed.), pp. 250-291. Holt, New York.

Castell, R., and Ploog, D. (1967). Zum Sozialverhalten der Totenkopfaffen (*Saimiri sciureus*): Auseinandersetzung zwischen zwei Kolonien. *Z. Tierpsychol.* **24**, 625-641.

Fiedler, W. (1956). Übersicht über das System der Primaten. *Primatologia* **1**, 1-267.

Hall, K. R. L., and DeVore, I. (1965). Baboon social behavior. *In* "Primate Behavior" (I. DeVore, ed.), pp. 53-110. Holt, New York.

Hill, W. C. O. (1960). "Primates," Vol. IV, Part A. Edinburgh Univ. Press, Edinburgh.

Itani, J. (1963). Vocal communication of the wild Japanese monkey. *Primates* **4**, 11-66.

Jay, P. (1965). The common langur of North India. *In* "Primate Behavior" (I. DeVore, ed.), pp. 197-249. Holt, New York.

Lorenz, K. (1966). A discussion on ritualization of behavior in animals and man. A. The psychological approach: Methods and results. *Philo. Trans. Roy. Soc. London* **B. 251**, 273-284.

MacLean, P. D. (1964). Mirror display in the squirrel monkey, *Saimiri sciureus. Science* **146**, 950-952.

Marler, P. (1965). Communication in monkeys and apes. *In* "Primate Behavior" (I. deVore, ed.), pp. 544-584. Holt, New York.

Moynihan, M. (1964). Some behavior patterns of platyrrhine monkeys. 1. The night monkey (*Aotus trivirgatus*). *Smithsonian Inst. Misc. Collections* **146**, 1-84.

Moynihan, M. (1966). Communication in the titi monkey, *Callicebus. J. Zool. London* **150**, 77-127.

Ploog, D. (1963). Vergleichende quantitative Verhaltensstudien an zwei Totenkopfaffen-Kolonien. *Z. Morphol. Anthropol.* **53**, 92-108.

Ploog, D. (1967). The behavior of squirrel monkeys (*Saimiri sciureus*), as revealed by sociometry, bioacoustics and brain stimulation. *In* "Social Communication Among Primates" (S. A. Altmann, ed.), pp. 149-184. Univ. of Chicago Press, Chicago, Illinois.

Ploog, D., and MacLean, P. D. (1963). Display of penile erection in squirrel monkeys (*Saimiri sciureus*). *Animal Behaviour* **11**, 32-39.

Ploog, D., Blitz, J., and Ploog, F. (1963). Studies on social and sexual behavior of the squirrel monkey (*Saimiri sciureus*). *Folia Primatol.* **1**, 29-66.

Ploog, D., Hopf, S., and Winter, P. (1967). Ontogenese des Sozialverhaltens von Totenkopfaffen (*Saimiri sciureus*). *Psychol. Forsch.* **31**, 1-41.

Reynolds, V., and Reynolds, F. (1965). Chimpanzees of the Bodongo Forest. *In* "Primate Behavior" (I. DeVore, ed.), pp. 368-424. Holt, New York.

Rowell, T. E., and Hinde, R. A. (1962). Vocal communication by the rhesus monkey (*Macaca mulatta*). *Proc. Zool. Soc. London* **138**, 279-294.

Schaller, G. B. (1965). The behavior of the mountain gorilla. *In* "Primate Behavior" (I. DeVore, ed.), pp. 324-367. Holt, New York.

Struhsaker, T. T. (1967). Auditory communication among vervet monkeys (*Cercopithecus aethiops*). *In* "Social Communication Among Primates" (S. A. Altmann, ed.), pp. 281-324. Univ. of Chicago Press, Chicago, Illinois.

Takeshita, H. (1962). On the delivery behavior of squirrel monkeys (*Saimiri sciureus*) and a mona monkey (*Cercopithecus mona*). *Primates* **3**, No. 1, 59-72.

Wappler, E. (1958). Vergleichende Untersuchungen zur Lautgebung von Cercopitheciden. Unpublished Diploma Thesis, Humbolt University, Berlin.

Wickler, W. (1966). Ursprung und biologische Deutung des Genitalpräsentierens männlicher Primaten. *Z. Tierpsychol.* **23**, 422-437.

Winter, P., Ploog, D., and Latta, J. (1966). Vocal repertoire of the squirrel monkey (*Saimiri sciureus*), its analysis and significance. *Exptl. Brain Res.* **1**, 359-384.

CHAPTER 10

The Learning and Sensory Capacities of the Squirrel Monkey in Phylogenetic Perspective

Duane M. Rumbaugh

I. Introduction

The purpose of this chapter is to place the learning and sensory capacities of the squirrel monkey (*Saimiri sciureus*) in perspective with those of other primates and, in a broader sense, other mammals. Since the intensive study of the squirrel monkey has spanned less than a decade, the reader should recognize that it is only within rather generous limits that the assigned task can be accomplished.

At the outset it should be made clear that psychologists interested in the comparison of diverse species and their behaviors are still devising and evaluating alternative strategies and methods of study. The extent to which direct comparisons of behaviors and performance levels in an absolute sense can be defended, for example, is still an open question, and the extent to which method of direct comparison should yield to those methods that pursue definition of behaviors specific to each species (Beach, 1960; Breland and Breland, 1961) is still an unsatisfactorily resolved issue.

To relate the behavior of any one species to the behaviors of all other species is one of the major undertakings of comparative psychology. That undertaking is clearly a difficult one, encumbered still by methods of comparison which in the day of atomic physics and space exploration are primitive beyond reasonable justification. However, until such time that the discipline of comparative psychology can command resources of the magnitude that have provided for rapid expansion of knowledge in the aforementioned areas, we must make do with techniques which, in the final analysis, are not technically commensurate with the complexities intrinsic to the task. Nevertheless, the fruits of those methods have made it possible to approximate an acceptable definition of *Saimiri* behavior relative to the order Primates. To examine what we know and do *not* know about *Saimiri* at this time hopefully will serve not only to expedite refined assessments of *Saimiri* capacities in future years but also serve to influence some of the basic approaches that behaviorists employ in their comparative studies.

Study of the squirrel monkey should begin only after taking full recognition of the fact that it is a unique form of primate life. It should be viewed neither as an advanced prosimian nor as a miniature version of some more advanced primate form. It has evolved to its present form in response to a novel combination of selective pressures. This point is neither a complex nor a new one, yet it is extremely important for the understanding of primates in general and the squirrel monkey in particular. Only by viewing primate species as unique evolutionary products of a variety of interacting genetic and environmental factors will we be able to gain a proper perspective of their relationships to each other.

II. Comparative Primate Behavior: Approach and Method

ABILITY TO LEARN AS AN INDEX OF INTELLIGENCE

One of the most important characteristics of probably all forms of animal life is the ability to learn, that is, to modify behavior as a consequence of interaction with the environment. It is the ability to learn that permits animals to adjust far more quickly and flexibly than plants to changing environmental pressures and demands. The ability to learn is not shared equally by all forms of animal life, however. Even a cursory survey of behaviors makes it apparent that the capacity for learning has increased with evolution of animal forms from amoeba to man.

Particularly with his own genus, *Homo*, man has found it defensible and useful to attempt quantification of certain complex behavioral processes, including those of learning, in a way that will yield an objective index of the more generalized concept of function, *intelligence*. Without exception all approaches to the definition of human intelligence assume a positive correlation between it and ability to learn; all human intelligence tests must correlate with ability to achieve and master complex tasks or else lose acceptance for lack of demonstrable validity. Accordingly, it is entirely reasonable that as attention is directed to the study of intelligence in nonhuman forms of life, measurement of learning ability be taken as a basic approach.

1. Animal Intelligence

A wide variety of tasks has been used in past years to estimate relative intelligence levels in diverse forms of animal life. The use of stick tools and other instruments in problem solving, for example, has been favored over the years since their power for inferring the operations of higher mental processes of chimpanzees was demonstrated by Köhler (1925). But the structuring of tool-using problem situations is frequently cumbersome and impractical at best for purposes of direct comparison; they do not readily lend themselves to a graduated series of increasing complexity appropriate to specific perceptual and motor skills of a variety of primate genera.

Other tasks used widely in interspecies studies in past decades, particularly the double alternation and delayed-response tasks, recently have been assessed by Warren (1965) as being of questionable value for the comparative psychology of learning. He concludes that these tasks, along with others devised with the intent of uniquely tapping the "symbolic" processes underlying animal behavior, have not fulfilled the promise they initially offered.

Warren's assessment of learning-set tasks was more favorable. Initially introduced by Harlow (1949) as a procedure for studying the process whereby animals *learn how to learn*, review of the research relating performance on learning-set tasks to phylogenetic rank provided the basis for the generalization that even the marmoset, a primitive primate form, is probably superior to all nonprimate forms, and through the series of monkeys from the marmoset to the rhesus macaque there is steady improvement in capacity for learning-set tasks (Warren, 1965, p. 110). Learning-set measurement has become broadly accepted as one of the most valuable methods of assessing the basic learning abilities of primates as well as infraprimate forms. The ways in which capacity for learning set relates to capacity for solving or mastering a wide variety of problem situations (including tool use) and to a variety of other behavioral propensities (including emotionality, curiosity, and sociability) need to be determined.

III. Learning Set: Its Nature and Value as a Tool for Measuring the Basic Intelligence of Primates

A. DEFINITION OF LEARNING SET

For many decades there has been growing recognition of the role that experience plays in providing the necessary skills for complex problem solving. Even the ardent nativists who attribute the basic abilities for mastering these tasks to genetic influence have been willing to allow the value of experience and training; but that there was a type of cumulative positive transfer of a generalized character which dramatically improved the ability of animals to solve problems of a given class was not convincingly demonstrated until the midpoint of this century.

By working with a small colony of monkeys, Harlow recognized the nonspecific yet definite improvement in the facility with which the subjects learned over the course of many discrimination experiments. He concluded that it was possible to define the experimental conditions under which animals learn how to be efficient problem solvers, ones that provide precise definition of experience with a given class of problems (Harlow, 1949). The basic learning task he utilized was object — quality discrimination, in which each problem consisted of a pair of three-dimensional (stereometric) objects, many of which were parts of children's toys or parts of common household items. One member of each problem pair was designated "correct," and if the animal responded to it on a given trial, it could take a food reward from a small well which was uncovered by displacement of that object. Choice of the "incorrect" object never resulted in food reward. The relative left — right positions of the objects were varied within the course of each problem so that position could not serve as a reliable cue. The rhesus monkeys (*Macaca mulatta*) he utilized worked on several hundred different two-choice problems, and each problem was presented for too few trials to permit mastery of a given problem during the initial portion of the experiment. By the end of more than 300 problems, however, the animals were rapidly learning the correct choice in most of the problems and by the end of the experiment were better than 95% correct on all but the first trials of the problems. (On first trials, of course, responses remain at chance levels.) The improvement in efficiency of learning had been orderly and systematic but the total effect had been that of changing the animals from "trial and error" learners into "insightful," i.e., one-trial, learners.

The major contribution of this finding was *not* that certain primates could solve complex problems with great rapidity and skill, for that fact had been known for decades. The main contribution was that a controlled method of investigating the manner whereby certain animals can become more efficient problem solvers had been demonstrated. Thus, it became possible to begin systematic inquiry into the nature of the process whereby complex learning capabilities develop and how various kinds of cues are employed for its acquisition and execution.

It is generally agreed that the capacity for learning set is not to be accounted for in terms of a capacity for single-problem learning. Measures based on the learning of a single discrimination problem have never reliably differentiated animals according to their phylogenetic rank or age. This is not to deny the possibility that a single problem might be devised that would be useful for this purpose, but it is particularly unlikely if the problem is the *first* as well as the only problem to be learned. The emotionality and initially erratic orientation of the animals prior to thorough adaptation to the procedures of a new problem situation augurs against their learning capacity being validly and reliably reflected in a single score, such as number of trials or amount of time required to learn a single problem.

B. Error Factor Theory

Harlow's approach (1959b) to understanding the formation of learning set has been based on analysis of the suppression of certain error-producing response tendencies which the animal brings to the training situation. According to "error factor theory" the learning-set training situation is viewed as an impediment to the animal's procurement of the incentive. The animal must respond to the discrimination problems in order to obtain the food incentive, but only by the elimination of certain response tendencies is it able to procure the incentive with efficiency. Elimination of these adverse response tendencies, or "error factors," is characteristically an orderly, systematic process. The four error factors that Harlow has identified are: (1) *Stimulus perseveration*. This error factor is reflected in the tendency of the animal to repeat selection of a stimulus object even though previous selection of it was unrewarded. Learned and unlearned preferences and aversions to objects are believed to be involved in this factor. (2) *Differential cue.* The operation of this factor, a very persisting one, entails resolution of the ambiguity of reinforcement of cues on correct trials. This ambiguity results from the fact that on any given reinforced trial both the selection of a specific object *and* its position on the stimulus tray are relevant, i.e., if, for example, the correct object is on the left and the animal choses it, the response to that object and also to the left position are rewarded. Position cues are not reliable ones for obtaining reward more than 50% of the time but it takes many trials for the subject to learn that this is the case. (3) *Response shift.* This factor is inferred from the observation that frequently an animal will make a response to the incorrect object of a given problem pair even though for several preceding trials the correct object has been consistently selected. Harlow has suggested that this error factor reflects a tendency on the part of the animal to explore and handle *both* objects of a given problem. When the incorrect object has not been responded to on the first few trials, that object retains a "novelty" value which the correct and familiar object loses as the animal responds to it. It is possibly for this reason that errors continue to occur even when the established learning set provides an essentially perfect performance. (4) *Position habit.* This factor is inferred whenever an animal develops a very strong tendency to persist in its response to either the left or the right food well regardless of the placement of the objects.

C. Learning-Set Capacity as Related to Phylogenetic Rank

Learning-set tasks have provided some of the most sensitive techniques for assessing learning ability on a comparative basis. Harlow (1959b, p. 508) reviewed evidence relevant to this point and concluded, "by and large the phylogenetic data demonstrate that learning-set formation is closely related to evolutionary position, as conventionally described, and to cortical complexity in so far as this characteristic has been effectively measured." Support for this conclusion has also been expressed by Riopelle (1960), Ratner and Denny (1964, p. 633), and Miles (1965). It would be a mistake to conclude, however, that the relationship between phylogenetic rank with its closely related dimension of cortical complexity and learning-set proficiency is necessarily a simple one. Recognition should also be given at this point to the fact that the learning-set capabilities of a given species might vary widely from one test situation to the next (Strong, 1965).

Learning-set proficiency has been found to be related significantly to both chronological and mental age in the human child. Reese's comprehensive review (1963) on the discrimination learning-set capabilities of children concludes that it is doubtful that the same kind of theory can account for learning-set formation in both monkeys and children. The acquisition of learning set in the child progresses at a rate quite different than in the monkey, with the result being that the curves appear to differ in shape as well as rate. It is also clear that error factors operate differentially in different genera of monkeys and also at different age levels of the child (Reese, 1963).

D. Learning-Set Capacity as Related to Level of Maturation

In their reviews both Miles and Reese comment on the evidence that relates the age variable to capacity for learning-set tasks. As the human child matures within the first 5 years of life his capacity for basic learning set is known to increase. It is also likely that the capacity for a wide variety of complex learning sets probably continues to increase even beyond the point where intelligence reaches asymptote, as measured by IQ tests, as contributions of varied and rich experience continue to be made to it.

The development of learning-set skills in the infant rhesus monkey has been explored in detail by Harlow (1959a) and his students (see Zimmerman and Torrey, 1965, for a recent review). Their studies clearly indicate that the 15-day-old macaque is able to learn a single spatial learning problem, with additional maturation providing only slight gain. The capacity for initial discrimination learning of single triangle—circle problems reached asymptote between 120 and 150 days. The capacity for delayed response matured somewhat later but it too was well-developed by 150 days of age. The capacity for object—quality discrimination learning set, though detectable by the age of 60—90 days, developed primarily within the second half of the first year of life and continued to improve far beyond that point. The ability to learn multiple-sign tests, as with the oddity problem in which the relationships among cues provided by more than two objects must be used, was assessed as incomplete by the age of 3 years. Full maturational development of learning abilities is believed to require from 4 to 5 years in the rhesus macaque. Studies of comparable scope have not yet been conducted on *Saimiri*.

IV. Learning-Set Skills of *Saimiri*

A. Initial Comparative Findings

Miles (1957) was first in reporting a learning-set (LS) function for *Saimiri*. It is remarkable that though only three squirrel monkeys (male) comprised the group, Miles' LS curve derived from it stands about as "normative" as can be reasonably hoped for in Wisconsin General Test Apparatus (WGTA) situations in which (1) stereometric objects comprise the LS problems, (2) those objects are manually displaced by the subjects to indicate choice on trials, and (3) the subjects are food-deprived and rewarded with highly preferred foods, such as grapes or raisins. Miles compared his squirrel monkey group's LS curve with similarly obtained curves for marmosets (*Callithrix jacchus*) and rhesus monkeys (Miles and Meyer, 1956). Evaluation of these curves (Fig. 1) indicates that: (1) All three are S-shaped. (2) After about 150 problems the rhesus group's level approximated the terminal performances of the other two groups. (3) The relative positions of the curves are in keeping with the phyletic standings of the groups. (4) Differences probably cannot be attributed to differences in visual capacities. (5) LS formation is a useful technique for comparative study of primates' learning abilities. Miles also appropriately pointed out that even though the LS performance of the squirrel monkeys was statistically superior to the marmosets, the number of cases was so small that the obtained difference might have limited generality (there was some overlap in scores of squirrel monkeys and marmosets).

Shell and Riopelle (1958) concluded from their study of LS in three New World primate groups that the spider monkey (*Ateles geoffroyi*) was superior to the cebus monkey (*Cebus albifrons*) and that the cebus, in turn, was

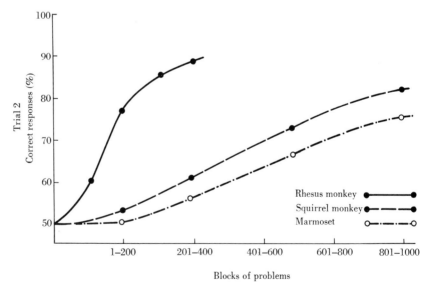

FIG. 1. Learning-set curves for rhesus monkeys, squirrel monkeys, and marmosets. (After Miles, 1957.)

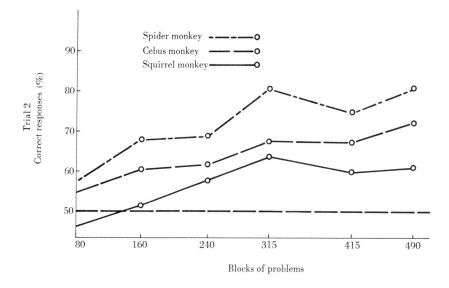

FIG. 2. Learning-set curves for three species of platyrrhine monkeys. (After Shell and Riopelle, 1958.)

superior to the squirrel monkey (Fig. 2). The squirrel monkey curve reasonably approximates the curve for that species reported earlier by Miles. Shell and Riopelle also concluded on the basis of data of studies published by others that all three of their New World primate groups were inferior in LS capacity to the rhesus monkey, chimpanzee, and human but superior to the marmoset, cat, raccoon, and rat.

Conclusions based on the results of these early comparative LS studies have stood without significant alteration (Polidora, 1964). Though groups frequently had as few as three specimens and rarely more than six, they yielded data that were consistent with each other.

B. MOTIVATION AND LEARNING SET

Motivational effects in *Saimiri* (1-, 5-, and 20-hour food privation) were studied with four subjects tested both on an easy and a difficult brightness discrimination in which reward consisted of a portion of grape (Miles, 1959). No difference in performance attributable to privation schedules was obtained. It was of interest, however, that the number of uneaten grape skins increased as privation level was reduced, i.e., only the choicest portions of the grape were consumed as motivation decreased. The monkeys were naive at the beginning of the study, and the test incentive (grape) was not included in the daily diet of the animals. Daily diet consisted of perishable fruits and vegetables, cooked eggs, bread, and a vitamin supplement. The results of this work serve to indicate that variation in drive level in *Saimiri*, as in rhesus (Meyer, 1951), is not a problem for the study of learning and is not related to performance accuracy. This author suggests, however, that factors influencing drive in *Saimiri* are not yet fully understood since investigators typically *do* employ food privation schedules with *Saimiri* and that without privation the animals frequently fail to respond at all.

Evidence in support of this last point is provided from a test conducted on monkeys that had just completed the discrimination reversal procedures of another experiment by Rumbaugh and Ensminger (1964). One group of three monkeys continued discrimination reversal training for an additional day, maintained on the 23-hour food privation schedule of the main experiment. A second group of four monkeys also continued training for an additional day but was allowed to feed freely for the intervening interval of 23 hours. The first group continued to perform as though the experimental program were still in progress. In the second group, however, two animals stopped responding almost immediately. They failed to resume responding despite repeated re-presentation of trials. The other two animals of the nondeprived group did, however, continue working throughout the session at accuracy levels approximating those of previous days. Though more study of this kind is needed, it would appear that if nondeprived monkeys work at all they are likely to do about as well as when deprived. It has been our experience in San Diego that privation schedules are advisable for insuring sustained performance in discrimination learning studies.

As a methodological note, collectively these observations may reflect the possibility that when squirrel monkeys are thoroughly adapted to procedures and personnel and tested in nonarousing (nonemotion-producing) situations, food *privation* is unnecessary if highly preferred foods are used as rewards. When food motivation is found necessary, permitting each monkey to feed on water-moistened chow for about 1½ hours after testing works well, keeping the animals in good health for a period of at least several weeks. Reducing free-feed body weights gradually, over 2 weeks, to about 82−85% also works very satisfactorily. Should animals be less than 2 years old, however, both of these methods of inducing motivation will probably interfere with their normal growth and development if employed for more than just a few weeks at a time.

C. STUDIES OF *Saimiri* TO EXPLORE THE NATURE OF
   LEARNING-SET AND DISCRIMINATION-REVERSAL SKILLS

The processes that support the formation of LS have been an area of prime interest since its, definition by Harlow (1949). It is beyond the scope of this chapter to review the extensive literature that relates to that line of inquiry (see Schrier, *et al.*, 1965, Vol. 1); only contributions to knowledge derived from the use of *Saimiri* in that study area will be reviewed.

1. Pretraining Effects

The classic learning-set training procedure entails the presentation of a series of discrimination problems, each comprised of a pair of stimuli; the formation of learning set has been viewed as some form of cumulative, positive transfer resulting from the learner's working on these discrimination problems. Detailed consideration of the learning-set testing procedure reveals that it is, in fact, a very complex one. For example, in addition to receiving discrimination training per se, the subject has visual encounter with the vast array of stimulus objects which, in pairs, comprise the series of discrimination problems. In addition, as learning-set forms, the learner receives reward at a higher rate, i.e., a greater proportion of its responses are correct.

A study by Rumbaugh *et al.* (1965a) was conducted to determine (1) whether the formation of learning set might be accounted for in terms of perceptual learning (as contrasted with discrimination learning) accruing as a result of encounter with a series of single objects of the kind used in conventional learning-set problems and (2) whether expectancies regarding the probability of responses being rewarded entered into the formation of learning set. The training apparatus was a modified WGTA (Fig. 3).

Phase I of the study consisted of 3000 trials which were given to the learning-set control group (group LS) in the conventional form of 500 six-trial LS problems. Of the experimental groups, one (group S-100%) encountered only *one* object whereas the remaining two groups (groups M-100% and M-50%) encountered a new object every sixth trial. *All* responses were rewarded in groups S-100% and M-100% but only three of the six responses to each object were rewarded in group M-50%.

In phase II all groups received an identical set of 200 LS problems, each for six trials, to test for the effect of groups' S-100%, M-100%, and M-50% pretraining experiences compared to the control group (group LS). Results are shown in Fig. 4. Data analysis indicated that groups S-100% and M-100% were at first learning set*less*, but subsequently they were neither accelerated nor retarded in LS formation. That neither of these groups evidenced well-established LS at the outset of phase II indicates that their extensive experiences in phase I were not of the kind germane to the formation of LS. Even the encounter with 500 single objects (provided for group M-100% but not for group S-100%), with whatever opportunity provided thereby for perceptual learning of the differences between the objects, failed to substitute for discrimination learning. It is of note, however, that group M-50% was significantly retarded in the formation of LS through

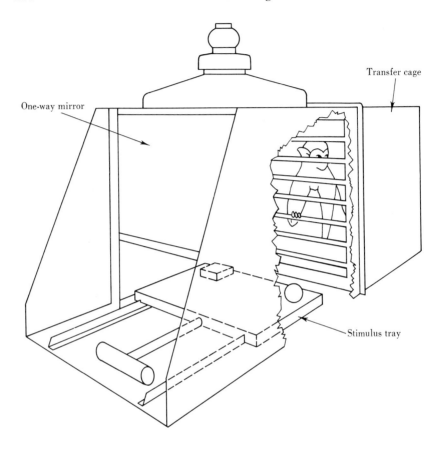

FIG. 3. The modified WGTA, less curtain at bottom edge of one-way vision mirror. (From Rumbaugh *et al.*, 1965a.)

the course of phase II, a finding that supports the notion that pre-established expectancies (in this case that only 50% of responses will be rewarded) can influence the rate of LS formation. The findings of this study in no way detract from the widely held view that LS is contingent upon the processes of discrimination learning which, in all probability, are best provided by the simultaneous presentation of both members of a problem pair on each of a series of trials.

2. Disruption of Learning Set

Once established, LS is a very stable skill, neither soon forgotten nor disrupted by contradicting experiences. Only temporary, but nonetheless significant, interruption of established LS was demonstrated with *Saimiri* subjects by Rumbaugh and Prim (1964). Three groups of four monkeys were matched for LS proficiency and then assigned to either continued LS training or to one of two conditions of discrimination-reversal (DR) training. The first group served as a control and received continued LS training with six-trial problems throughout the course of 900 trials. During this time one experimental group had successive reversals to a criterion (six consecutive correct responses) and the second experimental group had cue reversal every fourth trial regardless of performance accuracy. Groups were subsequently compared on a set of 50 six-trial LS problems. For the first 20 of those problems but not thereafter, the group that had cue reversal every fourth trial was significantly retarded in trial 2 but not trials 2−6 performance. The other experimental group showed no retardation. The effect was attributed to the probability that too frequent changes in cue values, with its concurrent consequent of intermittent reinforcement, interfered with the animals' abilities to execute their previously learned response tendencies or strategies necessary for efficient LS performance. A related experiment of similar design reported by Dalrymple and Stretch (1966) with rats as subjects in a position-reversal learning-set situation corrobor-

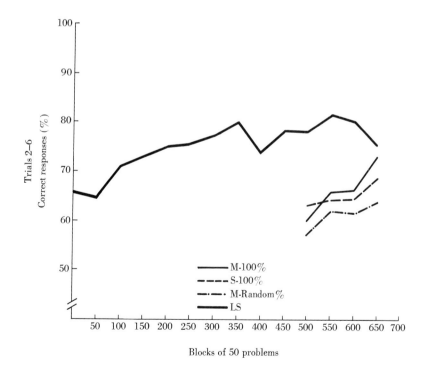

FIG. 4. Percent responses correct on trials 2 to 6. (From Rumbaugh *et al.*, 1965a.)

ates the disruptive effect that intermittent reinforcement at a low rate can have upon performance of a complex task. Rats, however, in sharp distinction to the *Saimiri* did not recover from the disruption.

3. Criterional Discrimination-Reversal (DR) Training with Single and Multiple Problems

Whether or not criterional reversals with a single problem were sufficient for the learning of DR skills by LS-sophisticated animals was the subject of a study reported by Rumbaugh and Ensminger (1964). The training phase consisted of 960 trials in which one group received successive reversals to the criterion of six consecutive responses correct while the second group learned and reversed to this same criterion, but each time with a new pair of objects. Very little improvement through the course of the training in the single-pair group was noted, a point that stands in contrast with the chimpanzee data from similar training reported by Schusterman (1962). The group that worked to criterion on each of a problem series required significantly fewer trials to learn than to reverse to the stated criterion.

In the first test phase both groups received 640 trials in which each received criterional, multiple-pair DR training, just as one group had received through training from the very beginning of the study. Both groups performed *equally* from the very beginning of this test phase, indicating that the observed difference between groups during training was only a performance difference, that is, under comparable test conditions both groups evidenced identical mastery (i.e., learning) of DR skills.

Schusterman (1962) had demonstrated earlier with naive chimpanzees that successive criterional reversals with only a very limited number of stimulus pairs will develop LS, as evidenced in a subsequent set of six-trial LS problems. Whether such training will develop LS in *Saimiri* has not been demonstrated but it clearly does establish DR skills.

Rhesus monkeys, as inferred from performance on a series of reversal problems, benefited from repeated criterional reversal training on an initial visual discrimination, whereas cats did not (Warren, 1965). It seems probable, therefore, that *Saimiri* stands much closer to rhesus than to cat in its ability to benefit from successive criterional reversal training in basic object — quality LS formation. Direct empirical demonstration of this assumption remains to be made, however.

4. Learning-Set Skills of Saimiri as Compared to Apes and Macaques

Studies of LS skills in groups of apes and monkeys at the San Diego Zoo (Rumbaugh and McCormack, 1967) provide extensive data for evaluation of *Saimiri* learning skills within the order *Primates*. Early findings (Rumbaugh and Rice, 1962) indicated that young apes were capable of developing LS in a situation in which problem objects were encased within Plexiglas bins, effects of which are discussed later in this chapter. That demonstration made it feasible to undertake a LS testing program, retaining standard usage of stereometric objects and noncorrection procedures even with apes of all age ranges and sizes.

The basic testing program included, as an initial stage, training to criterion in a simple form discrimination problem (red square versus red circle). Learning of that problem ensured that the animals had at least initially located the relevant cues (i.e., the discriminanda) within the transparent bins and provided an objective referent for definition of degree of adaptation and pretraining prior to subsequent LS training. The first LS training phase consisted of 500 six-trial LS problems and the second phase consisted of criterional LS training in which each problem was mastered to the criterion of 20 correct responses within a span of 25 trials (or for 800 trials maximum per problem) and in which training continued until an interproblem criterion was achieved (10 out of 12 consecutive problems in which the intraproblem criterion was met within the first 25 trials). A *test* of LS was then given in the form of 50 LS problems, each given for two trials. Results of that test are given in Fig. 5 by primate groups and by ages. Results from *Saimiri* tested in this basic format with objects encased within Plexiglas bins (as in Rumbaugh *et al.*, 1965b) are plotted appropriately above the age point for *adult* on the baseline.

Saimiri performance relative to all but the youngest of some great apes is clearly inferior; however, comparison of its performance with that of the gibbons requires careful interpretation. First, there is no question that the gibbons, regardless of age, performed at levels inferior to the great apes. It should not be concluded, however, that the gibbons and squirrel monkeys are in the same ability range, for that would require that we assume that the test situations were equally fair and appropriate for the two groups. Subsequent studies have revealed that at least one adult male gibbon could perform at levels commensurate with the best of the great apes (91 – 94% correct on trial 2 of LS) if first trained to ignore both irrelevant background and foreground cues, by use of criterional training procedures in which a single problem is successively mastered regardless of serial introduction of irrelevant cues which initially serve to distract. The gibbon/great ape findings indicate that the encasement of test objects probably made the training situation considerably more difficult for the gibbons than for the great apes, perhaps due to intrinsic differences in their perceptual processes. Thus we can not conclude that the test situations and methods of problem presentation were *necessarily* equivalent for all the primate groups studied. On the whole, however, the inferior performance of *Saimiri* in relation to the great apes can not be denied and, as in other studies, the squirrel monkey performance levels were commensurate with its zoological taxonomic standing.

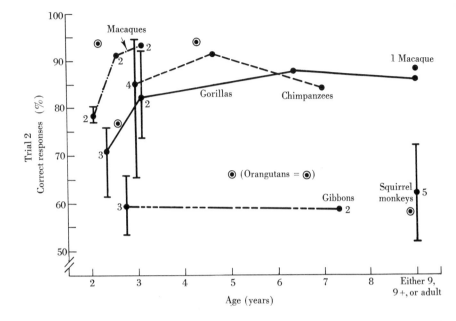

FIG. 5. Performance of primate groups (average percentages and ranges) by age on a learning-set test phase of 50 two-trial problems. Numbers by points indicate where *N* was other than 1. Orangutan points are not connected but they suggest a decline in test proficiency with age. Note that the *Saimiri* point is placed above the "adult" age level. (From Rumbaugh and McCormack, 1967.)

It should be noted that there is progressive improvement in LS capacity with age in macaques, chimpanzees, and gorillas. The deterioration of performance with age increments up to adult levels in the orangutan can not be satisfactorily explained at this point but very likely it reflects motivational changes.

5. Criterional versus Fixed-Trial Learning-Set Training

Progress in science frequently comes about when it is noted that certain observations are not in keeping with conclusions derived from prior research. Exceptions to generalizations or principles, regardless of how widely accepted they might be at the time, frequently provide opportunity for refining our scientific understanding of important events.

It was the initial failure that we encountered in attempting to establish LS in two young male squirrel monkeys (Brazilian) that led us to reconsider the variable of trials per problem in the formation of LS and eventually to the exploration of criterional training methods with the squirrel monkey. The two monkeys, healthy, responsive, and food-deprived, remained at chance performance levels over the course of 550 object — quality discrimination problems, each presented for six trials. That the objects were mounted about 1 inch from the leading edge of gray-painted wooden panels and that the monkeys pushed on the mounting panel's edge rather than on the object itself undoubtedly accounted for the failure (in 1958 we were not as sensitive to the importance of cue and response spatial contiguity). Our exasperation led to analysis of the situation, and we concluded the obvious — the monkeys had failed to develop LS by reason of insufficient cumulative transfer of learning from one problem to the next in the series. To counter this problem we required that the next series of problems had to be mastered to the criterion of 20 responses correct within a span of 25 trials.

Performance markedly improved and within the third block of eight criterional problems there was only one problem in which more than 25 trials were required for mastery, and that one required only 30 trials. Median numbers of trials for each of three successive blocks (eight problems each) for the better monkey were 44, 26, and 23. Responses correct on trials 2 to 6 for those blocks increased from 45%, to 75%, to 85%. What we had failed to obtain with 550 six-trial problems we obtained within relatively few criterional LS problems (the method of problem presentation had remained unchanged otherwise). The other monkey showed a similar, though less dramatic, effect, and the performance levels that differentiated them in this early study have held true over the subsequent 9 years.

Subsequently, Rumbaugh and McQueeney (1963) reported a study in which four naive squirrel monkeys were trained with criterional LS procedures. A different version of the WGTA was employed but its stimulus tray also provided for the mounting of the problem objects on sliding panels which covered food wells when in their forward positions. Two of the monkeys were young adults, and two were known to be 6 months of age as they were captive-born at the San Diego Zoo. All monkeys were trained to an interproblem criterion that required mastery (i.e., 20 correct choices within a span of 25 trials) within the first 25 trials on 10 out of 11 consecutive problems.

Learning set, as inferred from responses correct on trials 2 to 6 of the last block of 10 problems, was 88%. No difference between the two age pairs was indicated. Successful DR training followed.

Seven months later a retention test with 10 new DR problems was given, and with the exception of one animal that in the interim between training and the retention testing had received oddity training (unsuccessful), all animals did remarkably well. As far fewer total trials had been given these animals than given in previous six-trial LS studies (Miles, 1957), we interpreted the results as probably indicating that criterional procedures as employed had yielded more efficient LS than would have been the case had a small and fixed number of trials been given per problem. To place this interpretation in the context of other known data that were contrary to the position that trials per problem effectively altered the course of LS formation in a positive manner (Behar, 1961; Levine *et al.*, 1959) we proposed that it may well be only in the relatively primitive primates (such as *Saimiri*) that criterional training enhances LS, but that the criterional method, when effective, would not alter the basic properties of LS as a phenomenon.

Clearly, additional tests of the criterional approach were needed. We made a direct comparison to assess the effect when groups had either 6 or 60 trials per problem, in the fixed-trial LS conditions, or criterional training (Rumbaugh and Prim, 1963). Results were discouragingly negative, as were the results of a concurrently conducted study of similar design in another laboratory with rhesus monkeys (Sterritt *et al.*, 1963). The evidence against the proposed efficacy of the criterional LS method at this point was so great as to require reappraisal and restatement of position, which indeed was not without agony. Effects of early environment were assessed (Rumbaugh and Prim, 1964) and viewed as possibly accounting for the initial results. What we did not evaluate carefully enough were certain changes made in the stimulus tray, now a simple, flat tray with two small food wells at the leading edge. Stimulus objects covered these wells (there were no sliding panels to push) and the monkeys displaced them to indicate choice and to obtain reward. Now this is without doubt a much easier problem situation for the monkeys, for there is no chance that they will fail to attend to the relevant cues as they make their choices. They must attend to the objects in order to put a hand on them for pushing them aside. When objects are mounted on panels (as in the Rumbaugh and McQueeney study) this attentiveness might well be variable or even improbable.

It was the findings of others that stimulated reconsideration of our results in relation to the effectiveness of the criterional LS method. Accordingly, they are acknowledged with great pleasure.

A study that provided direct comparison of criterional and fixed-trial methods in a subprimate form was reported by Stevens (1964). Two groups of cats were used in a LS experiment, with one group receiving criterional training and the other receiving six-trials per problem. The results were dramatic and clear-cut — whereas LS developed in the criterional group, none was evident in the fixed-trial group *until* they were changed to criterional procedures in the second part of the study. Problem difficulty, as varied either by restriction of learning capacity or by making the discriminations more difficult, was the framework used by Stevens to interpret his results in support of the basic criterional hypothesis advanced earlier by Rumbaugh and McQueeney (1963). It was his study that led to the foregoing analysis of the stimulus tray and its probable effect in the Rumbaugh and Prim study.

Testing that same hypothesis with groups of black-hooded Norway rats, Kay and Oldfield-Box (1965) also obtained positive results in support of criterional training as a superior method for establishing LS in rats. King (1965), working with rock squirrels, concluded that the advantages of criterional LS methods were probably even more marked for squirrels than for squirrel monkeys (p. 275).

Results of those studies led us (Ternes *et al.*, 1965) to compare criterional methods with a training situation known to be highly refractory to even low-level LS formation in squirrel monkey, i.e., six-trial LS problems with objects encased in Plexiglas bins. Results were positive and in favor of criterional procedures for the first block of 50 six-trial problems, subsequent to either 1800 trials of criterional training or to an equivalent number of trials administered in the form of six-trial LS problems. However, the effect decayed (Fig. 6) thereafter and by the end of 200 six-trial test problems criterionally trained animals were not at all superior to those having six-trial problems throughout.

It now appears that criterional methods can facilitate the formation of LS in certain, but by no means all, training situations. Those situations in which LS formation benefits from criterional training have one common characteristic—they are all *difficult* ones. Whenever learning ability is restricted either by the characteristics of the animal form studied, or by age level (it is probably not effective with rhesus over 8−10 months of age), or wherever identification of the relevant cues might be difficult (as when they are encased or mounted on panels), or when the discriminations themselves are difficult to make given the perceptual capacities of the species being studied, criterional training procedures are likely to yield performance levels, assessed on an interproblem measurement, superior to fixed-trial procedures. In reference to the last of these conditions, it is of interest to note that Wilson (1965) finds criterional methods advantageous (though not necessarily a requisite) to the formation of tactual discrimination learning sets in macaque monkeys. The effectiveness of the criterional methods can now be described more confidently and positively than was permitted in light of evidence available just a few years ago (e.g., Miles, 1965).

6. Discrimination-Reversal Skills: The R/A Ratio

Comparative psychologists view the approach of direct comparison (in which the absolute behaviors of one species are directly compared with those of others) as having great potential but also replete with unknown hazards and pitfalls. Too many data obtained with this approach fit within an evolutionary framework to hold that the approach is without power.

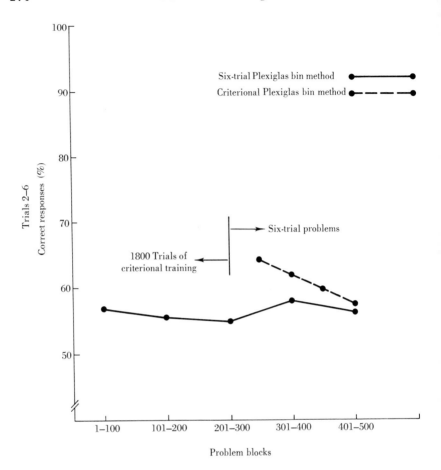

FIG. 6. Effects of criterional training and six-trial problem LS-training methods in which problem objects were encased in Plexiglas bins. (After Ternes *et al.*, 1965.)

There are also too many unknowns, however, reliably associated with the species variable, that have varying effects upon absolute levels of performance; thus it is difficult to feel completely confident in interpreting what has been observed and measured by direct comparison methods. Too frequently the experimenter is in the defenseless position of just assuming that the task is commensurate and equally applicable to all species under consideration. When closely related species are involved (as within families) that assumption is probably correct, but with increasingly unrelated forms the assumption of equally applicable techniques surely becomes increasingly untenable.

Rumbaugh and Jeeves (1966) have discussed alternatives to the method of direct comparison, those alternatives exemplified through a comparison of their respective discrimination-reversal indices. Rajalakshmi and Jeeves (1965) described the "reversal index" (RI) as a ratio between the number of trials (or errors) to criterion on the reversal trials and the number of trials (or errors) to criterion on the acquisition trials of a DR problem. The RI ratio is derived from the first (and *only*) DR problem learned, with *either* individual or group performance measures used in the computation. Rumbaugh and Pournelle (1966) described the R/A index as a ratio between percentage responses correct on the reversal trials of *a block* of discrimination-reversal problems and percentage responses correct on the acquisition trials of that same problem block; the problems were ones in which a fixed number of trials preceded and followed cue reversal. R/A values are calculated for *individual* animal's performances only, with values being derived from each of several blocks of problems (e.g., 20 problems per block).

Both indices avoid the problem of direct comparison of absolute performance levels through use of ratios that reflect performance on one aspect of a task (reversal) with that of another (acquisition). In this regard these indices bear resemblance to the approach espoused by Bitterman (1965), that approach being one of defining the *differential effects* of laws as they affect behaviors of various animal forms. Both indices are predicated on the assumption that to the degree that animals are able to execute efficient reversals of discriminations, they possess increased general problem-solving capacity which ultimately provides the basis for the one-trial LS ability of primates.

It should be made clear that perhaps either of these indices will undergo modification as more defensible, refined, and economical indices are sought. That possibility notwithstanding, the conceptual approach that these indices reflect should endure and lead to refinements in methodology and measurement.

Basic formulation for the R/A index stemmed from this author's observation that whereas apes and macaques scoring *above* the median percentage correct for their group on the acquisition trials of a block of fixed-trial DR problems *dropped* in percentage responses correct on reversal trials, those *below* the median *gained*. It was also observed that squirrel monkeys matched with ape/macaque subjects on the basis of percentage responses correct on acquisition (prereversal) performance dropped significantly on their reversal performance, whereas the ape/macaque subjects did as well on the reversal trials as on the acquisition trials.

Translation of the reversal performance (R% = responses correct) and prereversal performance (A% = responses correct) into R/A provided an index of the amount and direction of transfer from the prereversal to the reversal trials. Plotting R/A against A%, as an index of achievement and/or problem difficulty as inferred from the prereversal proficiency level, revealed two distinct functions (Rumbaugh and Pournelle, 1966). The one for apes and macaques reflected a preponderance of *positive* transfer while the one for squirrel monkeys reflected a preponderance of *negative* transfer. The R/A ratios for the groups differed most when A% approximated 65, e.g., when prereversal proficiency was relatively poor.

It is, of course, the positive correlation between A% and R% that provides for the R/A type of analysis, but the analysis provides more information than just the A% and R% values or the coefficient that defines the degree to which they are correlated. The analysis tells about the kind of transfer process operating through the course of discrimination reversal training, that with progression from the more primitive to the more highly evolved primates there is a reduction in amount of negative transfer and an increase in positive transfer. In addition, there is the suggestion that within those species in which adults characteristically exhibit positive transfer, there are maturational levels at which negative transfer dominates in the reversal performance.

It seems possible to me that it is such a basic difference as this direction and amount of transfer that probably permits learning-set tests in general to be sensitive to the phylogenetic and ontogenetic variables, as discussed earlier in this chapter.

If with the R/A method we compare species (or age levels within species) *only* when A% values are equal for the groups concerned, we circumvent the difficult problem of having to assume that the WGTA test situations are *precisely* equal and fair for all subjects, for we are comparing amounts and directions of transfer—not absolute performance levels. Figure 7 summarizes R/A values for a variety of primate groups when their prereversal performances are held constant (62–68% correct). It should be noted that *Saimiri* exhibit greater negative transfer than any of the other groups for which comparable data are available.

7. Response-Contingent Training Effects

Position habits are frequently very strong in *Saimiri*. Especially early in training, individuals may perseverate in response to either side for several hundred trials with no apparent attention to the array of stimuli encountered in dozens of LS problems. As one approach, we have employed with considerable success a correction procedure to handle this problem: the basic method consists of placing a plain block of wood as a stimulus object over the *non*preferred food well for two consecutive trials each time the monkey perseverates to a position response for 10 consecutive trials.

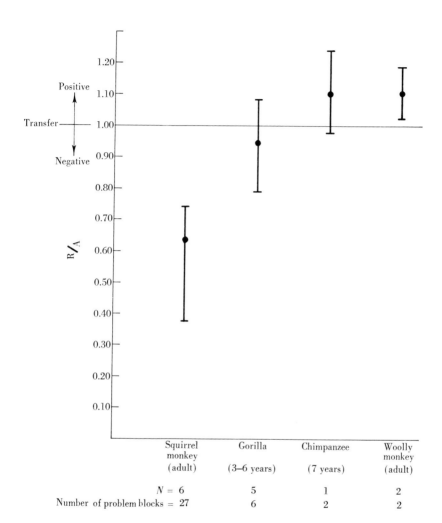

FIG. 7. R/A ratio (percentage correct on reversal trials divided by percentage correct on acquisition trials) means and ranges for four groups of primates. Only those R/A ratios from blocks of problems (20 per block and 5 blocks given to each subject) in which percentages of responses correct on the acquisition trials ranged between 62 and 68% are reported in this figure, i.e., all groups performed equivalently on prereversal trials. Note that there is no overlap between *Saimiri* and any other group.

Response-contingent LS methods (Abordo and Rumbaugh, 1965) also have proved extremely effective in coping with problems of position habits in *Saimiri*. The response-contingent (RC) procedure consists of changing the right—left position assignments of the members of each LS problem *only* on those trials that follow ones on which correct choices were made; hence, the procedure derives its name, for position assignments are totally contingent upon performance (except for trial 1).

The first demonstration of RC effectiveness was made in a WGTA test situation in which for the first 300 trials of discrimination training on LS-type problems two groups of naive monkeys were criterionally trained (9 correct responses within a span of 11 trials). Position assignments were made according to a predetermined sequence for one group (non-RC) and according to RC procedures in the second group. Test for effect consisted of a set of 50 LS problems each presented for three trials, the position assignment of objects following a predetermined non-RC sequence similar to that used in training for the non-RC group. Results were significantly in favor of the RC-trained group.

As the RC method reinforces a position alternation habit 100% of the time, it is possible, however, that prolonged RC training might adversely affect object-discrimination learning. Only if a given species is particularly inept at learning position alternation might extensive training by RC methods have no detrimental effect upon the acquisition of LS skills. (In a subsequently discussed study (Pournelle and Rumbaugh, 1966) in which 2100 trials of either non-RC or RC training were given to groups of squirrel monkeys, tamarins, and marmosets, those receiving RC training apparently were adversely affected in transfer test performances). It seems likely that RC training initially aids LS, both by discouraging position habits and *also* increasing the frequency of differential-cue trials (those trials on which object as separated from position on the tray is differentially reinforced). Harlow (1959b) reports that rhesus monkeys rarely have position preferences; hence we would predict with rhesus monkeys that RC methods would probably have no beneficial effect and possibly even an adverse effect by establishing position alternation.

8. A Modification of the WGTA for Use with Small Primates

Recent modifications in our WGTA were made to meet problems encountered in a study in which squirrel monkeys, tamarins, and marmosets were compared directly in a single test situation (Pournelle and Rumbaugh, 1965). The main problem was that they differed markedly in their ability to take food from the food wells, a problem that created differences in work and promptness of reward for correct responses. Magnets were imbedded where food wells had been located on the stimulus tray, and as problem objects had metal plates attached to their undersides, they were essentially immobile when positioned on these magnets. As the subjects were pretrained to simply *touch* (rather than displace) the object of choice for a given trial, they did not try to dislocate them except on rare occasions. The subject's choice, then, was indicated by its touching one of the objects. By use of a pellet dispenser, reinforcement was delivered directly into the restraining cage where it could be either picked or licked up according to the subject's preference. Dispensing of reinforcement for correct choices was controlled by the experimenter's use of an end switch. Learning was probably facilitated by the sound made by the dispenser, which provided immediate secondary reinforcement for the choice just made. As the experimenter did not have to retrieve rewards from food wells subsequent to trials on which errors were made by the subjects, and as there was never any problem in the animal procuring by hand or mouth its reward for correct responses, testing procedures were quite efficient.

9. Learning Set Compared for Squirrel Monkeys, Marmosets, and Tamarins

As part of the San Diego program of comparative primate studies, an intensive study (Pournelle and Rumbaugh, 1966) of learning and transfer of learning was made of three closely related groups of cebids: the squirrel monkey, the golden marmoset (*Leontideus rosalia*), and the cotton-topped tamarin (*Saguinus oedipus*). This experiment consisted of *training* all subjects on successive reversals of a black versus white cube problem to a criterion and then *testing for transfer* of that learning (1) on a set of fixed-trial DR problems and then (2) on a set of criterional DR problems. The apparatus described in the foregoing section was used throughout the study.

Results indicated that during the first phase (2100 trials of successive reversals, each to a criterion of six consecutive correct responses) there were no significant differences between species, with all groups showing significant increases in performance. Figure 8 shows the performance of the three primate groups, disregarding response-contingent training differences which in the training phase proved nonsignificant. Though the cotton-topped tamarins were initially poorer than the other groups, they were equal to the others in the last block of trials.

The performance on the first transfer test was affected both by species and training method. In the first transfer test those animals that received response-contingent training were inferior to those that had nonresponse-contingent training, presumably because the 2100 trials of response-contingent training were sufficient to establish a tendency to alternate choice of positions from trial to trial. The performance of the cotton-topped tamarins was inferior to that of the golden marmosets and squirrel monkeys, presumably because they perseverated in choice of object significantly more than did the other species. However, they tended to improve in this regard

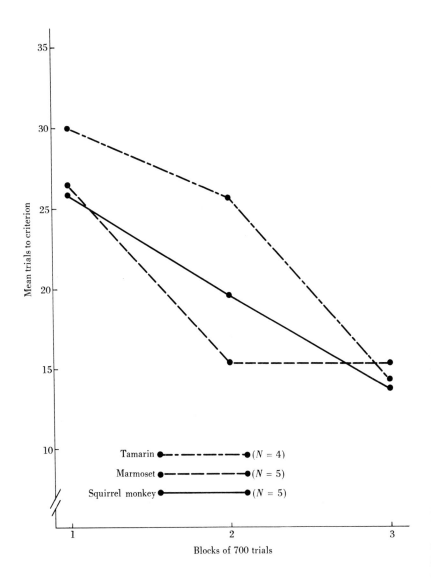

FIG. 8. Mean trials to criterion for each of three primate groups over the course of 2100 trials of successive reversal training. (From Pournelle and Rumbaugh, 1966.)

in the second transfer test. Squirrel monkeys exhibited the most appropriate usage of both position and object cues. The findings of this study thus indicate that associated with phyletic progression there are advances in the capacity for integrated usage of both position and object cues which, in turn, provide increased effectiveness in the operation of transfer of training mechanisms. This summary is in keeping with the strong position habits exhibited by a group of prosimians (*Tupia glis, Galago senegalensis, Galago crassicaudatus, Loris tradigradus, Perodicticus potto, Lemur fulvus,* and *Lemur catta*) in discrimination and delayed response tests (Jolly, 1964a,b). The very circumscribed ability of the tree shrew (*T. glis*), as assessed by Leonard *et al.* (1966) would place it appropriately below the taxonomic levels of the squirrel monkey, marmosets, and tamarins.

10. Role of Object-Contact Cues in Object-Quality Discrimination Learning

Peterson and Rumbaugh (1963) reported a study designed to assess the role of object-contact cues in the formation of LS in squirrel monkeys. Four squirrel monkeys learned two types of problems to a criterion. In one type the monkeys first were required to touch the object of choice, then withdraw the hand to push back on the leading edge of the panel on which the object was mounted. In the second type the monkeys could see but not touch the objects because of a clear Plexiglas shield interposed between them and the objects. Choice was indicated in the same manner—the monkeys had to touch the Plexiglas shield in an area behind which the object of choice was positioned, then withdraw the hand to push back the panel on which the object was mounted. The intraproblem criterion for each type of problem was 20 correct responses within a span of 25 trials, and all monkeys worked on alternate blocks of both types.

Results did not indicate a difference between these kinds of problems, and it was concluded that object-contact cues contributed little or nothing to conventional object discrimination learning. That the space which intervened between where the hand was placed and the object chosen, in the condition involving use of the Plexiglas screen, did not deter criterional learning led to the formulation of a refinement of Shuck's visual sampling gradient hypothesis (Shuck, 1960). Shuck postulated the operation of a gradient of visual sampling that was focused in the region of the monkey's hand as positioned for making a choice. The refinement offered was that it is on any normal plane that is beyond the hand and on the axis defined by the eye—hand relation at the time of choice that the visual gradient functions. This refinement, basically compatible with Shuck's belief that manipulation of the objects was of consequence *only* to the extent that it defined the point of focus for the visual sampling gradient, implies that under certain conditions there can be physical *dis*contiguity between the stimulus and hand without there being any loss in learning efficiency.

That object-contact cues appear to contribute little or nothing to the formation of *Saimiri* LS with conventional stereometric objects, does not mean, of course, that there are no other kinds of problems (or species) to which they might make a considerable contribution. When visual cues are deleted, for example, and only tactual cues are available, learning in macaques can still occur if the tactual cues are distinguishable to the subject (Wilson, 1965; Blakeslee and Gunter, 1966).

11. Other Studies of Discrimination Learning

a. Successive and Concurrent Discrimination Learning. The successive method of discrimination learning consists of giving all trials of one problem before presentation of subsequent problems' trials. By contrast, the concurrent or serial method consists of interposing between any two consecutive trials of a given problem one trial from each of all other problems which, collectively, form a "list." Miles' review (1965, p. 56) of findings obtained from these two methods suggests that the concurrent-discrimination method applied to nonhuman primates might yield interesting and varied findings relating retroactive and proactive interference effects to phylogeny.

King and Goodman (1966) report a study in which successive and concurrent method effects upon discrimination learning were compared in rock squirrels (*Citellus variegatus*) and squirrel monkeys. Each test session, in a modified WGTA, consisted of 64 trials, comprised of 16 trials for each of four discrimination problems. Problems were presented either successively (all 16 trials of each problem were given in an uninterrupted series), or divided into two concurrent lists (each containing two problems), or combined to form a single concurrent list of four problems which was presented for 16 runs (one trial from each of the four problems, then a second trial, etc.).

Squirrel monkeys made significantly more correct responses than the rock squirrels, but list length (1, 2, or 4 problems) had no significant overall effect on the performance (Fig. 9) of either group. (In the later runs on the longer lists, though, there was a lowering of squirrel monkeys', but not the rock squirrels', performances.)

Squirrel monkeys showed greater perseveration of object choice as list length increased. Position habits were not significantly related to either list length or species. Results were interpreted as suggesting that concurrent methods of training retarded learning primarily when an intermediate amount of intraproblem learning had occurred. For this reason no retardation was detectable in the learning of the rock squirrels and detectable in the squirrel monkeys only during their later runs.

b. Oddity. In oddity problems the correct object is never constant from trial to trial, for "correctness" is determined by one object being "odd"

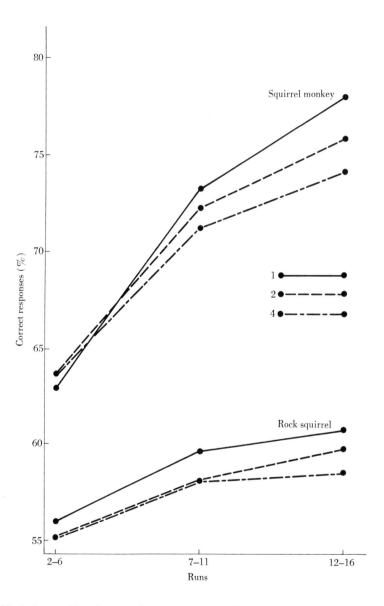

FIG. 9. Intraproblem learning for one-, two-, and four-problem lists. (After King and Goodman, 1966.)

relative to the other two objects which are usually identical. Problem solution is dependent upon the formation of an "oddity" concept. In an unpublished project conducted in our laboratory, Martin (1966) succeeded in demonstrating oddity concept formation with three adult male squirrel monkeys (Peruvian) known to be superior in LS performance. Criterional training was given on successive problems, and the most successful animal's trial scores (20 correct responses within a span of 25 trials) for eight problems were 1522, 127, 148, 74, 24, 137, 24, and 22. Clear evidence of interproblem transfer was indicated in this training situation in which all three positions were used for placement of the odd object. Subsequent testing on a series of one-trial problems, comprised of regrouped stimuli of the training problems, indicated that oddity achievement was about 70%. As is characteristic with all other animal forms capable of learning oddity discriminations, when all three positions are employed for odd and nonodd objects, the middle position for the odd object proved most difficult and accounted for all errors in the last two problems learned to criterion.

c. Conditional-Outcome Choice Behavior. In conditional-outcome training situations, subjects must make a discrimination between alternative and discriminable stimuli for responses to be rewarded; in nonconditional situations, there is no discrimination possible to be made between stimuli, for they are identical and choice of them is essentially "blind." If one controls for rate or frequency of reinforcement in both situations, trains all subjects in both situations, and then on certain test trials gives subjects a choice between the two, an estimate can be made of *preference* for a task in which discriminative choices and responses related to those choices control the occurrence of reward. Logan (1962) concluded that rats do not exhibit any significant preference of this kind, but Weir (1965) found that a preference for the conditional-outcome situation was demonstrable with children. Working with squirrel monkeys, Green and Moore (1966) found evidence of preference in one animal. They concluded that the performance of this subject and the findings of Weir indicate that Logan's conclusion based on rat behavior might not hold for primates. More data are needed on this problem, but if Green and Moore are correct it indicates that still in one additional manner the behavior of the squirrel monkey bears resemblance to other primates rather than to the behavior of nonprimate mammals.

d. Position-Reversal Learning Set. Gossette and Inman (1966) assessed the abilities of three squirrel monkeys and capuchins to master successive, criterional position (spatial) reversals in a WGTA-type apparatus with the intent of evaluating the sensitivity of that kind of task for broader use in comparative studies of learning. The capuchins were superior to the squirrel monkeys over the course of 19 reversals. Major findings of that study are shown in Fig. 10, which reveals progressive improvement in both

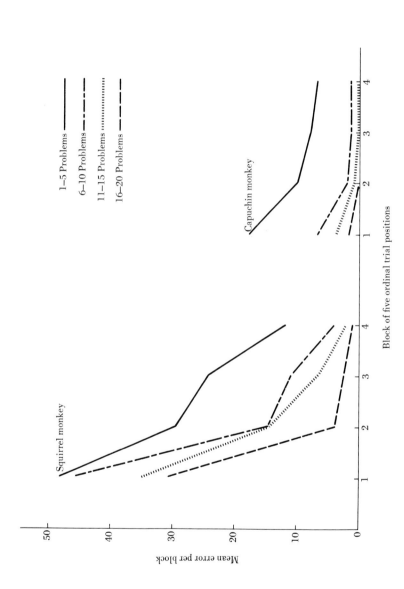

FIG. 10. Mean ordinal trial position error across blocks of five trial positions and five problems. (After Gossette and Inman, 1966.)

groups throughout the series of successive reversals to criterion. At the end of training, the capuchins typically made only one error before reversing while the squirrel monkeys were still making three to five errors. It should be noted, however, that the squirrel monkeys were still giving signs of improving; with continued training they might have equalled the capuchins' performances. On the other hand, the *Saimiri* strong position preference difficulties observed in learning-set training might indicate a restricted ability for position-reversal tasks. Of additional interest, Gossette and Inman reported that whereas the capuchins made their maximum error scores on the original discrimination, the squirrel monkeys made their maximum error scores on the first reversal. (This observation is of value as it relates to the profound negative transfer exhibited by squirrel monkeys in the reversal trials of discrimination reversal problems, a matter discussed earlier in this chapter.) Gossette and Inman concluded that this kind of reversal task is sensitive and appropriate to the task of cross-species studies of learning as indicated by the major finding that the capuchins were superior to the squirrel monkeys, a finding consistent with their taxonomic standings.

V. Delayed-Response Skills

Fletcher (1965) assesses the delayed-response problem, "With no close rival, past or present, . . . the one behavioral test most sensitive to the widest range of experimental treatments." In the delayed-response test subjects are exposed briefly to certain information (usually visual) regarding the placement of an incentive and then after an enforced delay are permitted to act upon that information to obtain the incentive. How well they do is believed to relate to orientation and skills of symbolic retention of information. Fletcher's review includes phylogenetic differentiation according to delayed-response performances, with cat and raccoon showing almost no retention by the end of 30 seconds, marmoset and gibbon remembering about 70−75% by 30 seconds, and rhesus remembering about 80% after the same delay.

The delayed-response performance of *Saimiri* typically has been assessed as falling somewhere between marmoset and rhesus. Treichler's study (1964) of *Saimiri* led him to conclude that it was closer to rhesus than to marmoset, though in learning-set skills *Saimiri* is closer to the marmoset. Thus, though rank ordering of these species by learning set and delayed response is the same, distance between successive ranks is believed to differ. With delays of 1 second the squirrel monkeys' choices were about 90% correct, there being a linear decay in performance associated with longer intervals up to 50 seconds by which time choices were only 60% correct.

King and Clawson (1966) report findings that coincide closely with Treichler's values. They also reported differences due to conditions that prevailed during the delay interval. In one condition the test tray and surrounding area remained illuminated, in a second condition there was darkness, and in a third condition there was total darkness but there were also cue glo lights, one underneath each of the two food wells, covered by identical white blocks. For delays from 5 to 60 seconds performance was uniformly better (by about 10%) under the condition in which the test tray remained illuminated, with no suggestion of a difference between the other two conditions (Fig. 11). This finding does not support the argument that performance in delayed response testing deteriorates due to visual distractions during the delay interval. Preliminary findings by King *et al.* (1968) also indicate that fox squirrels do better than squirrel monkeys in delayed

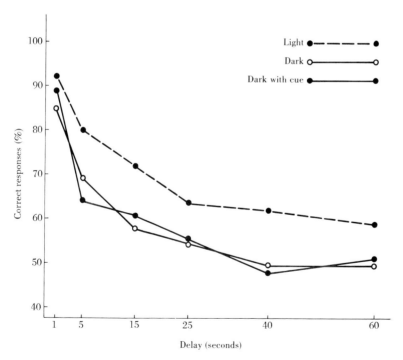

FIG. 11. Distribution of correct responses as a function of delay interval and delay condition. Each of the three delay conditions included 2880 trials. (After King and Clawson, 1966.)

response tests, a fact attributed to the fox squirrels' ability to maintain an orientation to the baited well more reliably for longer intervals of time.

Miles (1967) has extended assessment of *Saimiri* delayed-response abilities by systematically varying both length of delay periods and number of response alternatives. Four adult specimens received extensive training (5000 to 6000 trials) in a modified WGTA. Eight food wells (1½ inches apart) were located along the leading edge of the test tray. On a given trial, with a specified number of food wells covered with identical stimulus cubes (2, 3, 5, or 7), the food well under one cube was baited in full view of the subject. After a specified delay interval in darkness had transpired (3, 5, or 10 seconds), the test tray was illuminated and positioned to permit the subject to execute a choice. Choice was defined by the subject's hand touching a stimulus block. When the choice was correct, the experimenter withdrew the block by means of an attached cord to permit access to the food reward; when the choice was incorrect, the tray was immediately withdrawn to prevent choices of other blocks. Figure 12 shows the test situation, with the stimulus tray in position for the subject to choose among seven alternatives, and performance levels for the last 100 test trials under the designated delay-choice conditions. The results indicate that with extensive training the squirrel monkey can perform essentially without error after a 10-second delay if only two choice alternative are used. Increasing the number of choice alternatives resulted in a performance decrement at each delay interval, the decrement increasing linearly between 3 and 10 seconds. Miles' squirrel monkeys did considerably better at the 10-second delay than the monkeys of the two studies described immediately above. This fact, probably reflecting differences in testing techniques, serves to caution against use of any single delayed-response measurement as an absolute index for a given species' capacity.

Quite probably the skills that enable one animal to benefit in problem solving by being given the opportunity to observe another animal's work also relate to performance in delayed-response tasks. Mahan and Rumbaugh (1963) reported difficulty in getting squirrel monkeys to observe attentively responses of another in a discrimination situation, and while significant evidence of observational learning was obtained, it was only slightly above chance (about 50% when chance was 25% for being correct in a four-choice task).

French (1959) reported on the delayed response performance of squirrel monkeys when systematic variations were made in the accessibility of the negative and positive loci during trial-setting and delay periods of the problems. The squirrel monkeys were observed to orient toward the position of reward during the delay interval, a tendency that has been observed in other New World monkeys (see Fletcher, 1965). Placement of a barrier

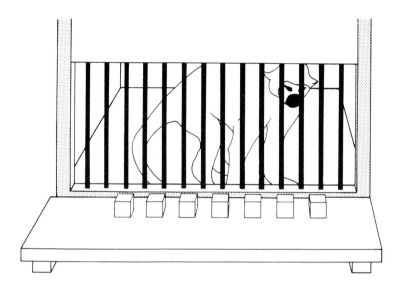

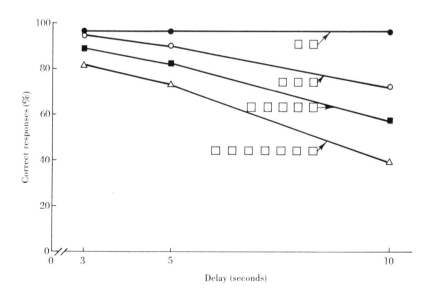

FIG. 12. The test situation and performance for groups according to delay intervals and number of alternatives as indicated by the number of squares. (Miles, 1967.)

over the positive locus during either the trial-setting or delay period adversely affected performance, whereas a barrier similarly placed over the negative locus did not interfere. In French's discussion of the results it was concluded that squirrel monkeys "trained on the classical problem learn to identify the positive locus on each trial, to orient toward it and respond to it, but not to discriminate clearly between it and the negative locus" (French, 1959, p. 744). Orienting responses of the body apparently obviated the learning of a discrimination *between* the cues associated with the rewarded and nonrewarded positions.

It would be worthwhile to determine whether or not a relationship exists between delayed response and learning-set skills for a group of *Saimiri*. Probably the relationship would be a positive one in which monkeys attentive in a delayed-response task would also excel in discrimination learning. If so, measurement of learning-set "capacity" might be confounded with the presence of skills and habits that relate most directly to delayed-response task performance. In addition, whether training in either learning set or delayed response facilitates performance in the other might be of great value in the development of methods appropriate to a variety of species. The report by Leonard *et al.* (1966) that the tree shrew (*T. glis*) is very poor on *both* learning set and delayed response, being inferior even to the cat, exemplifies the relationships suggested by the foregoing discussion.

VI. Patterned-String Studies

Ability to perform well in patterned-string problems has been used extensively to assess learning ability of primates (Harlow and Settlage, 1934; Finch, 1941; Riesen *et al.*, 1953). Cha and King (in press) have studied *Saimiri* capacity for patterned-string problems and report that *Saimiri* as well as rhesus, learn simple parallel problems with virtually no error. By contrast, King and Witt (1966) reported that rock squirrels had considerable trouble mastering such problems even when the strings were far apart. Cross and pseudo-cross problems (in the latter, the strings converge and appear to cross but actually do not) were learned, with evidence of strong negative transfer from the former to the latter. An intermixed series of crosses and pseudo-crosses was exceedingly difficult for most animals; in fact, some squirrel monkeys did not learn them at all. Cha and King interpret the poor performance of the squirrel monkeys on the intermixed series as indicating that they probably had failed on previous problems to learn to follow the string to the food cup, but were instead learning each problem as a simple discrimination. The same conclusion had been reached by King and Witt about the one rock squirrel that learned the same patterns. Results of their study are in keeping with the phyletic standing of *Saimiri* in relation to rock squirrels and rhesus monkeys.

VII. Operant-Conditioning Studies

One of the first studies to report a comparison between the performance of the squirrel monkey and another species was by Kelleher and Cook (1959). Squirrel monkeys and rats were compared on concurrent schedules comprised of fixed-ratio (FR) responding for food and a Sidman schedule of shock avoidance. The subjects were trained first on the FR schedule to press a lever for food; then after 20 reinforcements (all responses reinforced), the concurrent Sidman avoidance schedule was started in which failure to respond led to shock, delivered every 30 seconds. Responses postponed shock for 30 seconds. The squirrel monkeys' performances were qualitatively similar to those of the rats, but on the avoidance component of the schedule their response rates were higher. It was also discerned that when no shocks were delivered, pauses developed following food reinforcement in both species, with responses otherwise occurring at high rates. Response rates were highest just prior to food reinforcement on the FR schedule. When no food was delivered, low rates of responding occurred as is typical of the avoidance schedule. Kelleher *et al.* (1963) have described the squirrel monkey's performance on simple or multiple schedules of positive and negative reinforcement as comparable to that of the rhesus monkey (also see Kelleher, 1965, for a review).

The effects of multiple-link chain schedules (in which conditioned schedules are combined in a variety of ways) upon *Saimiri* behavior have been reported by Segal (1964). There were two chains which appeared in sequence, each chain having a fixed-interval (FI) schedule as its first link. One chain had a FR schedule while the other had a variable interval (VI) schedule as the second link, both of these schedules entailing food reinforcement. The only reinforcement of the FI schedule of both chains was the opportunity to work for food reinforcement on the second link. Colored stimulus cues signaled the commencement of whatever schedule was then in effect; however, the colored cues did not indicate whether it was the first, second, third, or fourth (at a maximum) of a given schedule in the entire sequence. Even so, the monkeys mastered the complete sequence of four FI VI and four FI FR chains, their responding being appropriate not only to the schedule of the moment but to the schedule as it was sequenced in a pattern that lasted 24 minutes. An increase in response rates in the FI links with successive repetitions of the FI VI chain and a decrease in response rates in the FI links with repetitions of the FI FR chain, was attributed to possible emotional changes associated with unequally preferred schedules of reinforcement.

A study of the ability of the squirrel monkey to space its responses through time as affected by positive and negative reinforcements (Segal and Rumbaugh, 1964) revealed that timing was very good under the schedule for which reward was positive (sucrose) but quite poor under negative reinforcement (noise). Timing behavior deteriorated toward the later training sessions under the condition of noise offset, suggesting either an adaptation to the noise or a hearing loss or some other change affecting the reward value of the event. The possibility that the noise elicited emotional behaviors incompatible with effective timing was also suggested.

Dews (1965) interrupted certain portions of a FI food reinforcement schedule with an intermittently appearing white light, never immediately followed by food reward. Had such interruption disrupted the smooth acceleration of responding which is typically observed in a FI schedule, it would have indicated that the imminence of reward for responding was in some manner indicated to the animal by the gradually accelerated response rate. However, interruption in this manner did not, in fact, disrupt *resumption* of a response rate with the smooth, increasing acceleration characteristic of that which precedes reinforcement in a FI schedule. As this finding was true of both pigeons and squirrel monkeys, it seems unlikely that some high-order brain mechanism mediates response patterning in FI schedules of positive reinforcement.

VIII. Punishment Effects

The inhibitory effect of shock upon previously established adaptive behavior in *Saimiri* was suggested in a study by Appel (1961). It had been known from earlier studies of other investigators that though shock would effectively inhibit such behaviors as bar-pressing for food in the rat and pigeon, the effect was temporary. With shock omitted, bar-pressing returned to normal rates within a few days. Appel's study extended observations of this order to two adult squirrel monkeys trained to bar-press for food. Body weights had been reduced to 80% of free-feeding levels. On a VI-6 (bar presses were rewarded variably and on the average once every 6 minutes) with no shock, each monkey bar-pressed about 2500 times during each of the first seven, 8-hour daily sessions. On the eighth day when shock was associated with each bar press, only 65 and 29 responses were given by the two monkeys. Appel concluded that the squirrel monkey may be more sensitive than the rat and pigeon to punishment effects.

An alternative to electric shock as a reinforcer in avoidance conditioning of *Saimiri* has been reported recently by Polidora and Boyer (1967). Consistent shuttle avoidance behavior developed more rapidly in groups for which jets of high-pressure air served as reinforcers than in other groups for which either continuous or discontinuous electric shocks delivered via a grid floor were used. The effect was attributed to the observation that an air blast does not elicit the violent and chaotic behaviors commonly associated with the subject's receipt of its first electric shocks, those behaviors probably interfering with the learning of the specific responses that will terminate the noxious stimulation.

IX. Light as a Reinforcer

With only one exception (*Aotes*), monkeys and all apes are diurnal animals. This knowledge gives rise to questions about the reinforcing properties of light for the order Primates and the way in which it affects their behavior. Parker (1966) conducted a series of studies in which squirrel monkeys were individually maintained in small chambers that could be darkened. In one study in which an adult female squirrel monkey was kept in this unit for 29 consecutive days, the only light it obtained was that accompanying the depression of a bar protruding through a wall. During the first 7 days, when ambient light was provided for 5 seconds by each bar press, incidence of bar-pressing increased monotonically from about 4500 to well over 9000 per day. As the amount of light per bar press was increased on each subsequent day from 10 seconds to 4 minutes, incidence of pressings dropped to a level of less than 1000. As light per press was again shortened, bar-pressing increased back to previous levels. However, as the light period was shortened to less than 5 seconds (i.e., $2\frac{1}{2}$ seconds and 1 second), rate of responding again dropped off. It was concluded that both light onset and duration of light were powerful variables influencing the bar-pressings of this monkey. Observation of the animal's behavior through a viewing port on one side of the unit suggested why light intervals less than 5 seconds were not sufficient to sustain the high response rate found with longer intervals. The monkey would depress the bar, immediately traverse the unit's floor to procure a piece of chow, but would drop it the moment the light went off. Though it would procure food in the light, it did not eat in darkness to any appreciable degree. Light was a requisite both to procuring *and* eating.

In another study of this series, Parker modified the apparatus to pit procurement of food and light against one another even more effectively. The light was on *only* when the monkey was on a perch at one end of the unit. Food and water were available at the other end of the unit but could not be procured by the animal unless it left the perch, which, in turn, produced total darkness. As the food was a gruel, it could not be retrieved in any quantity to be eaten on the perch with light on. For the first three continuous days when light was left on to familiarize the monkey with the location of food and water, it spent less than 10% of the time on the perch. On the fourth day, however, when the availability of light was contingent upon being on the perch, the monkey was on the perch almost 100%. No water was consumed and what little eating occurred consisted of the monkey leaving the perch, dipping its hand into the gruel, hastily returning to the perch where it then, in the light, leisurely licked its hand clean. As so little food could be obtained per trip in this manner, the animal engaged in this feeding activity most of the day. Parker concluded that total darkness might be used as a very effective, yet intrinsically harmless punishment in certain studies in which punishments are necessary but in which use of strongly aversive stimuli are either unwarranted or imcompatible with other desired procedures, such as the taking of physiological recordings.

LEVELS OF AROUSAL

Reynolds (1964) studied the reaction time of a squirrel monkey in a situation in which it had been trained to press and hold down a lever for food reward whenever a blue light was turned on and to subsequently release it at the appearance of a white circle. Duration of the foreperiod (time during which the white circle was shown) was either held constant at 2 seconds or varied unpredictably from 0 to 5 seconds following the lever press. Under the fixed foreperiod condition reaction time was about 30 msec slower than under the variable foreperiod one. These findings, just the opposite of those reported for humans under comparable conditions, were attributed to possible effects of prolonged training or to the chance that the squirrel monkey is maintained in a higher state of arousal in the variable foreperiod condition and, accordingly, responds more quickly than in the fixed condition.

X. Fear Studies

The etiology of fears frequently expressed by primates to certain classes of stimuli, such as snakes, is beyond the scope of this chapter. The reader is referred to other sources to pursue that topic (Hebb, 1946; Wolin *et al.*, 1963). It should be noted, however, that the squirrel monkeys of our colony are particularly aroused (standing erect, withdrawing, vocalizing, turning away, etc.) by some snakelike objects, such as certain kinds of wire cable and toy models of prehistoric animals. Aversive responses to the latter have been so common that we no longer use them as stimuli in learning-set training situations without first mutilating their form. Removal of the head and tail usually suffices to render the models neutral but at other times the grain suggested by the backs of the forms has also had to be roughened and otherwise altered.

Of particular interest to us has been the sensitivity of the squirrel monkeys to real snakes (they need not be in motion) within gallon glass jars. Squirrel monkeys and gibbons have been found, in our studies of learning set, to be inept at looking through Plexiglas-fronted bins to the discriminanda placed within when only six trials per problem are allowed (Ternes *et al.*, 1965). Nonetheless, they detect *immediately* whether a jar is empty or whether there is a snake within. This sensitivity has been so marked and so resistant to extinction, with the fear evidenced in response to jar + snake not generalizing readily to empty jars, that we have used it as a test situation to determine recovery levels of squirrel monkeys subsequent to exposure to near-vacuum atmospheric pressures. The etiology of such fear is not known to us but we are inclined to agree with Wolin *et al.* (1963) on the points that it is probably easier to condition fear within primates to certain classes of objects or environments than others and that snakes might possess certain qualities that make them prepotent as stimuli to which fear can be readily conditioned. Also viewed as reasonable is their point that young primates reared where snakes are not really a threat, as in a laboratory, might learn to fear certain things by being stimulated by the terror and fear exhibited by previously conditioned members of the colony. In my judgment, the squirrel monkey is an excellent candidate for studies of the origins of fears and the effects of fear upon instrumental and social responses.

Fear responses of golden marmosets (*Leontideus rosalia*), cotton-topped tamarins (*S. oedipus*), and squirrel monkeys to a series comprised of alternate groups of fear-inducing and neutral stimuli were recorded in an unpublished study by Pournelle and Ternes in our laboratory. All stimuli were pretested for effect with independent groups of animals. Fear stimuli included prehistoric animal models and a live snake in a jar; neutral stimuli were unpainted blocks of wood of irregular shape and size. The subjects first were trained to take food from a red plastic square on a tray whenever positioned before them in a WGTA (when all had earlier LS training). Serial presentations of the stimuli then were made, each stimulus in turn being positioned 1—2 inches behind the locus of the food. Each trial terminated whenever the animal either took the food or failed to take it within 3 minutes. Squirrel monkeys and golden marmosets behaved comparably, becoming afraid equally (as reflected in food-taking latencies) in response to the first stimuli that effectively induced fear. The cotton-topped tamarins, however, were by comparison significantly more fearful and also less subject to adaptation over the course of encountering subsequent stimuli. Once thoroughly frightened by a fear stimulus, the cotton-topped tamarins broadly generalized their fear to all stimuli, as indicated by their chronic balks to the food even on trials in which neutral stimuli were presented. In contrast, squirrel monkeys and golden marmosets quite readily adapted and soon came to take the food whenever it was paired with neutral stimuli. Such a study serves to caution against drawing broad, nonspecific statements regarding behaviors of closely related primates, for though the marmosets are more closely related to the tamarins than they are to the squirrel monkeys, behaviorally they were more like squirrel monkeys in this test situation. That this similarity coincides with the performance of these same groups in a learning-set training situation suggests that more attention should be given to relating learning abilities to emotional characteristics of species studied.

XI. Curiosity

Studies such as those reported by Harlow *et al.* (1950) have served to revitalize attention toward behaviors that do not provide any apparent metabolic reward or incentive for the animal. That rhesus monkeys which repeatedly disassembled a mechanical puzzle, consisting of a hasp and hook, were disrupted rather than facilitated in this behavior by the introduction of food reward into the puzzle situation, served to challenge traditional thought regarding the exclusive role of basic physiological drives in the determination of behavior patterns. Subsequent studies, such as those by Menzel (1964), have expanded our knowledge of how responsiveness of primates to a broad class of stimuli of this kind can be influenced by environmental variations during infancy.

Glickman and Sroges (1966) have published results of an extensive testing program in which a wide variety of zoo animals, from reptiles through primates, were given a set of stimulus objects to which to respond. Wooden blocks, steel chains, wooden dowels, rubber tubing of three different sizes, and a ball of crumpled paper comprised the set of objects. Responses of two male and three female squirrel monkeys were significantly more restricted than that of three male and two female Cebus (*Cebus capucinus* and *Cebus nigrivittatus*). Whereas three of the five capuchins gave no response to the objects, according to the scoring method employed, the remaining two contacted the objects with a variety of reactions. Draping of the tubing around the neck, holding of the dowel in the mouth while rubbing it with the hands, and mouthing of the paper ball were included among listed responses. Five spider monkeys (*Ateles ater*, 1 M, 1 F) and three woolly monkeys (*Lagothrix cana*, 1 M, 1 F, 1?) were judged as fairly responsive; however, their approach movements to the stimuli were more "lethargic" than the capuchins. No squirrel monkey made sustained contact with any of the objects, all contacts being brief and intermittent during test sessions. The squirrel monkey with the highest response score made only one actual contact, that being with the crumpled paper ball. Clearly, at least these five squirrel monkeys failed to respond as vigorously and in as varied ways as many of the other monkeys tested. Representatives of Callithricidae were but three in number, each of a different species, but the relatively great responsiveness of the golden marmoset (*L. rosalia*, sex unknown) is of interest. This animal grasped the rubber tubing with its hands, bit it, looked through it, and rubbed it against his belly, among other responses made. Overlap between at least families of primates (Callithricidae and Cebidae) is suggested, with the squirrel monkeys being an exception according to these tests. Except for the loris, the prosimians tested (4 lemur, 2 loris, and 4 galago) were similar in behaviors to *Cercocebus*, *Allenopithecus*, and *Macaca*. In fact, the prosimians were more responsive than were the four gibbons (*Hylobates*) tested. The most responsive primates of all tested in this study were the baboons and macaques.

Glickman and Sroges in their summary (1966, p. 177) note that the primates as a group exhibited a relatively large amount of purely visual exploration, but in particular this characterized the tree-living forms, which includes the squirrel monkey. That many factors could contribute to visual exploratory behavior, such as kind and length of captivity, general health and age of the animal, and the limited variety of stimuli comprising a testing program of the kind conducted, serves to caution against any conclusive statement at this time, and certainly with regard to the squirrel monkey whose characteristics are the subject at hand.

This approach, with appropriate refinements in method of presenting stimuli and recording the variety and intensity of responses made to them, holds considerable promise for increasing our understanding of important aspects of primate behavior, nonetheless. To study responsiveness systematically according to stimulus class of objects, endogenous and foreign to the ecology of various primates, can tell us much regarding the way primates perceive and respond to their environments. The effects of any number of treatment and subject variables studied in this fashion might prove more meaningful, in the final analysis, than is the case when such effects are assessed within the highly artificial situations of the operant conditioning box and the discrimination learning task.

Jolly's study (1964a,b) of prosimians' manipulation of and performance in simple object problems leads to conclusions that place them below the marmoset, and by implication the squirrel monkey. Jolly points out that good vision and fine manipulation ability contribute much to the adaptive intelligence manifested by the more highly evolved primates. As evaluated in the performance of the prosimians, however, vision and manipulatory ability are preadaptations only, for the "intelligent" behavior expressed in the test situations was limited. Differences in the attention span, orientation (visual), and manipulation ability of loris, galago, tupai, and various lemurs were demonstrably related to food procurement behaviors and to their own species' specific biology. Those that feed on insects which are likely to fly away, wait and pounce with precision, for example.

XII. Maze Learning

The use of mazes in assessing the learning abilities of primates has been relatively infrequent compared to use of other kinds of apparatus, notably versions of the WGTA. Zimmerman and Torrey (1965) review the studies of the Wisconsin Regional Primate Center in which mazes were used to chart the ontogeny of both spatial and nonspatial learning skills in young rhesus monkeys.

The relatively infrequent use of the maze with primates can probably be attributed to the fact that at least one manifestation of their simple spatial discrimination skills can be studied very readily with WGTA techniques in all specimens old enough to have well-developed use of the hand. With nonprimates, such as the rat, the whole-body response of selecting and traversing one route of the maze instead of another substitutes for their not having the extraordinary forelimb development and hand of the primate. It is of interest that WGTA modifications have recently been made for the rat, however, the choice response being to push with the nose on an object (Rollin *et al.*, 1963).

J. W. Davenport (1966) reports data from a Y-maze study of spatial discrimination learning skills of 16 male albino rats, 10 adult female squirrel monkeys, and 6 adolescent male rhesus monkeys, all animals being naive to the maze initially. Rat—monkey pairs were tested concurrently in Y-mazes identical in all detail except size. Incentives were 45-mg pellets for rats and 97-mg sucrose pellets for monkeys. Animals were confined within an arm of the maze for magazine training (a bar-pressing apparatus was situated in each arm of the maze). After preliminary training, in which both left and right alley choices were rewarded, spatial discrimination training was given. The "correct" arm for each animal was its nonpreferred arm during pretraining.

The performance of the rats was much superior to that of the monkeys, with no difference detected between the rhesus and squirrel monkey groups (Fig. 13). Some rhesus and squirrel monkeys were performing at chance levels even at the end of 80 trials, though with continued training they did reach the criterion of 10 consecutive trials correct within two test sessions. Davenport describes the behavior of both rhesus and squirrel monkeys, once learning has met criterion, as similar to rat behavior in that regular speed measures and long series of consecutive correct choices are obtained. There does not appear to be any strong tendency for response shift to occur with monkeys in a maze situation, in contrast with their choice behavior in a WGTA. Reversal training was successful for 8 of the 10 squirrel monkeys, considerably more trials being required to reach criterion on reversal than on acquisition for all but one monkey. Davenport considers the possibility that among the differences between rats and monkeys which may in part account for the obtained difference in initial learning is the liklihood that rats are more naturally oriented to spatial cues while monkeys orient more readily to visual cues. There seems general agreement, however, that no entirely satisfactory explanation for the difference in maze learning currently exists.

Whatever in the final analysis proves the best accounting of these interesting findings, it should be noted that while maze situations might accommodate the skills of rats, they do not necessarily prove conducive to learning by other animal forms considered superior to the rat in learning ability. *Possibly* the difference might be accounted for in terms of how cues are selected and attended to by these animals. Rats might prove generally su-

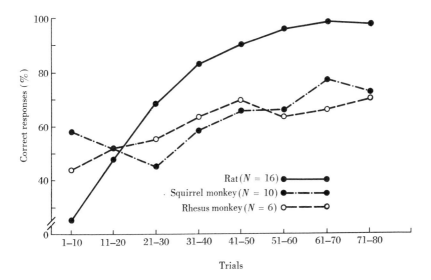

FIG. 13. Learning curves for rats and for rhesus and squirrel monkeys in a Y maze. (After J. W. Davenport, 1966.)

perior to primates in use of cue stimuli positioned beyond reach by any part of the body, e.g., the forelimb. Note that in the WGTA, in which monkeys can learn well via selection of stimuli through use of a hand, even slight distances between the location of relevant cues and where the choice response is made *can* preclude learning. However, the primate's hand is not used for cue selection in the maze where choices are made with "whole body" orientation and movements. Perhaps this factor (i.e., the ineffective use of the hand for selecting cues) keeps monkeys from exhibiting their full learning abilities in mazes. This line of thought suggests that modification in maze design to permit (or require) the primate to use its hand for selection of certain cues and not others at the points of choice might profoundly enhance its learning and performance.

XIII. Stereotyped Behaviors

Certain human retardates exhibit recurring movement patterns, many of which are highly repetitive and persistent over time (Berkson and Davenport, 1962). R. K. Davenport and Menzel (1963) assessed these kinds of movements (stereotypies) in chimpanzees, some of which were born in captivity and reared under various degrees of environmental restriction and others of which were wild-born and reared under relatively enriched captive environments. Whereas all 16 captive-born and restricted-reared chimpanzees developed stereotypies (one exhibiting a rhythmical activity of the whole body) the wild-born animals developed remarkably few stereotypies (e.g., none of the latter engaged in whole-body rocking or thumb-sucking). But as the authors had no record of stereotypies in captive-born but mother-reared chimpanzees, they concluded that stereotypies of the kind recorded were typical of nursery-reared chimpanzees and that they were not unique to animals raised under conditions of environmental restriction. They attributed the development of stereotypies in the chimpanzee to insufficient stimulation that is ordinarily provided by the mother as she carries and cares for the infant during its early months. The author has observed stereotypies, including thumb-sucking and whole-body rocking while sitting, in a gibbon (*Hylobates lar × moloch*) but not in a gorilla, both of which were born within 1 week's time and nursery-reared at the San Diego Zoo.

Captive-born squirrel monkeys, mother-reared, normally do not exhibit varied and sustained stereotypies. However, recently King (1967) has observed chronic sucking of thumb and genitals and also whole-body stereotyped rocking in two squirrel monkey infants hand-raised from birth. This report suggests that there might be conditions, as yet unexplored, that will bring about in *Saimiri* stereotypies similar to those observed in chimpanzees and children raised in impoverished or restricted conditions. Frequently in our WGTA studies, wild-born squirrel monkeys have been observed to engage in stereotypies. These behaviors typically have been either backward flips or some type of pacing movement, not infrequently including a backward or sideways throwing of the head as the direction of body movement changed. Undoubtedly it is significant that even in normally reared animals stereotypies are the rule, rather than the exception, during the intertrial interval in the WGTA test situation. However, squirrel monkeys, in contrast to chimpanzees, are not given to in-place stereotypies such as body-rocking while sitting or thumb-sucking.

Stereotypies and general spontaneous behavior emitted by different primate forms as they relate to performance levels in test situations are of interest and possible significance. Parker's account (1961) of squirrel monkeys in a WGTA situation indicated that they remained active throughout testing sessions, pacing about in the cage in stereotyped circles between trials. In contrast, spider monkeys either hung from a handhold on the cage side or reclined on a side, reaching up from that position to respond upon trial presentation. In marked contrast to the squirrel and spider monkeys, macaques tended to sit in front of the problem presentation portion of the apparatus and frequently chewed or banged with their hands on the apparatus between trials, some smearing feces with fingers onto the glass screen. It would seem that these behaviors suggest greater problem orientation and aggression as well as frustration on the part of the macaques in contrast to the other monkeys referred to above.

Unfortunately, intertrial behaviors are only infrequently described in various testing situations. How they vary among age levels and between sexes and how they relate to performance levels might be very revealing. Certainly these behaviors are too diverse among primate species to ignore and discount in assessment of learning abilities. Such behaviors might be approached fruitfully as reflections of various levels of arousal, characteristic of the species in certain situations, and studied as Mason (1965) and his associates have studied the social behaviors of captive chimpanzees.

XIV. Sensory Capacities of *Saimiri*

A. COLOR VISION

Color vision, inferred when organisms can discriminate wavelengths independent of their relative intensities, is known to be a relatively atypical characteristic of mammals other than primates. Some mammals, such as the cat, although possessing well-developed lateral geniculate nuclei have,

nonetheless, appeared to be relatively insensitive to color. In the case of
the cat, however, some ability for red — green discriminations has been
demonstrated (Sechzer and Brown, 1964).

De Valois (1965) has discussed at length basic characteristics of the primate visual system, most of his data being obtained from the macaque. It
remains to be seen to what extent the *Saimiri* color vision system coincides
with the macaque's, but probably points of similarity will be far more impressive than ones of dissimilarity.

Klüver (1933) studied not only the capacity of *Saimiri* to choose the
larger of two figures (to obtain reward) but to discriminate color as well.
One of his *Saimiri* subjects tended to prefer the darker of two hues, a preference more recently noted by Green *et al.*, (1966).

It was Miles (1958) who first reported that the squirrel monkey was deficient in ability to discriminate the longer wavelengths (reds) of the spectrum. Cebus monkeys were already known to be deficient in discriminating
reds (Malmo and Grether, 1947) and Miles' studies indicated that *Saimiri*
was by comparison probably even more deficient in this ability. As *Saimiri*
successfully discriminated yellow-green, green, and blue, but not red, it
was suggested that it possessed a two-color visual system of the red-blind
type characteristic not only of the cebus monkey, but the human protano-

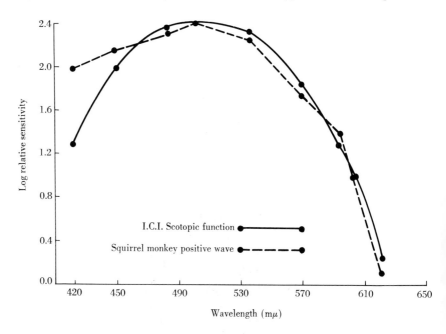

FIG. 14. Spectral sensitivity of the ERG positive wave. (After Jacobs *et al.*, 1963.)

pia. As De Valois (1965) concludes that the macaque's color visual system is probably identical to man's and as Miles assessed *Saimiri* as more deficient than the cebus in capacity to perceive red, it appears that the squirrel monkey has color vision capabilities commensurate with its relatively primitive taxonomic standing among primates.

Jacobs *et al.* (1963) assessed the electroretinograms (ERG) of eight squirrel monkeys in response to both single light pulses and flickering monochromatic light. The spectral sensitivity curve, based on an equal-response criterion (65 μV), corresponded closely with the International Commission on Illumination scotopic function, except at 420 mμ (Fig. 14). Purkinje-shift data were also reported (Fig. 15), clearly indicating a differentiation of the scotopic and photopic components in *Saimiri* ERG.

Jacobs (1963) also reported on the spectral sensitivity and color vision of *Saimiri*, supporting Miles' earlier report of red deficiency and, in addition, a loss of relative sensitivity in long wavelengths for the species. The Pur-

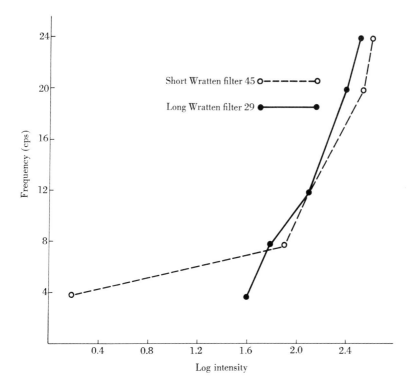

FIG. 15. An ERG demonstration of Purkinje shift. The two curves are equated at 12 cps. (After Jacobs *et al.*, 1963.)

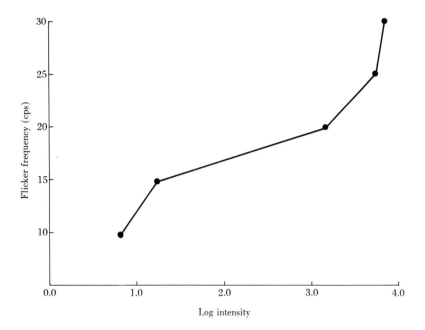

FIG. 16. Flicker thresholds for white light. (After Jacobs, 1963.)

kinje shift was again demonstrated and the critical flicker frequency (CFF) intensity for white light (Fig. 16) closely resembled that previously defined for humans. CFF data obtained through use of two color filters (480 and 630 mμ) indicated retinal duplicity (Fig. 17), the scotopic — photopic crossover points for both determinations being at about the same frequency locus as for humans (15 − 20 cps). Jacobs concluded that trichromatic protanomaly characterized *Saimiri* color vision.

B. Visual Acuity and Discrimination Skills

Woodburne's assessment (1965a) of their visual acuity, by use of the method of minimum separable lines discriminable, placed the squirrel monkey midway between rhesus (0.67) and cebus monkeys (0.95). The *Saimiri* visual angle threshold was established at 0.84 minutes of visual angle (threshold of 75% responses correct in a modified WGTA). A decrease in correct responses in the task of discrimination was associated with increased response latency. Woodburne (1965b) also demonstrated that *Saimiri* ability to differentiate slightly different geometric forms is commensurate with its visual acuity.

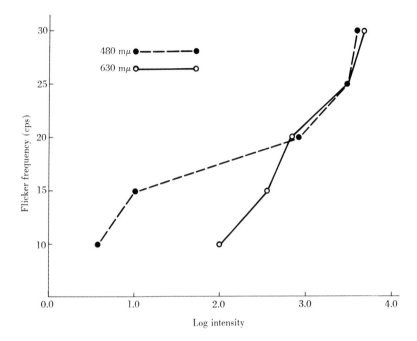

FIG. 17. Flicker thresholds for colored light. The two functions are equated at 25 cps. (After Jacobs, 1963.)

More recently it has been reported by Cowey and Ellis (1967) that *Saimiri* visual acuity threshold is lower than that reported by Woodbourne. Comparisons based on measurements by a modified method of limits indicated that the minimum separable visual acuity of 12 *Saimiri* was about 0.74 minute of arc. Ranked acuity scores of 12 *M. mulatta* were significantly superior to those of *Saimiri*, the visual acuity for the macaques being 0.65 minute of arc. Differences in test methods and amounts of training probably account for the differences in these estimates for *Saimiri*, with the more extensive training given subjects in the Cowey and Ellis study probably permitting definition of the lower threshold. Though *Saimiri* visual acuity appears slightly inferior to that of *M. mulatta*, it was pointed out that because of its smaller eye size, *Saimiri* in fact resolves a finer retinal image than *Macaca*.

Brooks (1966) reported discrimination thresholds, expressed as Weber fractions in relation to the log of background intensity, obtained from three squirrel monkeys in a test situation in which choices of the brighter of two targets were food rewarded. The targets differed in brightness for a period of only 1 second commencing 25 seconds after the initiation of a given trial.

These thresholds (Fig. 18) bear close resemblance to those obtained from rhesus monkeys and humans (Crawford, 1935). Brooks points out that the flattening of the curves at the higher background intensities might reflect the real limit of *Saimiri* discriminative ability, but it is also possible that it simply reflects some artifact of the particular test method employed.

   Saimiri visual discrimination learning skills were studied as affected by contextual variables involving the manner of stimulus presentation (Nash and Michels, 1966). Of the variables studied, the number of shapes (2 to 4) appearing together in each ground, relative position (systematic or random) among shapes, sidedness (either four or six-sided), and redundancy among shapes on the stimulus plates, only the latter proved to have a significant main effect revealed by analysis of variance. High redundancy facilitated learning when there were four shapes in each plate (a first-order interaction) and was effective only when shapes were randomly positioned. The usefulness of *Saimiri* for basic studies of the psychophysics of shape as it interacts with contexts in which there is, for example, a multiplicity of shapes as in nature, was indicated by the success of this study. Psycho-

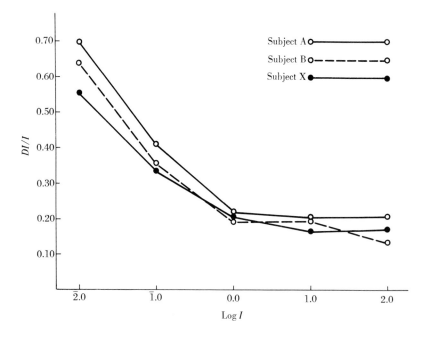

FIG. 18. Discrimination thresholds expressed as the Weber fraction *DI/I*, as a function of log *I* or background intensity. (After Brooks, 1966.)

physical studies of visual discrimination skills, of the kind conducted with sea lions (Schusterman *et al.*, 1965) and with seals (Feinstein and Rice, 1966) are needed for a variety of animals including *Saimiri*. Such data would be helpful in relating such skills to phylogeny.

The effect of maintenance in total darkness was studied with three squirrel monkeys by Manzoni and Riesen (1966). All animals were first trained to grasp a vertically suspended thread so as to receive a small segment of food attached at its end which was kept from view. The threads were of varying sizes, were presented one at a time against a plain white background, and were suspended from any one of a number of points so as to prevent acquisition of response to a specific position. The largest thread was 1/1000 inch and the remaining threads consisted of either one, two, three, four, five, or six strands each having a known diameter of 0.000669 inch. Two such threads intertwined subtended an angle of 1.08 minutes whereas the angle of one thread was 0.46 minute of an arc at 5 inches.

Prior to light privation, all monkeys were trained until they responded 100% to even the smallest thread. Three intervals of light privation were employed, 48 hours, 72 hours, and 7 days. When taken from the darkness each animal was tested within the first minute with the largest thread and successively with each of the smaller threads in the series to determine threshold. In the event that a monkey did not respond to presentation of a thread, the last one successfully responded to was presented once again before testing with the next smaller thread resumed. Testing continued for each subject after each light-privation period until the smallest thread was successfully responded to on each of three successive trials.

Minutes of testing to reach the stated criterion was just short of 1 hour for two monkeys after 48 hours in darkness and the same for all three monkeys after 7 days. Practice effects among successive deprivation experiences were marked, the number of minutes required to criterion being halved even though time of darkness was increased from 48 to 72 hours. Though all animals drank water while light-deprived, food intake was reduced to the point that it presented a problem for long-term dark maintenance. Methods of ensuring daily adequate food intake in monkeys being maintained in darkness should be explored. Liquified nutrients might remedy this problem as drinking appears not to be interfered with as completely as are biting and chewing (see discussion of Parker's studies earlier in this chapter).

More work will be needed to refine assessments of how *Saimiri* visual processes are altered by maintenance in darkness, but Manzoni and Riesen view their initial data as consistent with data procured on human subjects.

C. AUDITION AND VESTIBULAR FUNCTION

Myers and Bernstein (1965), in a study of salicylate ototoxicity, included a curve defining the hearing threshold for a group of 12 squirrel monkeys (Fig. 19). The data were obtained from an avoidance conditioning situation in which movement over a hurdle terminated shock. Prior to shock onset a 4-second tone was sounded; avoidance responses were used to infer whether or not the tone was perceived. Though satisfactory for the purpose of the study from which it came, Fig. 19 should not be interpreted as "the" normative curve for *Saimiri* (and, indeed, Myers and Bernstein did not present it as such). As hearing threshold functions are subject to so many methodological variables and as the data on *Saimiri* hearing is very limited, we must stop short of any conclusion other than the one that its hearing is keen and yields threshold curves of the same shape as other primates. Fujita and Elliott (1965) reported mean audiograms for pairs of squirrel, rhesus, and cynamolgus monkeys as inferred from performances in both punishment and reward training situations. The audiograms indicated comparable threshold values (to 32 K in the reward situation) for all three species, though by reason of there being only two animals per species the audiograms were not reported as constituting normative data.

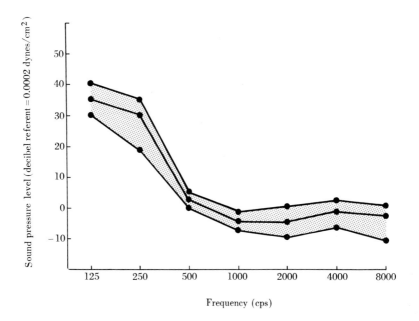

FIG. 19. A threshold of hearing curve for a group of *Saimiri*. (After Myers and Bernstein, 1965.)

D. TASTE

Using four squirrel monkeys, Wagner *et al.* (1965) assessed the pair comparison method for determining glucose preference (5, 10, 20, 30, and 40% solutions). Each monkey was given the choice daily of drinking from a pair of solutions presented simultaneously in graduated cylinders. That consumption curves were greatest at the intermediate concentrations was interpreted as compatible with other curves obtained from more thoroughly tested animals such as the rat. Use of the pair comparison method was recommended as a way of resolving disparate findings of past studies in which amounts consumed or operant indices (such as bar-pressing rates) have been employed.

E. OLFACTION

No studies assessing *Saimiri* olfactory capabilites have been found in a search of the literature through June 1967. Informal observations suggest, however, that *Saimiri* possesses such capability and, furthermore, uses it to identify females in estrous and to select certain preferred nutrients over others.

XV. Discussion

Review of the research findings indicates that *Saimiri* learning and sensory capacities are fundamentally like those that characterize all monkeys and apes. It possesses a well-developed capacity for the learning of complex principles and stratagems, excellent visual acuity and color vision, and auditory sensitivity that spans a broad range of frequencies, some of which are inaudible to man. Behaviorally as well as physically, *Saimiri* is properly included in the order *Primates*.

The most refined estimate of *Saimiri* average capacity for learning-set tasks is that it is grossly superior to that of tree shrews, somewhat superior to those of the tamarins and marmosets, and somewhat inferior to those of the larger ceboids and cercopithecoids. *Saimiri* specimens vary widely in their basic learning-set skills to the extent that if one uses trial 2 performance as the criterion, equivalent training conditions will net essentially perfect and efficient performance on the part of few (better than 90% correct — as good as the best macaques and apes) and equally impressive *im*-perfect and *in*efficient performance on the part of others (to the extent that they remain learning-set*less*). In view of Schrier's conclusion, " . . . that, at most, only small differences in asymptotic learning-set can be expected among the cercopithecoid monkeys" (1967, p. 309) it seems unlikely that

Saimiri racial differences (Chapter 1) in learning ability will be marked, if even extant.

Saimiri capacity for delayed-response tasks appears to be in keeping with its taxonomic classification, i.e., superior to Callithricidae and inferior to the larger ceboids and cercopithecoids. It appears possible, however, that *Saimiri* delayed-response capacity is relatively *more* restricted than its learning-set capacity. If this impression is a correct one, it suggests that within the order Primates the capacity for learning complex tasks evolved *prior* to the capacity that makes it possible for the organism to take in cue information (as in the delayed-response task) and to store it for appropriate use at a later date. With the exception of man, all primates appear particularly restricted in their ability to formulate responses appropriate to information perceived at an earlier point in time. In this regard, man's capacity appears infinitely superior to that of all other primates.

Saimiri visual acuity and color vision appear to be commensurate with those of the family Callithricidae, which, in turn, quite closely approximate *Macaca*, of subfamily Cercopithecinae, and the apes (and man) of the superfamily, Hominoidea. Not enough is known of the visual systems of other primate groups to make appropriate comment. The *Saimiri* visual system is, then, remarkably developed and advanced, its relatively minor deficiency in the reds providing an interesting challenge to those who might wish to determine what, if any, adaptation value might be provided thereby.

Its visual discriminations appear to be particularly sensitive to disruption by irrelevant cues. The author suggests that perhaps the peculiar head turning and twisting, particularly characteristic of young *Saimiri* as they visually inspect novel objects or views, might accommodate some perceptual process that filters the varied cues of the visual field so as to enhance figure — ground definitions.

Touch cues appear to provide little or nothing to discrimination learning when conventional stereometric objects comprise the problem pairs, those objects providing an abundance of visual cues which are used to establish the discriminations. Yet *Saimiri* does appear to have certain tactual preferences and aversions, but the parameters of these are not known. In the final analysis, except for vision, little is known about *Saimiri* sensory characteristics and capacities.

Saimiri operant conditioning characteristics are, in general, neither remarkable nor distinct from those of other primate and nonprimate forms. Only in reference to its hypersensitivity to punishment and to the effects of avoidance conditioning schedules does *Saimiri* operant behavior suggest qualitative distinction from rat and pigeon. It is probably more capable than the rat and pigeon (and other nonprimates) when mastery of a complex schedule chain is the criterion, mastery being indicated by response rates being appropriate not only to the schedule of the moment but also to the sequence of schedules in the chain (Segal, 1967).

Evidence is contradictory on the issue of motivation as its strength affects *Saimiri* performance accuracy and readiness to work in a training situation. It is common practice, however, to envoke food privation schedules when *Saimiri* responses are to be selectively reinforced with food incentive. It is suggested that *Saimiri* finds little by way of intrinsic reward in the kinds of activities afforded by most experimental tasks and situations. *Saimiri* gives the researcher little reason to conclude, for example, that it responds to the WGTA training situation as either intrinsically positive or negative, a point of possible contrast with other primates such as macaques, apes, and man.

Saimiri is neither an efficient learner of string-type problems nor a spontaneous user of tools. Inferior even to many nonprimates in this regard, it seems to lack all skills germane to the calculation of relationships between functional elements of mechanical-type problems even though it does have capacity for mastery of the complex oddity principle. So limited are these skills that it is only rarely necessary, for example, to lock transfer cage or home cage doors. Even when locking is necessary, a simple twist of a small wire will imprison *Saimiri* indefinitely though the wire is readily accessible for manipulation. With macaques and apes quite the opposite is the case, laboratory and zoo maintenance procedures entailing rather sophisticated procedures to foil escape.

In summary, as is the case with every other primate form, *Saimiri* provides a unique profile of learning and sensory capacities. Though none of its known capacities are qualitatively unique from each and every other primate form, the composite of quantitative differences presented by *Saimiri* defines a primate form which is unique and, in many respects, remarkable. As is true for primates in general, when compared to man, *Saimiri* sensory capacities appear to be more highly developed than its cognitive or learning capacities. If in some defensible manner it were possible to calibrate cognitive and perceptual capacities in terms of physical weight of the organism so as to obtain an efficiency quotient, *Saimiri* would, no doubt, have the most favorable quotient of all primates, including man. Its small size and light weight provide for a wealth of learning and perceptual skills essentially minimal in nonprimates yet characteristic of all other primates commonly viewed as "more highly evolved" than *Saimiri*. It is in this light a remarkably efficient biological system. Probably for this reason, more than any other, it has come to be a preferred primate for research and domestic enjoyment.

As stated at the beginning of this chapter, it is only within rather generous limits that the behavioral capacities of *Saimiri* can be assessed phyletically at this point. Research of the future will surely lead to the re-evaluation of most, if not all, the data that have been used in the current undertaking, for it seems probably that as researchers become more knowledgable and their studies more technically adequate and appropriate, with a primate form as efficient as *Saimiri,* dramatic new levels of behavioral capacity will be uncovered. It seems probable that when numbers of *Saimiri* infants become available for group studies to assess effects of early environments and rearing conditions upon such behaviors as curiosity, attention, emotionality, learning, and retention, considerable surprise will be in store. It is suspected that there will be a progressive upgrading of estimates regarding *Saimiri* capacities, for that has characterized the past few years of research as revealed in the literature. As breeding colonies of *Saimiri* become stabilized, selective breeding programs based on behavioral parameters will become possible, and with them, in turn, the horizons of research on *Saimiri* ultimate behavioral *potentials* will become infinitely broadened.

ACKNOWLEDGMENTS

Studies conducted by the author and his students were supported by grants from the National Science Foundation and facilitated by the cooperation extended by the Zoological Society of San Diego, the Institute for Comparative Biology, and the San Diego State College Foundation. The assistance of Gerald Steinmetz, Sylvia Triska, Joyce Nease, and my wife, Phyl, in completion of this manuscript is gratefully acknowledged. The sustained interest and critical comments of my friend, Prof. Maurice P. Smith, expressed frequently throughout the writing of this chapter were both helpful and deeply appreciated. Finally, the early impetus given by Robert B. Voas to my studies of *Saimiri* is acknowledged with particular pleasure, for it brought both new interests and varied experience to my research.

REFERENCES

Abordo, E. J., and Rumbaugh, D. M. (1965). Response-contingent learning-set training in the squirrel monkey. *Psychol. Rept.* **16,** 797-802.
Appel, J. B. (1961). Punishment in the squirrel monkey. *Science* **133,** 36.
Beach, F. (1960). Experimental investigations of species-specific behavior. *Am. Psychologist* **15,** 1-18.
Behar, I. (1961). Analysis of object-alternation learning in rhesus monkeys. *J. Comp. Physiol. Psychol.* **54,** 539-542.
Berkson, G., and Davenport, R. K., Jr. (1962). Stereotyped movements of mental defectives. I. Initial survey. *Am. J. Mental Deficiency* **66,** 849-852.
Bitterman, M. E. (1965). Phyletic differences in learning. *Am. Psychologist* **20,** 396-410.
Blakeslee, P., and Gunter, R. (1966). Cross-modal transfer of discrimination learning in cebus monkeys. *Behaviour* **26,** 76-90.
Breland, K., and Breland, M. (1961). The misbehavior of organisms. *Am. Psychologist* **16,** 681-684.
Brooks, B. A. (1966). Neurophysiological correlates of brightness discrimination in the lateral geniculate nucleus of the squirrel monkey. *Exptl. Brain Res.* **2,** 1-17.
Cha, J. A., and King, J. E. (1969). The learning of patterned strings problems by squirrel monkeys. *Animal Behaviour* (in press).

Cowey, A., and Ellis, C. M. (1967). Visual acuity of rhesus and squirrel monkeys. *J. Comp. Physiol. Psychol.* **64**, 80-84.

Crawford, M. P. (1935). Brightness discrimination in the rhesus monkey. *Genet. Psychol. Monographs* **17**, No. 2, 71-162.

Dalrymple, S. D., and Stretch, R. (1966). Disruption of a position-reversal learning set in the rat. *Quart. J. Exptl. Psychol.* **18**, 250-253.

Davenport, J. W. (1966). Studies of Y-maze discrimination learning: A comparative study of rats, squirrel monkeys, and rhesus monkeys. Unpublished study, University of Wisconsin, Madison, Wisconsin.

Davenport, R. K., Jr., and Menzel, E. W., Jr. (1963). Stereotyped behavior of the infant chimpanzee. *Arch. Gen. Psychiat.* **8**, 99-104.

De Valois, R. L. (1965). Analysis and coding of color vision in the primate visual system. (Reprinted from *Cold Spring Harbor Sympo. Quant. Biol.* **30**, 567-579.) Indiana University, Bloomington, Indiana.

Dews, P. B. (1965). The effect of multiple S$^\Delta$ periods on responding on a fixed interval schedule. II. In a primate. *J. Exptl. Anal. Behavior* **8**, 53-54.

Feinstein, S. H., and Rice, C. E. (1966). Discrimination of area differences by the harbor seal. *Psychon. Sci.* **4**, 379-380.

Finch, G. (1941). The solution of patterned string problems by chimpanzees. *J. Comp. Psychol.* **32**, 83-90.

Fletcher, H. J. (1965). The delayed-response problem. In "Behavior of Nonhuman Primates" (A. M. Schrier, H. F. Harlow, and F. Stollnitz, eds.), Vol. 1, pp. 129-165. Academic Press, New York.

French, G. M. (1959). Performance of squirrel monkeys on variants of delayed response. *J. Comp. Physiol. Psychol.* **52**, 741-745.

Fujita, S., and Elliott, D. N. (1965). Thresholds of audition for three species of monkey. *J. Acoust. Soc. Am.* **37**, 139-144.

Glickman, S. E., and Sroges, R. W. (1966). Curiosity in zoo animals. *Behaviour* **26**, 151-188.

Gossette, R. L., and Inman, N. (1966). Comparison of spatial successive discrimination reversal performances of two groups of new world monkeys. *Perceptual Motor Skills* **23**, 169-170.

Green, K. F., and Moore, J. W. (1966). Conditional-outcome choice behavior in squirrel monkeys. *Psychon. Sci.* **4**, 369-370.

Green, K. F., Moore, J. W., and Sargent, T. D. (1966). Color preference in squirrel monkeys *(Saimiri sciureus). Psychon. Sci.* **4**, 367-368.

Harlow, H. F. (1949). The formation of learning sets. *Psychol. Rev.* **56**, 51-65.

Harlow, H. F. (1959a). The development of learning in the rhesus monkey. *Am. Scientist* **47**, 459-479.

Harlow, H. F. (1959b). Learning set and error factor theory. In "Psychology: A Study of a Science" (S. Koch, ed.), Vol. 2, pp. 492-537. McGraw-Hill, New York.

Harlow, H. F., and Settlage, P. H. (1934). Comparative behavior of primates. VII. Capacity of monkeys to solve patterned strings tests. *J. Comp. Psychol.* **18**, 423-435.

Harlow, H. F., Harlow, M. K., and Meyer, D. R. (1950). Learning motivated by a manipulation drive. *J. Exptl. Psychol.* **40**, 228-234.

Hebb, D. O. (1946). On the nature of fear. *Psychol. Rev.* **53**, 259-276.

Jacobs, G. H. (1963). Spectral sensitivity and color vision of the squirrel monkey. *J. Comp. Physiol. Psychol.* **56**, 616-621.

Jacobs, G. H., Jones, A. E., and De Valois, R. L. (1963). Electroretinogram of the squirrel monkey. *J. Comp. Physiol. Psychol.* **56**, 405-409.

Jolly, A. (1964a). Prosimians' manipulation of simple object problems. *Animal Behaviour* **12**, 560-570.

Jolly, A. (1964b). Choice of cue in prosimian learning. *Animal Behaviour* **12**, 571-577.

Kay, H., and Oldfield-Box, H. (1965). A study of learning-set in rats with an apparatus using 3-dimensional shapes. *Animal Behaviour* **13**, 19-24.

Kelleher, R. T. (1965). Operant conditioning. *In* "Behavior of Nonhuman Primates" (A. M. Schrier, H. F. Harlow, and F. Stollnitz, eds.), Vol. 1, pp. 211-247. Academic Press, New York.

Kelleher, R. T., and Cook, L. (1959). An analysis of the behavior of rats and monkeys on concurrent fixed-ratio avoidance schedules. *J. Exptl. Anal. Behavior* **2**, 203-211.

Kelleher, R. T., Gill, C. A., Riddle, W. C., and Cook, L. (1963). On the use of the squirrel monkey in behavioral and pharmacological experiments. *J. Exptl. Anal. Behavior* **6**, 249-252.

King, J. E. (1965). Discrimination and reversal learning in the rock squirrel. *Perceptual Motor Skills* **20**, 271-276.

King, J. E. (1967). Personal communication.

King, J. E., and Clawson, J. A. (1966). Delayed response by squirrel monkeys under various delay lighting conditions. *Psychon. Sci.*, **6**, 429-430.

King, J. E., Flaningam, M. R., and Rees, W. W. (1968). Delayed response with different delay conditions by squirrel monkeys and fox squirrels. *Animal Behaviour* (in press).

King J. E., and Goodman, R. R. (1966). Successive and concurrent discrimination by rock squirrels and squirrel monkeys. *Perceptual Motor Skills* **23**, 703-710.

King, J. E., and Witt, E. D. (1966). The learning of patterned strings problems by rock squirrels. *Psychon. Sci.* **4**, 319-320.

Klüver, H. (1933). "Behavior Mechanisms in Monkeys." Univ. of Chicago Press, Chicago, Illinois.

Köhler, W. (1925). "The Mentality of Apes." Routledge & Kegan Paul, London.

Leonard, C., Schneider, G. E., and Gross, C. G. (1966). Performance on learning set and delayed-response tasks by tree shrews *(Tupaia glis)*. *J. Comp. Physiol. Psychol.* **62**, 501-504.

Levine, M., Levinson, B., and Harlow, H. F. (1959). Trials per problem as a variable in the acquisition of discrimination learning set. *J. Comp. Physiol. Psychol.* **52**, 396-398.

Logan, F. A. (1962). Conditional-outcome choice behavior in rats. *Psychol. Rev.* **69**, 467-476.

Mahan, J. L., and Rumbaugh, D. M. (1963). Observational learning in the squirrel monkey. *Perceptual Motor Skills* **17**, 686.

Malmo, R. B., and Grether, W. F. (1947). Further evidence of red blindness (protanopia) in cebus monkeys. *J. Comp. Physiol. Psychol.* **40**, 143-147.

Manzoni, R. S., and Riesen, A. H. (1966). Effects of short-term visual deprivation on visual acuity of the squirrel monkey. Unpublished study, University of California at Riverside.

Martin, M. (1966). Unpublished project.

Mason, W. A. (1965). Determinants of social behavior in young chimpanzees. *In* "Behavior of Nonhuman Primates" (A. M. Schrier, H. F. Harlow, and F. Stollnitz, eds.), Vol. 2, pp. 335-364. Academic Press, New York.

Menzel, E. W., Jr. (1964). Patterns of responsiveness in chimpanzees reared through infancy under conditions of environment restriction. *Psychol. Forsch.* **27**, 337-365.

Meyer, D. R. (1951). Food deprivation and discrimination reversal learning of monkeys. *J. Exptl. Psychol.* **41**, 10-16.

Miles, R. C. (1957). Learning-set formation in the squirrel monkey. *J. Comp. Physiol. Psychol.* **50**, 356-357.

Miles, R. C. (1958). Color vision in the squirrel monkey. *J. Comp. Physiol. Psychol.* **51**, 328-331.

Miles, R. C. (1959). Discrimination in the squirrel monkey as a function of deprivation and problem difficulty. *J. Exptl. Psychol.* **57**, 15-19.

Miles, R. C. (1965). Discrimination-learning sets. *In* "Behavior of Nonhuman Primates" (A. M. Schrier, H. F. Harlow, and F. Stollnitz, eds.), Vol. 1, pp. 51-95. Academic Press, New York.

Miles, R. C. (1967). Personal communication.

Miles, R. C., and Meyer, D. R. (1956). Learning sets in marmosets. *J. Comp. Physiol. Psychol.* **49**, 219-222.

Myers, E. N., and Bernstein, J. M. (1965). Salicylate ototoxicity. *Arch. Otolaryngol.* **82**, 483-493.

Nash, A. J., and Michels, K. M. (1966). Squirrel monkeys and discrimination learning: Figural interactions, redundancies, and random shapes. *J. Exptl. Psychol.* **72**, 132-137.

Parker, C. E. (1961). Trials per problem and species as learning-set formation variables in primates. Unpublished Master's Thesis, San Diego State College, California.

Parker, C. E. (1966). Total darkness as an aversive stimulus condition for the squirrel monkey. *Psychon. Sci.* **6**, 111-112.

Peterson, M. E., and Rumbaugh, D. M. (1963). Role of object-contact cues in learning set formation in squirrel monkeys. *Perceptual Motor Skills* **16**, 3-9.

Polidora, V. J. (1964). Learning abilities of New World monkeys. *Am. J. Phys. Anthropol.* [N.S.] **22**, 245-252.

Polidora, V. J., and Boyer, W. N. (1967). Avoidance learning by squirrel monkeys: Measures and motivators. *Psychon. Sci.* **7**, 175-176.

Pournelle, M. B., and Rumbaugh, D. M. (1965). A modified Wisconsin General Test Apparatus for use with a variety of small primates. *Perceptual Motor Skills* **21**, 489-490.

Pournelle, M. B., and Rumbaugh, D. M. (1966). A comparative study of learning in the squirrel monkey, the golden marmoset, and cotton-topped tamarin. Paper read at the *Southeastern Psychol. Assoc., New Orleans 1966.*

Rajalakshmi, R., and Jeeves, M. A. (1965). The relative difficulty of reversal learning (reversal index) as a basis of behavioral comparisons. *Animal Behaviour* **13**, 203-211.

Ratner, S. C., and Denny, M. R. (1964). "Comparative Psychology: Research in Animal Behavior." Dorsey Press, Homewood, Illinois.

Reese, H. W. (1963). Discrimination learning set in children. *In* "Advances in Child Development and Behavior" (L. P. Lipsitt, and C. C. Spiker, eds.), Vol. 1, pp. 115-145. Academic Press, New York.

Reynolds, R. W. (1964). Reaction time as a function of fixed vs. variable fore-period in the squirrel monkey. *Psychon. Sci.* **1**, 31-32.

Riesen, A. H., Greenberg, B., Granston, A. H., and Fantz, R. L. (1953). Solutions of patterned strings problems by young gorillas. *J. Comp. Physiol. Psychol.* **46**, 19-22.

Riopelle, A. J. (1960). Complex processes. *In* "Principles of Comparative Psychology" (R. H. Waters, D. A. Rethlingshafer, and W. E. Caldwell, eds.), pp. 208-249. McGraw-Hill, New York.

Rollin, A. R., Shepp, B. E., and Thaller, K. E. (1963). A modified Wisconsin General Test Apparatus for the rat. *Am. J. Psychol.* **76**, 500-502.

Rumbaugh, D. M., and Ensminger, L. W. (1964). Discrimination reversal training with single and multiple stimulus pairs in the squirrel monkey. *J. Comp. Physiol. Psychol.* **57**, 304-306.

Rumbaugh, D. M., and Jeeves, M. A. (1966). A comparison of two discrimination-reversal indices intended for use with diverse groups of organisms. *Psychon. Sci.* **6**, 1-2.

Rumbaugh, D. M., and McCormack, C. (1967). The learning skills of primates: A comparative study of apes and monkeys. *In* "Progress in Primatology" (D. Starck, R. Schneider, and H.-J. Kuhn, eds.), pp. 289-306. G. Fischer, Stuttgart.

Rumbaugh, D. M., and McQueeney, J. A. (1963). Learning set formation and discrimination reversal: Learning problems to criterion in the squirrel monkey. *J. Comp. Physiol. Psychol.* **56**, 435-439.

Rumbaugh, D. M., and Pournelle, M. B. (1966). Discrimination-reversal skills of primates: The reversal/acquisition ratio as a function of phyletic standing. *Psychon. Sci.* **4**, 45-46.

Rumbaugh, D. M., and Prim, M. M. (1963). A comparison of learning-set training methods and discrimination reversal training methods with the squirrel monkey. *Am. Psychologist* **17**, 408. (Abstr.).

Rumbaugh, D. M., and Prim, M. M. (1964). Temporary interference of insolvable discrimination reversal training upon learning set in the squirrel monkey. *J. Comp. Physiol. Psychol.* **57**, 302-304.

Rumbaugh, D. M., and Rice, C. (1962). Learning-set formation in young great apes. *J. Comp. Physiol. Psychol.* **55**, 866-868.

Rumbaugh, D. M., Sammons, M. E., Prim, M. M., and Phillips, S. (1965a). Learning set in squirrel monkeys as affected by pretraining with differentially rewarded single objects. *Perceptual Motor Skills* **21**, 63-70.

Rumbaugh, D. M., Ternes, J. W., and Abordo, E. J. (1965b). Learning set in squirrel monkeys as affected by encasement of problem objects in plexiglas bins. *Perceptual Motor Skills* **21**, 531-534.

Schrier, A. M. (1967) Learning-set formation by three species of macaque monkeys. *In* "Progress in Primatology" (D. Starck, R. Schneider, and H.-J. Kuhn, eds.), pp. 307-309. G. Fischer, Stuttgart.

Schrier, A. M., Harlow, H. F., and Stollnitz, F., (1965). "Behavior of Nonhuman Primates," Vols. 1 and 2. Academic Press, New York.

Schusterman, R. J. (1962). Transfer effects of successive discrimination-reversal training in chimpanzees. *Science* **137**, 422-423.

Schusterman, R. J., Kellogg, W. N., and Rice, C. E. (1965). Underwater visual discrimination by the California sea lion. *Science* **147**, 1594-1596.

Sechzer, J. A., and Brown, J. L. (1964). Color discrimination in the cat. *Science* **144**, 427-429.

Segal, E. F. (1964). A serial conditioned reinforcement effect in a multiple-chain schedule in a squirrel monkey. *Psychon. Sci.* **1**, 175-176.

Segal, E. F. (1967). Personal communication.

Segal, E. F., and Rumbaugh, D. M. (1964). Timing behavior in squirrel monkeys as a function of positive vs. negative reinforcement. *Psychon. Sci.* **1**, 371-372.

Shell, W. F., and Riopelle, A. J. (1958). Progressive discrimination learning in platyrrhine monkeys. *J. Comp. Physiol. Psychol.* **51**, 467-470.

Shuck, J. R. (1960). Pattern discrimination and visual sampling by the monkey. *J. Comp. Physiol. Psychol.* **53**, 251-255.

Sterritt, G. M., Goodenough, E., and Harlow, H. F. (1963). Learning set development: Trials to criterion vs. six trials per problem. *Psychol. Rept.* **13**, 267-271.

Stevens, D. A. (1964). Learning-set formation in Burmese cats: Fixed-trial and criterional training methods compared. Paper read at the *Western Psychol. Assoc., Portland, Oregon 1964.*

Strong, P. N. (1965). Learning and transfer of oddity as a function of apparatus and trials per problem. *Psychon. Sci.* **3**, 19-20.

Ternes, J. W., Abordo, E. J., and Rumbaugh, D. M. (1965). Effect of criterional learning-set training where problem objects are encased in Plexiglas bins. *Perceptual Motor Skills* **21**, 544-546.

Treichler, R. F. (1964). Delayed response performance by the squirrel monkey. *Psychon. Sci.* **1**, 129-130.

Wagner, M. W., Green, K. F., and Manley, M. B. (1965). Paired comparison method for measurement of sugar preference in squirrel monkeys. *Science* **148**, 1473-1474.

Warren, J. M. (1965). Comparative psychology. *Ann. Rev. Psychol.* **16**, 95-118.

Weir, M. W. (1965). Children's behavior in a two-choice task as a function of patterned reinforcement following forced-choice trials. *J. Exptl. Child Psychol.* **2**, 85-91.

Wilson, M. (1965). Tactual discrimination learning in monkeys. *Neuropsychologia* **3**, 353-361.

Wolin, L. R., Ordy, J. M., and Dillman, A. (1963). Monkey's fear of snakes: A study of its basis and generality. *J. Genet. Psychol.* **103**, 207-226.

Woodburne, L. S. (1965a). Visual acuity of *Saimiri sciureus*. *Psychon. Sci.* **3**, 307-308.

Woodburne, L. S. (1965b). Geometrical shape discrimination by *Saimiri sciureus*. *Psychon. Sci.* **3**, 309-310.

Zimmerman, R. R., and Torrey, C. C. (1965). Ontogeny of learning. *In* "Behavior of Nonhuman Primates" (A. M. Schrier, H. F. Harlow, and F. Stollnitz, eds.), Vol. 2, pp. 405-447. Academic Press, New York.

CHAPTER **11**

Brain Mechanisms in the Behavior of the Squirrel Monkey

Lawrence R. Pinneo

I. Introduction

The squirrel monkey is rapidly replacing the cat as the most widely used species for the study of mammalian brain function. There are several good reasons for this. Since it is a primate, its brain structure and function (and the resulting behavior) more closely resemble man's than do the cat's. Yet, like the cat it is small and tractable and is inexpensive to buy and maintain. Furthermore, special instruments and techniques developed over the years for brain research on the cat can be used with relatively little modification on the squirrel monkey. In these days of high research costs, especially in regard to primates, this feature has become a very practical consideration for the small laboratory.

Unfortunately, very little research has been carried out on the squirrel monkey just to find out about the brain of the squirrel monkey. Although the animal is widely used for brain/behavior studies, most of the investigations might as well have been carried out on other species. As a consequence, not too much can be said here of the unique properties of the squirrel monkey brain in relation to behavior. Therefore this chapter will be limited to: (1) a description of the characteristic features of the squirrel monkey brain and special methods for studying it in relation to behavior; (2) a brief review of some of the major studies relating brain activity to certain aspects of behavior; and (3) a description of a new approach to the study of brain mechanisms in behavior developed on and for use with squirrel monkeys.

II. Characteristic Features of the Squirrel Monkey Brain

According to some investigators the singular advantage of using the squirrel monkey in brain/behavior research is the size and weight of its brain relative to its body. This is predicated upon the assumption that intelligence is related to the ratio of brain weight to body weight. There are many arguments that make this assumption tenuous at best, and some evidence to suggest that "intelligence" — whatever that may be — is in proportion to the ratio of the weight of the brain to the weight of the spinal cord in the same animal (Krompecher and Lipak, 1966). Nevertheless, whenever brain/behavior experiments require a primate, the squirrel monkey is an obvious choice because while its brain is about the size and weight of the cat's, its body size and weight are less than one-fourth those of the cat, at least suggesting that the squirrel monkey is the brighter animal.

Figure 1 illustrates various aspects of the squirrel monkey brain and indicates major landmarks and cortical areas. Most distinctive is the smoothness of the cortical surface ("semilissencephalic"), showing few invaginations relative to the cat, as well as to other primates. This feature is especially valuable for cortical microelectrode studies since it is often desirable, even necessary, to introduce the electrode as nearly perpendicular to the surface as possible. Subcortical features of the squirrel monkey brain may be found in one or the other of two elegant stereotaxic atlases showing the structures in stereotaxic coordinates (Gergen and MacLean, 1962; Emmers and Akert, 1963). It is of definite advantage for an investigator to own both of these atlases since there are some major differences between them that are complementary. In particular, the Emmers and Akert atlas illustrates the position of the brain relative to the skull and identifies gross features, while the Gergen and MacLean atlas illustrates the brain in longitudinal sections as well as cross section.

Table I gives some representative body and brain measurements (Carmichael and MacLean, 1961); also see Beischer and Furry (1964).

Of the few studies that have been concerned with the squirrel monkey brain per se, the most extensive have dealt with cortical representation. A

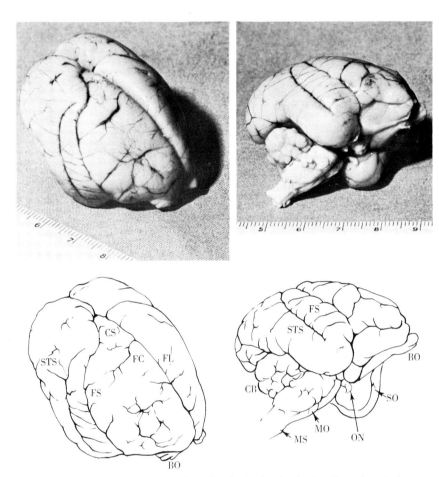

FIG. 1. Two aspects of the squirrel monkey brain showing landmarks and cortical areas. Key: CS, central sulcus; FS, Sylvian fissure; STS, superior temporal sulcus; FC, central fissure; FL, longitudinal fissure; BO, olfactory bulb; Cb, cerebellum; MS, medulla spinallis; MO, medulla oblongata; ON, optic nerve; and SO, orbital sulcus.

series of reports from the Laboratory of Neurophysiology of the University of Wisconsin present detailed maps of the somatic afferent areas I and II, the cortical projections of dorsal roots and sensory nerves, and the "motor" areas for somatic musculature. These maps are extremely useful for investigations of brain/behavior mechanisms involving these systems.

Benjamin and Welker (1957) report that representation in somatic sensory area I (Fig. 2) is similar to that of the macaque monkey. They point out that the most striking change in phylogenetic development of this area from rat to primate is the relative and absolute increase in amount of cortex concerned with distal portions of arms and legs, and a distortion of cerebral localization patterns of these parts associated with phylogenetic develop-

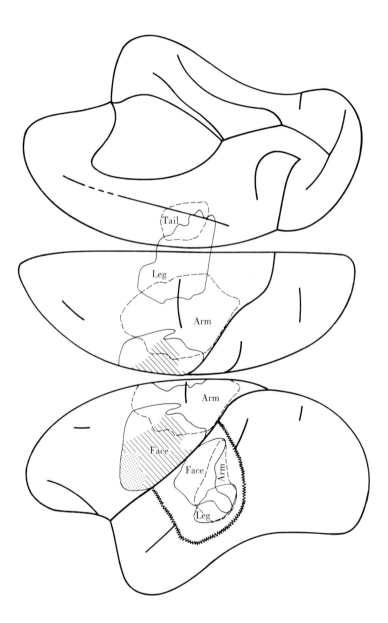

FIG. 2. Diagram of somatic sensory areas revealed by somatic stimulation and cortical evoked responses, with bilateral (hatching) and ipsilateral (black) representation. (After Benjamin and Welker, 1957.)

TABLE I

SOME REPRESENTATIVE BODY AND
BRAIN MEASUREMENTS OF THE SQUIRREL MONKEY[a]

Measurement	Number of animals	Mean	Standard deviation
Weight	76	717 gm	±170.4
Body length	49	26 cm	±2.47
Tail length	50	36 cm	±2.14
Total length	48	63 cm	±3.57
Head length	45	5.4 cm	±0.22
Head width	45	4.1 cm	±0.36
Brain weight	21	26 gm	±1.72
Brain length	29	4.9 cm	±0.21
Brain width	30	3.5 cm	±0.71

[a] After Carmichael and MacLean, 1961.

ment of the brain. Of particular advantage to the biobehavioral investigator is the fact that the map of somatic area II obtained by these authors is more complete than anything available for most other primates. In somatic areas I and II similar somatotopic organization, or specialization, was found, with the largest area in both devoted to the arm. Since some areas of the cortex responding to somatic stimuli actually lie outside of areas I and II shown in Fig. 2, a complete map of the somatosensory cortex which includes the effects of dorsal root and sensory nerve stimulation is given in Fig. 3. One major difference between these results and those illustrated in Fig. 2 is that the leg area is somewhat larger (Blomquist and Lorenzini, 1965).

A similar map of the cortical organization of muscular control is shown in Fig. 4 (Welker *et al.*, 1957). On the basis of topographical organization, threshold current to direct cortical stimulation, and cytoarchitectural criteria, four cortical areas were found to be involved in movement of the skeletal musculature. Body movement representation was found in both the pre- and postcentral gyri, where the topographical pattern between the two is a mirror image (see Fig. 4). In addition to the pre- and postcentral motor areas, a supplementary motor area was found with higher thresholds to stimulation and without facial representation. This area lies rostral and medial to the precentral motor region. The fourth area, the so-called "secondary" motor area coincides with the secondary somatic area for the squirrel monkey (labeled Sm II in Fig. 3). The details of organization of these motor patterns are described as paralleling those found in other primates.

Several other studies have been concerned with cortical and subcortical representation to which the reader is referred. The visual system has been

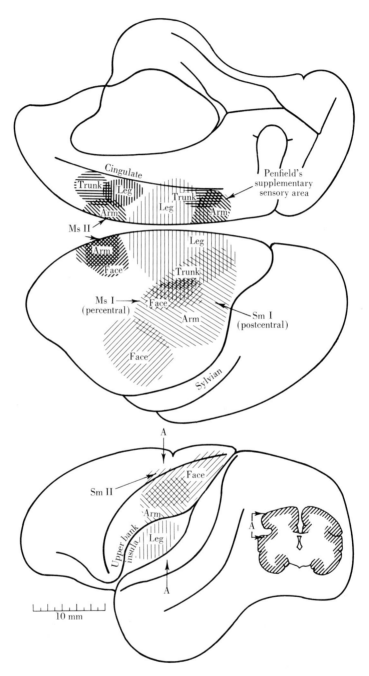

FIG. 3. Diagram of squirrel monkey somatic sensory areas as projections of dorsal roots and sensory nerves. (After Blomquist and Lorenzini, 1965.)

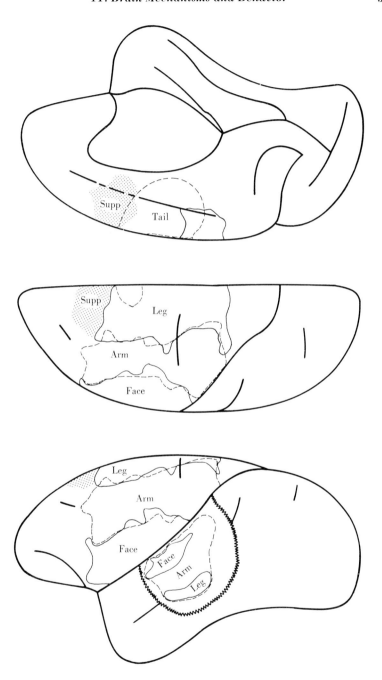

FIG. 4. Diagram of the squirrel monkey cortical motor representation as a result of direct stimulation. (After Welker *et al.*, 1957.)

explored for several species of primates, including the squirrel monkey, by Hassler (1966), and anatomical details of the squirrel monkey lateral geniculate nucleus have been described by Doty *et al.* (1966). Hast and Milojevic (1966) have found the cortical motor area for the vocal folds (thyroarytenoid muscle) important for studies involving vocalizations. In the auditory system Goldberg and Moore (1967) studied the ascending connections of the lateral leminiscus through the inferior colliculus and the projections upon the thalamus, while Hind *et al.* (1958) mapped the auditory cortex and Benjamin and Emmers (1960) determined cortical responses to stimulation of the chorda tympani. Moskowitz (1965) has made a comparative study of central auditory nuclei between the squirrel monkey, the slow loris, and the elephant shrew. Blomquist *et al.* (1962) mapped the thalamic areas related to afferents from the tongue, while interconnections between the fornix and hippocampus have been described by DeVito and White (1966). Of additional anatomical interest, and especially for comparative neurology, Creswell *et al.* (1964) have shown that aldehyde—fuchsinpositive neurons in the squirrel monkey brain are closely associated with phylogenetically old cellular structures and fiber systems of the brain. Also see Rosabal (1967), Shende and King (1967), and Yokota *et al.* (1967).

III. Techniques for Neurophysiological and Chronic Brain/Behavior Studies

A. Normal Vital Signs

Normal physiological values for the squirrel monkey, important from the point of view of a viable animal during surgery or studies involving autonomic nervous system activity, have been published by Beischer and Furry (1964); some values obtained from restrained squirrel monkeys are reproduced in Table II and are within the range obtained in this author's laboratory by telemetry from unrestrained animals. In working with squirrel monkeys, expecially when they are restrained, it is not unusual to see elevations of body temperature to 40°C, heart rate to 360—410 beats per minute, and respiration rate to 160 inspiration/expirations per minute.

B. Tranquilizers and Anesthetics

Squirrel monkeys on the whole are relatively docile animals. Like most animals, however, they do not particularly care to be restrained and if at all possible in our chronic work we leave them free to move in a testing cage or compound. On the occasions when we must restrain them, we attempt to make the initial few experiences as nontraumatic as possible. Three meth-

TABLE II
PHYSIOLOGICAL DATA OF RESTRAINED SQUIRREL MONKEY[a]

Sex	Body weight (grams)	No. of measurements	Body temperature (axillary) (°C)		Respiratory rate		Heart rate	
			Mean	Range	Mean	Range	Mean	Range
F	324	22	36.7	35.9–38.0	66	55–110	276	260–360
M	375	19	43.4	36.1–39.7	78	64–112	292	250–330
M	498	25	43.3	36.4–39.3	54	40–92	242	180–300
F	368	23	37.1	36.4–37.8	63	50–80	230	180–300
F	490	21	37.2	36.3–38.1	67	60–80	290	270–320
F	332	20	36.4	35.8–37.3	72	60–84	264	230–310
F	339	17	39.3	38.4–40.4	106	76–160	242	220–300
F	376	22	37.4	36.5–39.0	61	50–88	243	200–290
F	495	24	38.3	36.1–39.2	76	64–84	245	220–280
M	349	25	36.8	35.1–39.1	51	40–60	185	140–260

[a] After Beischer and Furry, 1964.

ods work particularly well. For situations in which monkeys must be placed in a chair several times a day for an hour or so, most of the stress and difficulty of the first few days is avoided by administering an anesthetic dose of nitrous oxide just prior to placing the animal in the chair. This is done in a small airtight wooden "gas box" with a plastic window for observation. The induction takes about $1\frac{1}{2}$ minutes, after which the animal is removed from the box and locked in the restraining chair within the 30 to 40 seconds it takes for complete recovery. Animals so treated are much calmer for the subsequent testing than monkeys not so treated, show none of the fluctuations of vital signs indicated in Table II, and generally show no ill effects. Once animals are habituated to the testing situation, especially if the task itself is rewarding, no special procedures are required for placing them in the chair.

For experiments requiring restraint of over an hour, small intramuscular injections of the tranquilizer Tranvet (Diamond Laboratories) are used. A dosage of about $0.1-0.2$ mg per kilogram of body weight per hour is sufficient for most procedures and can be used safely for many days in succession. We have not observed any untoward effects upon either learning or discrimination ability in these monkeys; in fact, the tranquilization, if not too deep, usually results in better performance, apparently because the stress of restraint is removed. The reader is warned *not* to use the tranquilizer Inovar-Vet (McNeil Laboratories) on squirrel monkeys; though it is considered by us to be the tranquilizer of choice for rhesus monkeys, in the experience of the author even very small doses invariably killed squirrel monkeys.

The third method for "easy" restraint is more tedious for the investigator, but has the advantage of not using drugs or anesthetics. This involves leash-training the animal to leave its home cage voluntarily to climb into the chair himself in order to be fed. This technique takes anywhere from 2 days to 2 months to accomplish.

Our anesthetic techniques with squirrel monkeys have passed through several periods of success and frustration. For long procedures a tranquilizer such as Largon (Wyeth Laboratories) or Tranvet in a dosage of about 0.3 mg per kilogram body weight given intraperitoneally (i.p.), is followed by 20 mg per kilogram of Nembutal (Abbott Laboratories) also i.p. It is usually wise to add about 0.2 ml of 0.2% atropine to prevent excess fluid development in the mouth, trachea, and lungs. Though this combination is generally satisfactory, surgery is often followed by a prolonged period of depression. This period can be reduced by using 15 mg per kilogram of Seconal (Eli Lilly and Company) instead of Nembutal for the barbiturate. In both cases, however, it is wise to intubate the animal (if a sufficiently small endotracheal tube can be found, such as a no. 2 French) and have immediately available a respirator with full oxygen supply and a nembulizer with a bronchial dilator solution such as Micronefrin (Bird Corporation) and sterile water.

Since intubation may be required, another solution to the anesthesia problem is the use of a gas anesthetic with a wide margin of safety. This also allows the surgeon to control very closely the depth of anesthesia, and the animal is usually awake within minutes following surgery. To intubate the animal we premedicate with Tranvet and induce a light anesthesia with Penthrane (Abbott Laboratories) using only a few drops on a gauze-covered nose cone. After intubation, the monkey is then changed to Flouthane (Ayerst Laboratories) using a small-animal anesthetic apparatus. Intubation and short operative procedures such as repairing minor wounds around implanted electrodes may also be done efficiently on the squirrel monkey with a short-acting barbiturate such as Brevane (Corvel Laboratories) given intravenously, or phencyclidine hydrochloride (Sernylan, Parke, Davis & Company) given intramuscularly.

C. Surgical Procedures and Special Techniques

Every investigator undoubtedly has his own preferred surgical procedures, so very little detail will be given here. Some of the implantation methods we have used, however, may be of interest to those readers using squirrel monkeys the first time and will be described briefly.

After our monkeys are anesthetized, intubated, and placed on the stereotaxic instrument, we find it useful to routinely monitor heart rate on an oscilloscope and an audio amplifier and speaker. This is needed when implanting electrodes in the brain stem (see Section V), for it is very easy to accidentally place an electrode into cardiac centers where the mechanical stimulation of the electrode presence is sufficient to stop the heart. If the electrode is left in place for over 60 seconds, the animal will probably die, though no lasting damage appears if it is withdrawn immediately.

Electrode implants are done by one of two methods, depending upon the particular experiment. In one type, after the skin and scalp muscles are reflected, holes just large enough for passage of electrodes are made with a stereotaxic drill press. If multiple electrodes are required for the same hole, a commercially available* stainless steel array is used; these are constructed of no. 316 wire, 0.003 inch in diameter, with quad Teflon-coated leads and six contacts 2 mm apart. Each set of electrodes is fixed to the skull with a small amount of self-curing dental plastic (Formatray, Kerr Manufacturing Company). When all electrodes have been implanted, the plug to which they are connected is also cemented to the skull; reinforced

---

*Mr. Henry Schryver, Developmental Design, 110 West Packard Avenue, Fort Wayne, Indiana.

attachment of the plastic to the skull is made by three stainless steel "Pop-it" rivets using the method described by Roth (1966); rivets are preferred to screws if the animal is to be used for over a year. The skin wound is closed around the cap by silk suture or wound clips. Excess skin is removed by electrosurgery and cautery; this procedure enables the skin to adhere to the underlying periosteum and so closes the wound against infection.

The second type of implant is the chronic method described for the squirrel monkey by MacLean (1967). In this technique a predrilled platform is attached to the skull under anesthesia. After the monkey has recovered, the skin under any desired hole can be locally anesthetized, a small hole drilled in the skull, and macro- or microelectrodes lowered to the required depth in the fully awake or tranquilized monkey. This method is particularly useful to reduce the trauma of surgery; it eliminates the need for open surgery at the time of an experiment; it allows for a considerable number and variety of stereotaxic coordinates; and the electrodes may be kept in place for long periods of time or removed after one experiment. Of course the greatest advantage is that various depths of the brain can be explored in a given stereotaxic locus in an awake animal. In addition, local chemical stimulation may be carried out with the platform device (MacLean and Delgado, 1953).

Various other special techniques have been devised for brain/behavior research in the squirrel monkey, including a restraining chair (Carmichael and MacLean, 1961), cryosurgery (Cutt *et al.*, 1965), and radiotelemetry systems for remote brain stimulation (Upson *et al.*, 1962), among others.

IV. Brain Mechanisms and Behavior

It was pointed out in the introduction to this chapter that not too much can be said of the unique properties of the squirrel monkey brain in relation to behavior since very little work has been concerned with the squirrel monkey in contrast to other species. Nevertheless, the squirrel monkey is a primate, its cerebral cortex has many of the properties peculiar to primates, and its behavior in many respects is much like man's. Consequently, while the experiments discussed below are by no means exhaustive, they do illustrate the wide variety of investigations that are being or could be done to elucidate brain mechanisms in the behavior of the squirrel monkey.

A. Sensory-Perceptual Mechanisms

Undoubtedly, the most widely studied sensory process of the squirrel monkey in relation to his brain is his vision. One of the more important papers (Brooks, 1966) not only describes the brightness discrimination

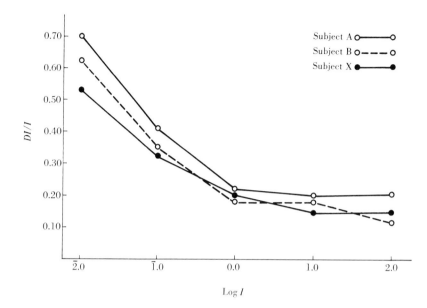

FIG. 5. Brightness discrimination, or Weber, function of the squirrel monkey, where DI/I versus I is the just noticeable difference in flash intensity (DI) necessary to perceive the flash against a background luminance (I) as that luminance is varied over a factor of 10,000 times. (After Brooks, 1966.)

curve, or Weber function, for the squirrel monkey, but also for the first time directly relates this to neural activity in the primary visual pathway. Three squirrel monkeys, with electrodes chronically implanted in the lateral geniculate nucleus, were trained to displace one of two targets if a threshold-intensity light flash DI was perceived upon the steady intensity of background illumination I of the targets. The background intensity I was varied over a range of four logarithmic units, or a factor of 10,000. Figure 5 illustrates the Weber function for the three squirrel monkeys, where the ratio of a threshold light flash intensity to its background illumination DI/I is plotted as a function of background illumination I. This curve is quite similar to that obtained psychophysically from human subjects.

Electrophysiologically, Brooks averaged the instantaneous overall activity of the geniculate as a function of the level of background illumination and the intensity of the test flash. As background illumination increased, the neural activity decreased as a power function of the intensity of the light. Figure 6 shows the change in the overall, or tonic, activity of the geniculate with background illumination, plotted in logarithmic coordinates. Of major significance is the fact that the form of the function in Fig. 6 for the geniculate change parallels very closely the human brightness discrimina-

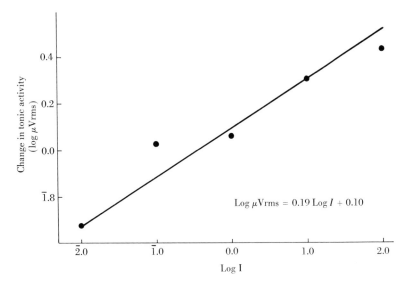

FIG. 6. Change in the level of overall, or tonic, activity in the lateral geniculate nucleus of the squirrel monkey as a function of background illumination. The actual change was a decrease in activity that was larger with larger background illumination. From this curve of neural activity alone the Weber function of Fig. 5 can be predicted. (After Brooks, 1966.)

tion function as described by Stevens (1962). Brooks also found that the light flash *DI* produced an increase in the geniculate activity but that the increase was reduced by the depressive effect of increased background illumination in the same proportion that the perception of the flash was depressed (Fig. 5). These results strongly suggest that the interaction of tonic and transient, or phasic, activity of the primary visual pathway is the neural basis for brightness vision.

Several investigations have been concerned with acute recordings from sensory systems of squirrel monkeys. Bignall and Singer (1967) have mapped cortical evoked responses in the squirrel monkey to photic, auditory, and somatic stimulation, in both classic primary sensory areas and other areas outside the primary cortex. Jacobs (1964) has made single-unit recordings from the lateral geniculate nucleus in response to different wavelengths and intensities, while Wolin *et al.* (1966) made recordings with gross electrodes from the superior colliculus in response to color. Cuenod *et al.* (1965), Casey *et al.* (1965), and Gergen and MacLean (1964) have investigated unit recordings in the limbic system of the squirrel monkey in response to photic stimulation to show that the visual modality probably plays a direct and significant role in emotional behavior and the regulation of neuroendocrine functions. Other important sensory functions were studied in an experiment by Casey (1966) on the response of single units of thalamic nuclei to noxious stimulation of the body.

B. LEARNING AND BEHAVIORAL DEFICITS

The advantage of the squirrel monkey in brain/behavior research is clearly seen in learning studies in which unit analysis from the nervous system is required. Travis and Sparks (1967) report a study in which discharge patterns of units in the extrapyramidal motor system vary with the conditioning procedures. An adult monkey was semirestrained in a chair and performed relatively complicated behavioral discriminations while microelectrodes explored various regions of the brain. In this procedure the squirrel monkey was the experimental animal of choice because of its size, learning capacity, and primate brain. These advantages are reflected in the importance of the data obtained, for probably in no other way could it be shown that single units play such an important part in learning. For example, Travis and Sparks found that certain cells respond differentially to two stimuli, suggesting that these convey information about the nature of a conditioned stimulus. On the other hand, certain other cells responded with complex graded discharge patterns which presumably are concerned with anticipating the time of reinforcement. Such data would not be obtained from the cat as easily.

A similar advantage in using squirrel monkeys is seen in learning experiments in which direct stimulation of the brain is used to modify conditioned responses. Pecci-Saavedra *et al.* (1965) trained squirrel monkeys to respond to bilateral stimulation of the nucleus centrum medianum to avoid cutaneous shocks. They were interested in whether or not recruiting responses in a primate would adversely affect learning or learned behavior, since literature on cats and dogs had suggested that recruiting interfered with learning. Their results showed that even though large recruiting responses appeared in the dorsal neocortex anterior to the central sulcus, including the sensorimotor cortical area representing the arm used to make the conditioned response, there was no interference with learning or behavior.

Much of the literature on brain mechanisms in learning is concerned with the effects of cortical ablation, such as the effects of frontal lobe lesions on delayed response, learning sets, discrimination learning, and the like. Reports of frontal lobe deficits in squirrel monkeys, such as by Miles and Blomquist (1960), again suggest the utility of the squirrel monkey for brain/behavior research. Among other things, they trained squirrel monkeys on delayed response and discrimination before and following removal of frontal granular cortex on the lateral surfaces of both hemispheres, and on learning sets following surgery only. All subjects receiving delayed response training showed marked deficits following frontal removal, whereas discrimination was unaffected. In contrast with their delayed response performance, the monkeys with frontal ablations showed no deficiency in developing learning sets.

C. SEXUAL BEHAVIOR AND EMOTION

Of the work carried out on brain mechanisms in the behavior of the squirrel monkey, perhaps none is as new, exciting, and of as great practical importance in an overpopulated world as the work on sexual function in the brain by MacLean and his co-workers at the National Institutes of Health. Their work is too extensive to review here, and the reader is referred to various publications for details (in particular, MacLean and Ploog, 1962; Dua and MacLean, 1964; MacLean, 1966; but also see Maurus *et al.*, 1965; Hendley, 1966). Their work is important because prior to their investigations there was little direct evidence that sexual functions were represented in the brain above the level of the hypothalamus. They showed that such diverse areas as the septum, anterior hypothalamus, dorsal thalamus, and the mamillo-thalamic tract were involved in penile erection alone. This is strong evidence that higher nervous structures may influence gonadal functions through their interaction with the hypothalamus, and further shows how somatic impulses reach the hypothalamus. This is critical to an analysis of emotional behavior, since stimulation of the areas investigated results in additional behavior changes such as vocalization, urination, and cardiac changes, as well as gonadal responses.

V. BRAINS: A New Approach to the Study of Brain Mechanisms in Behavior

BRAINS is an acronym for "Behavior Replication by Analog Instruction of the Nervous System." It is descriptive of a new method developed in the author's laboratory for analysis of brain function in the behavior of the squirrel monkey (it is useful for other species too). The method was devised to provide a more direct, rapid, and accurate examination of brain function than afforded by the classic or other contemporary approaches described in preceding sections of this chapter.

The principle is simple in concept: (1) electrodes are chronically implanted in selected areas of the brain; (2) electrical stimulation of any *one* electrode elicits some elementary response, such as the flexion of an arm at the elbow, or a slight increase in heart rate, or a momentary change in the neural activity mediating a primary sense modality; and (3) stimulation of two or more of the implanted electrodes in a programmed sequence produces a series of responses that are analogous to a similar series of responses carried out, or experienced, by the animal in his normal repertoire of behavior. The power of this approach is that if behavior is indeed replicated by programmed stimulation of the brain, and if the behavior is an analog function of the stimulation, then how the brain normally mediates the replicated behavior is implicit in an analysis of the brain sites involved and the parameters of stimulation.

A. PROGRAMMED STIMULATION AND PURPOSIVE MOVEMENT

A brief description of some of our research on the control of purposive movement over the past 3 years will illustrate the method; details have been published elsewhere (Pinneo, 1966a,b). Many studies have shown that electrical stimulation of the brain can produce skeletal motor activity. For example, movements of the head, foreleg, hind quarters, and muscles of the face have been elicited by stimulation of diencephalic structures (Hess, 1949). Other movements, including "normal" progressions of behavior in time and space such as attack, avoidance, sitting, standing, preening, seeking and eating of food, have been initiated by stimulation of the brain stem and red nucleus (Delgado, 1965; von Holst and von St. Paul, 1960, 1962). The difficulties with these experiments for determining brain mechanisms in purposive movement are three. (1) A given group of muscles is used in a variety of ways in normal behavior, but stimulation as in the studies cited above did not allow for any variability in behavior using the same electrodes. (2) Histology of the brain sites involved in these movements has not revealed separate centers for the representation of specific functions, making exact replication very difficult. (3) The type and complexity of the movements depended too much upon antecedent conditions, such as whether the animal was asleep or awake, or reclining versus erect.

What was needed was a set of discrete brain centers which, whenever stimulated, always resulted in relatively simple movements, and the same movements each time the sites were stimulated. Experiments by Brodal *et al.* (1962), Pompeiano (1959), and others (Dow and Moruzzi, 1958) on decerebrate rigidity suggested a clue. They showed that electrical stimulation of cerebellar nuclei, vestibular nuclei, and other nuclei of the caudal brain stem in the cat produced elementary movements such as flexion or extension of a paw, foreleg, or hip. The movements were quite discrete, in many instances the loci for stimulation were somatotopically organized, and stimulation at a given locus always produced the same movement.

Our procedure was in three steps. The first was to closely observe naturally occurring behavior of squirrel monkeys freely living in a compound. Motion pictures were taken of simple motor acts of juveniles and adults, singly and together, involved in eating, grooming, locomotion, and the more complex motor acts involved in play, aggressive behavior, and responses to novel stimuli. By use of a motion picture film analyzer, details of the elementary movements and patterns of movements in purposive behavior were then worked out (see Deutsch, 1966, for details of the same method on rhesus monkeys).

The second step was to carry out extensive brain mapping studies using barbiturate-anesthetized squirrel monkeys to produce elementary movements. A single concentric stainless steel electrode was stereotaxically placed at all possible positions between the mesencephalic reticular formation and the rostral end of the spinal cord (to about C2), with the exception of the cerebral and cerebellar cortices. Major nuclei of interest included the interpositus, fastigial, and dentate of the cerebellum, and the superior, medial, lateral, and inferior vestibular nuclei, as well as other brain stem nuclei. Almost countless locations were found in which elementary movements could be produced, including: flexion and extension of all four limbs at the wrist, elbow, shoulder, ankle, knee, or hip; clenching and spreading of the fingers; opening and closing of the mouth; movements of the tongue in and out; curling or sideways movement of the tail; movements of the eyes, singly and together, and dilatation of the pupils; various forms of vocalization; and finally, control of heart rate and the rate and volume of respiration.

In all cases it was found that the extent and complexity of movement was directly related to current strength. Threshold current, or the lowest current that produced the maximum movement in one elementary response, was 200 to 300 rectangular pulses per second, $0.1-1.0$ msec pulse duration, $50-200$ μA base-to-peak, monophasic with the active electrode negative. Each threshold site was very specific, since if the electrode was moved as little as 100 μ the elicited response ceased. It could be re-elicited either by an increase in current or by repositioning of the electrode at the former site. At any given locus, an increase in current significantly above threshold produced more than one elementary response. This was presumably due to spread of current to adjacent sites, since movement of the electrode up, down, or laterally, produced each movement separately at low current values. Upon completion of mapping in a particular animal, the brain was perfused and normal histological control carried out to determine the loci of stimulation.

The final step was to combine the results of the free behavior studies and the brain mapping experiments to directly control behavior in an awake animal by programmed electrical stimulation of the brain. Under barbiturate anesthesia and sterile surgery, up to 30 electrodes were chronically implanted in the cerebellar nuclei and selected nuclei of the brain stem of each of 20 squirrel monkeys. Final position of each electrode was chosen by the effects of stimulation while the electrode was lowered. When all electrodes were placed they, and the electrical connector to which they were attached, were cemented to the skull, the skin wound closed, and tests again made with the electrodes. (See Fig. 7).

Two to 4 weeks following the implant, programmed stimulation of the implanted electrodes was begun in awake animals in a primate chair. It was found that a wide variety of behaviors could be initiated and controlled using only relatively few electrodes. For example, with six electrodes and a particular program of stimulation, we have had a squirrel monkey reach out to a dish in front of him, pick up a piece of food, and bring it rapidly and smoothly to his mouth (Fig. 8). Using exactly the same electrodes, but a different program, the monkey was made to reach up as though climbing a cage. With still another program but the same electrodes, upon programmed stimulation he reached back and scratched the base of his tail. And so on through seemingly endless variations.

To insure that it was our stimulation of the cerebellar and brain stem nuclei alone that was producing the movements, and that voluntary acts or sensory inputs to the animal were not entering into the results, we deliberately destroyed the left motor cortex for the voluntary control of the right

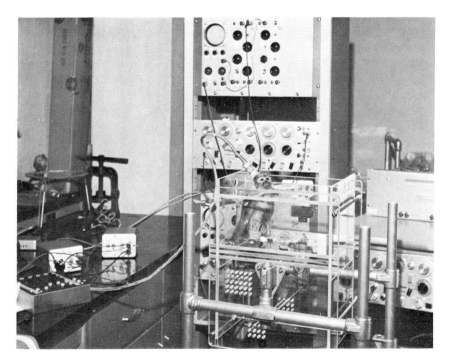

FIG. 7. A squirrel monkey with 30 chronically implanted electrodes in a primate chair being tested 1 month after surgery. Stimulating and programming apparatus are in the background.

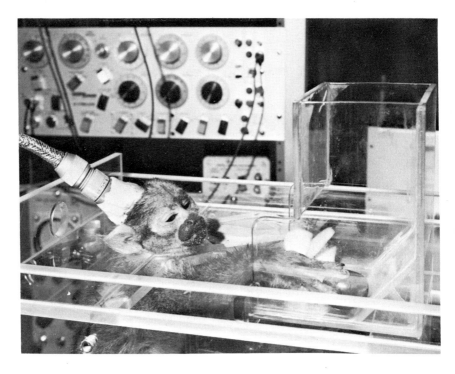

FIG. 8. The same monkey shown in Fig. 7 with programmed stimulation causing him to reach for a piece of apple with his right hand. This could be accomplished, and the food brought to his mouth with further programmed stimulation, even when his right arm was paralyzed to voluntary movement by an "experimental stroke."

arm and hand of this monkey. Of course this produced paralysis in that limb just as a cerebral stroke does in man. Yet, with both single electrode and programmed stimulation, the same movements and sequence of movements (that did not differ in any way from those elicited prior to monoplegia) were produced after the lesion.

This "artificial stroke" experiment sharply points to the fact that the BRAINS technique can be used for more than studies on brain function. Since the level of integrative organization of the elementary responses elicited in these studies is at the level of the caudal brain stem and spinal cord (Pinneo, 1966b), it may well be possible in the future to similarly stimulate the brains of human beings afflicted with paralysis from cerebral strokes, or to control Parkinsonism, epilepsy, and other diseases of the nervous system in order to restore "normal" motor function and voluntary control of purposive movement.

B. Control of Sleep, Arousal, and Attention

Early in our research with chronic animals it became evident that level of arousal was critical if we were to be able to observe what electrical stimulation in a single electrode could accomplish. Though the programmed stimulation pre-empted and over-rode other forms of motor activity in the limbs involved, the stimulated movement was nevertheless in constant competition with other motor acts, sometimes severely so. Furthermore, differences in response to stimulation often were associated with changes in level of arousal, orienting response, and attention to stimuli not involved in the purposive movement we were attempting to replicate. And, of course, level of arousal is well known to be important in various aspects of normal behavior (Alexander, 1965; Hebb, 1955; Lindsley, 1951; Malmo, 1959).

A large part of our effort, therefore, was spent in attempting to produce *any* level of arousal and control it for any length of time, from deep sleep to convulsive states. This was accomplished by mapping studies, as with the motor experiments described above, and chronic implantation, and testing. To produce sleep, electrodes were implanted in the preoptic nucleus (Clemente and Sterman, 1963; Hernandez-Peon and Ibarra, 1963), the nucleus reticularis, the inferior thalamus (Hess, 1954; Parmeggiani, 1964), and the caudate nucleus (Parmeggiani, 1964). The most consistent locus for producing arousal was the mesencephalic reticular formation (Moruzzi and Magoun, 1949).

To date it has been relatively simple to produce arousal with reticular formation stimulation in the chronic squirrel monkey, including awakening of an animal from a light barbiturate anesthesia. Sleep has been more difficult to produce and often is confused (in stimulating effects) with what best can be termed "behavioral arrest." The latter state is decidedly different from sleep in that the animal, though awake, simply does not respond to any stimulus. Nevertheless, both behavioral arrest and what appeared to be "true" sleep were elicited from several squirrel monkeys, and when produced in conjunction with stimulated arousal allowed behavior to be subtly balanced and maintained from deep sleep through drowsiness, alertness, to excitement. Thus, by finely counterbalancing current in sleep-producing and arousal-producing electrodes simultaneously, states of attention, arousal, tranquilization, and even orienting responses can be placed under the close control of the experimenter in order to evaluate the effects of arousal on other functions of the nervous system such as sensation, perception, and learning.

One very important and rather exciting result of control of arousal is that in chronic animals some stimulation-elicited motor responses actually

changed with level of arousal. For example, stimulation at a particular locus in one monkey under either electrical or chemical tranquilization produced pupillary dilitation, head turning, and poststimulus vocalization.
However, stimulation at the same location and with the same electrical
parameters, but without tranquilization, produced a distinct movement of
raising the right arm and scratching the chest. This phenomena has only
occurred in roughly 40% of the electrodes producing motor movement; in
all others the *same* movement appeared when awake as when tranquilized
except with a lowered stimulus threshold. The implication of this result is
that the loci stimulated in the critical 40% do not have direct outputs to the
lower motor centers as might be supposed for the other 60%. Rather, movements associated with the 40% apparently involve multisynaptic pathways
in higher centers, and this synaptic organization is actually modified with
changes in level of arousal.

C. CONTROL OF SENSATION, PERCEPTION, AND LEARNING

If the BRAINS technique is to be successful in the study of brain mechanisms in behavior, it must be capable of eliciting and producing aspects of
behavior other than skeletal motor activity and changes in level of arousal,
such as sensation, perception, and learning. Our first attempts in this
direction have only recently begun, yet enough progress has been made to
suggest that the programmed stimulation method will be successful. The
approach is the same as that used in the motor and arousal experiments:
stimulation of critical brain areas in such a way that the nervous tissue acts
as it would under "normal" stimulation.

Several studies over the past decade have provided strong evidence that
the neural basis of sensation is the interaction of tonic and phasic activity
of neurons in the primary sensory pathway (Pinneo, 1966a). In the visual
system, for example, tonic activity alone is recorded in the optic nerve and
lateral geniculate nucleus under conditions of maintained illumination of
the retina (Arduini and Pinneo, 1961, 1962, 1963). Brooks (1966) has shown
that this tonic activity in the squirrel monkey is modulated by phasic responses to transient light, and that the monkey's brightness discrimination
function can be described accurately by the interaction of phasic and tonic
activity in the lateral geniculate nucleus (see Section IV). Perception of
flicker, fusion, brightness enhancement, and the Talbot brightness associated with intermittent light stimulation of the retina also have been
shown to depend directly upon the interaction of phasic and tonic activity
(Pinneo and Heath, 1967).

Our approach to replicating brightness vision was to control the level of
tonic and phasic activity in the optic nerve by programmed stimulation. In
this case polarizing negative currents were introduced at the level of the

optic chiasm and the lateral geniculate nucleus to control tonic activity. Using a range of 0.5 — 2.0 mA, tonic activity could be increased (simulating "less bright") or decreased (simulating "more bright") depending upon the amount of current employed; that is, lower currents produced decreases in tonic activity while higher currents were followed by increases. Phasic responses of any magnitude could then be superimposed in any pattern upon the existing tonic level by sequential single shocks through a second electrode in the optic nerve. Thus, the activity of the primary visual pathway in response to steady and transient illumination of the retina was replicated by programmed stimulation.

We do not yet know whether the effects of programmed stimulation actually result in "brightness vision," or whether similar effects can be obtained in other sensory modalities. To determine this, we are presently implanting squirrel monkeys with chronic electrodes in the visual pathways. Later they will be placed in dark chambers and given a "brightness discrimination" task to perform, in which "brightness" will be produced only by programmed stimulation. Following this procedure the monkeys will be tested in an actual light discrimination situation. If the previous programmed stimulation of the visual pathway truly replicates the actual sensory-perceptual experience of "brightness," then the monkey should make fewer errors than the controls. If it does not, then the programmed stimulation will be modified in progressive steps until such discriminations do take place.

Our "learning" studies are proceeding along three lines. The first is to evaluate the role of reinforcement, or rather the lack of reinforcement in the usual sense. A chronically implanted squirrel monkey is placed in a discrimination learning situation requiring some form of instrumental response by the animal, such as displacement of one or two "targets" by the right hand. When the discriminitive stimuli are presented, the monkey is caused to make the correct displacement by programmed stimulation of the brain so that he never makes an error. There is no deprivation of food, water, or other basic need, and no other "reward" is given for the correct response. Our task is then to determine whether under usual instrumental conditioning procedures treated subjects take significantly fewer trials to form this discriminative response than animals not previously subject to programmed stimulation.

The other two lines of our investigations into the learning process involve attempts to establish unique responses not ordinarily present in the animal's behavior. In one case, stimulation of two areas in the brain stem are paired in the classical conditioning paradigm: one area upon being stimulated never results in overt motor activity (the CS), while the other area when stimulated always results in motor activity (the UCS). Our question is: will the "neutral" brain area, after many pairings of the CS with the

UCS, take on the properties of the "positive" brain area so that stimulation of the neutral area now results in the overt motor response associated with the UCS? In the second case, motor activity not normal to the animal but still producible by programmed stimulation is used as an instrumental response by the monkey to a discriminative stimulus (both with and without the usual reinforcement). The question is: once the programmed stimulation is removed, will the monkey continue using this abnormal-to-him form of responding to the discriminative stimuli? This last line of investigation also lends itself to developmental studies in which young monkeys may be "taught" behaviors that are not characteristic of the species.

D. Control of Physiological Homeostasis, Emotion, and Social Interaction

It is well known that the "state of the organism" is the substrate for all behavior, normal and abnormal, rational and emotional, personal and social. Not only are disease states reflected by changes in visceral function but so is any reaction to stress whether physiological or psychological. Furthermore, there is convincing evidence to suggest that changes in physiological homeostasis in reaction to stress also modify behavior, as in affective states. Finally, of all the physiological reactions of the body those primarily concerned in visceral function are the most sensitive to changes in body chemistry and to drugs.

Analysis of the nervous control of autonomic function suggests that similar mechanisms operate in visceral activity as in skeletal motor and sensory activities. That is, the organization of control is largely through discrete functional systems within the brain. Electrical stimulation within these systems exerts gross and fine adjustments of heart rate and cardiac output, respiration rate and volume, gastric motility, glandular secretion, pupillary dilatation and contraction, and the like. Such autonomic activity should be as subject to control by programmed stimulation as is sensory and motor activity.

To date we have carried out only a few experiments on the control of physiological homeostasis and emotion but the results are encouraging. For example, in the brain stem of the squirrel monkey we have found two loci that upon electrical stimulation either increased or decreased heart rate. Programmed stimulation of one site and then the other resulted in a variation of heart rate from as low as 80 beats per minute to as high as 420 beats per minute. By appropriate use of sensing electrodes, cardiotachometers, comparators, and programmed stimulation of these sites, it should be possible to keep the heart rate at any level and to stay within prescribed limits, even under stressful situations that would ordinarily cause large variations.

Other visceral organ activity, including glandular secretion, may be controlled in the same way. For example, by stimulation of various sites in the squirrel monkey brain (MacLean, 1966; see Section IV,C), we have produced penile erection and ejaculation. Similarly, ovulation by the female may be produced indirectly by posterior hypothalamic stimulation. Evidently, if programmed stimulation of appropriate skeletal muscles is combined with production of genital function in a male and female, then it should be possible to replicate the complete sexual act from approach, through presentation, intromission, ejaculation, and ovulation.

Of course more complicated affective mechanisms and their effects upon social situations also can be studied with the BRAINS technique. Using the telestimulation method devised by Delgado (1964), we are producing various forms of attack, avoidance, and threat behavior of squirrel monkeys living together in a compound, whereby docile animals can be made dominant and vice versa. Simple and complex facial expressions, and movements of the head, limbs, or tail, which are of great social significance in primate behavior (Hinde and Rowell, 1962), can be produced by programmed stimulation of the brain under various social situations in order to evaluate their relative strengths in social organizations or disorganization. Dominance hierarchies may be modified, or even completely reversed, by making hostile animals docile, or by "calming" frightened and intimidated monkeys. Thus, BRAINS affords a very powerful technique for the study of brain mechanisms in behavior from the most simple to the most complex.

ACKNOWLEDGMENTS

Much of this work was carried out while the author was on the faculty of the Delta Regional Primate Research Center, Tulane University, and was supported by grants FR-00164 and NB-04951 from the National Institutes of Health, U.S. Public Health Service, and Contracts Nonr-475 (11) and N00014-68-C-0184 from the Office of Naval Research. The author thanks Miss Patricia O'Neil for valuable assistance in the preparation of this chapter.

REFERENCES

Alexander, M. F. (1965). Arousal effects on activity and response time in the squirrel monkey (*Saimiri sciureus*). *Dissertation Abstr.* **26**, 1769-1770.
Arduini, A., and Pinneo, L. R. (1961). Attività nel nervo ottico e nel genicolato laterale nell'oscurita 'e durante l'illuminazione continua. *Boll. Soc. Ital. Biol. Sper.* **37**, 430-432.
Arduini, A., and Pinneo, L. R. (1962). Properties of the retina in response to steady illumination. *Arch. Ital. Biol.* **100**, 425-448.
Arduini, A., and Pinneo, L. R. (1963). The tonic activity of the lateral geniculate nucleus in dark and light adaptation. *Arch. Ital. Biol.* **101**, 493-507.

Beischer, D. E., and Furry, D. E. (1964). *Saimiri sciureus* as an experimental animal. *Anat. Record* **148,** 615-624.

Benjamin, R. M., and Emmers, R. (1960). Localization of separate cortical areas for taste and tactile tongue afferents in squirrel monkey (*Saimiri sciureus*). *Federation Proc.* **19,** 291.

Benjamin, R. M., and Welker, W. I. (1957). Somatic receiving areas of cerebral cortex of squirrel monkey (*Saimiri sciureus*). *J. Neurophysiol.* **20,** 286-299.

Bignall, K. E., and Singer, P. (1967). Auditory, somatic and visual input to association and motor cortex of the squirrel monkey. *Exp. H. Neurol.* **18,** 300-312.

Blomquist, A. J., and Lorenzini, C. A. (1965). Projection of dorsal roots and sensory nerves to cortical sensory motor regions of squirrel monkey. *J. Neurophysiol.* **28,** 1195-1205.

Blomquist, A. J., Benjamin, R. M., and Emmers, R. (1962). Thalamic localization of afferents from the tongue in squirrel monkey (*Saimiri sciureus*). *J. Comp. Neurol.* **118,** 77-88.

Brodal, A., Pompeiano, O., and Walberg, F. (1962). "The Vestibular Nuclei and their Connections, Anatomy and Functional Correlation." Oliver & Boyd, Edinburgh and London.

Brooks, B. A. (1966). Neurophysiological correlates of brightness discrimination in the lateral geniculate of the squirrel monkey. *Exptl. Brain Res.* **2,** 1-17.

Carmichael, M., and MacLean, P. D. (1961). Use of squirrel monkey for brain research, with description of restraining chair. *Electroencephalog. Clin. Neurophysiol.* **13,** 128-129.

Casey, K. L. (1966). Unit analysis of nociceptive mechanisms in the thalamus of the awake squirrel monkey. *J. Neurophysiol.* **29,** 727-750.

Casey, K. L., Cuenod, M., and MacLean, P. D. (1965). Unit analysis of visual input to posterior limbic cortex. II. Intracerebral stimuli. *J. Neurophysiol.* **28,** 1118-1131.

Clemente, C. D., and Sterman, M. B. (1963). Cortical synchronization and sleep patterns in acute restrained and chronic behaving cats induced by basal forebrain stimulation. *Electroencephalog. Clin. Neurophysiol.* Suppl. **24,** 172-187.

Creswell, G. F., Reis, D. J., and MacLean, P. D. (1964). Aldehydefuchsin positive material in brain of squirrel monkey *(Saimiri sciureus). Am. J. Anat.* **115,** 543-549.

Cuenod, M., Casey, K. L., and MacLean, P. D. (1965). Unit analysis of visual input to posterior limbic cortex. I. Photic stimulation. *J. Neurophysiol.* **28,** 1101-1117.

Cutt, R. A., Wolfson, R. J., Ishiyama, E., Rothwarf, F., and Myers, D. (1965). Preliminary results with experimental cryosurgery of the labyrinth. *Arch. Otolaryngol.* **82,** 147-158.

Delgado, J. M. R. (1964). Free behavior and brain stimulation. *Intern. Rev. Neurobiol.* **6,** 349-449.

Delgado, J. M. R. (1965). Sequential behavior induced repeatedly by stimulation of the red nucleus in free monkeys. *Science* **148,** 1361-1363.

Deutsch, J. (1966). Analysis of positional behavior in the rhesus monkey *(Macaca mulatta).* Tech. Rept. 66-1. Office Naval Res., Dept. Navy.

DeVito, J. L., and White, L. E. (1966). Projections from the fornix to the hippocampal formation in the squirrel monkey. *J. Comp. Neurol.* **127,** 389-397.

Doty, R. W., Glickstein, M., and Calvin, W. H. (1966). Lamination of the lateral geniculate nucleus in the squirrel monkey, *Saimiri sciureus. J. Comp. Neurol.* **127,** 335-340.

Dow, R. S., and Moruzzi, G. (1958). "The Physiology and Pathology of the Cerebellum." Univ. of Minnesota Press, Minneapolis, Minnesota.

Dua, S., and MacLean, P. D. (1964). Localization for penile erection in medial frontal lobe. *Am. J. Physiol.* **6,** 1425-1434.

Emmers, R., and Akert, K. (1963). "A Stereotaxic Atlas of the Brain of the Squirrel Monkey *(Saimiri sciureus)."* Univ. of Wisconsin Press, Madison, Wisconsin.

Gergen, J. A., and MacLean, P. D. (1962). "A Stereotaxic Atlas of the Squirrel Monkey's Brain *(Saimiri sciureus)."* U.S. Public Health Serv. Publication No. 933, Washington, D.C.

Gergen, J. A., and MacLean, P. D. (1964). The limbic system: Photic activation of limbic cortical areas in the squirrel monkey. *Ann. N.Y. Acad. Sci.* **117**, 69-87.

Goldberg, J. M., and Moore, R. Y. (1967). Ascending projections of the lateral lemniscus in the cat and monkey. *J. Comp. Neurol.* **129**, 143-156.

Hassler, R. (1966). Comparative anatomy of the central visual systems in day- and night-active primates. *In* "Evolution of the Forebrain" (R. Hassler and H. Stephan, eds.), pp. 419-434. Thieme, Stuttgart.

Hast, M. H., and Milojevic, B. (1966). The response of the vocal folds to electrical stimulation of the inferior frontal cortex of the squirrel monkey. *Acta Oto-Laryngol.* **61**, 196-204.

Hebb, D. O. (1955). Drives and the CNS (Conceptual Nervous System). *Psychol. Rev.* **62**, 243-254.

Hendley, C. D. (1966). Penile erection by brain stimulation in the squirrel monkey: Effect of drugs. *Federation Proc.* **25**, 386.

Hernandez-Peon, R., and Ibarra, G. C. (1963). Sleep induced by electrical or chemical stimulation of the forebrain. *Electroencephalog. Clin. Neurophysiol.* Suppl. 24, 188-198.

Hess, W. R. (1949). "Das Zwischenhirn." Benno Schwabe, Basel.

Hess, W. R. (1954). The diencephalic sleep center. *In* "Brain Mechanisms and Consciousness" (E. D. Adrian, F. Bremer, and H. H. Jasper, eds.), pp. 117-136. Thomas, Springfield, Illinois.

Hind, J. E., Benjamin, R. M., and Woolsey, C. N. (1958). Auditory cortex of squirrel monkey *(Saimiri sciureus). Federation Proc.* **17**, 71.

Hinde, R. A., and Rowell, T. E. (1962). Communication by postures and facial expressions in the rhesus monkey *(Macaca mulatta). Proc. Zool. Soc. London* **138**, 1-121.

Jacobs, G. H. (1964). Single cells in squirrel monkey lateral geniculate nucleus with broad spectral sensitivity. *Vision Res.* **4**, 221-232.

Krompecher, S., and Lipák, J. (1966). A simple method for determining cerebralization. Brain weight and intelligence. *J. Comp. Neurol.* **127**, 113-120.

Lindsley, D. D. (1951). Emotion. *In* "Handbook of Experimental Psychology" (S. S. Stevens, ed.), pp. 473-516. Wiley, New York.

MacLean, P. D. (1966). Studies on the cerebral representation of certain basic sexual functions. *In* "Brain and Behavior" (R. A. Gorski and R. E. Whalen, eds.), Vol. III, pp. 35-79. Univ. of California Press, Los Angeles, California.

MacLean, P. D. (1967). A chronically fixed stereotaxic device for intracerebral exploration with macro- and micro-electrodes. *Electroencephalog. Clin. Neurophysiol.* **22**, 180-182.

MacLean, P. D., and Delgado, J. M. R. (1953). Electrical and chemical stimulation of fronto-temporal portion of limbic system in the waking animal. *Electroencephalog. Clin. Neurophysiol.* **5**, 91-100.

MacLean, P. D., and Ploog, D. (1962). Cerebral representation of penile erection. *J. Neurophysiol.* **25**, 29-55.

Malmo, R. B. (1959). Activation: A neuropsychological dimension. *Psychol. Rev.* **66**, 367-386.

Maurus, M., Mitra, J., and Ploog, D. (1965). Cerebral representation of the clitoris in ovariectomized squirrel monkeys. *Exptl. Neurol.* **13**, 283-288.

Miles, R. C., and Blomquist, A. J. (1960). Frontal lesions and behavioral deficits in monkey. *J. Neurophysiol.* **23**, 471-484.

Moruzzi, G., and Magoun, H. W. (1949). Brain stem reticular formation and activation of the EEG. *Electroencephalog. Clin. Neurophysiol.* **1**, 455-473.

Moskowitz, N. (1965). Comparative aspects of the central auditory nuclei. *Anat. Record* **151**, 467.

Parmeggiani, P. L. (1964). A study on the central representation of sleep behavior. *Progr. Brain Res.* **6,** 180-190.

Pecci-Saavedra, J., Doty, R. W., and Hunt, H. B. (1965). Conditioned reflexes elicited in squirrel monkeys by stimuli producing recruiting responses. *Electroencephalog. Clin. Neurophysiol.* **19,** 492-500.

Pinneo, L. R. (1966a). On noise in the nervous system. *Psychol. Rev.* **73,** 242-247.

Pinneo, L. R. (1966b). Electrical control of behavior by programmed stimulation of the brain. *Nature* **211,** 705-708.

Pinneo, L. R., and Heath, R. G. (1967). Human visual system activity and perception of intermittent light stimuli. *J. Neurol. Sci.* **5,** 303-314.

Pompeiano, O. (1959). Organizzazione somatotopica delle risposte flessorie alla stimolazione elettrico del nucleo interposito nel gatto decerebrato. *Arch. Sci. Bio. (Bologna)* **43,** 163-176.

Rosabal, F. (1967). Cytoarchitecture of the frontal lobe of the squirrel monkey. *J. Comp. Neurol.* **130,** 87-108.

Roth, J. G. (1966). A method for attaching apparatus to the skull. *Electroencephalog. Clin. Neurophysiol.* **20,** 618-619.

Shende, M. C., and King, R. B. (1967). Excitability changes of trigeminal primary afferent preterminals in brain-stem nuclear complex of squirrel monkey *(Saimiri sciureus).* *J. Neurophysiol.* **30,** 949-963.

Stevens, S. S. (1962). The surprising simplicity of sensory metrics. *Am. Psychologist* **17,** 29-39.

Travis, R. P., Jr., and Sparks, D. L. (1967). Changes in unit activity during stimuli associated with food and shock reinforcement. *Physiol. and Behavioral* **2,** 171-177.

Upson, J. D., King, F. A., and Roberts, L. (1962). A constant-amplitude transistorized unit for remote brain stimulation. *Electroencephalog. Clin. Neurophysiol.* **14,** 928-930.

von Holst, E., and von St. Paul, U. (1960). Von wirkungsgefug der triebe. *Naturwissenschaften* **18,** 409-422.

von Holst, E., and von St. Paul, U. (1962). Electrically controlled behavior. *Sci. Am.* **206,** 50-59.

Welker, W. I., Benjamin, R. M., Miles, R. C., and Woolsey, C. N. (1957). Motor effects of stimulation of cerebral cortex of squirrel monkey *(Saimiri sciureus).* *J. Neurophysiol.* **20,** 347-364.

Wolin, L. R., Massopust, L. C., and Meder, J. (1966). Differential color responses from the superior colliculi of squirrel monkeys. *Vision Res.* **6,** 637-642.

Yokota, T., Reeves, A. G., and MacLean, P. D. (1967). Intracellular olfactory response of hippocampal neurons in awake, sitting squirrel monkeys. *Science* **157,** 1072-1074.

CHAPTER **12** _____

The Squirrel Monkey in Aerospace Medical Research

Dietrich E. Beischer

For nearly 10 years the squirrel monkey has served aerospace research
in two related roles: (1) in the laboratory as surrogate for man in the exploration of hazardous, space flight-connected conditions and (2) in actual
flight as forerunner in the exploration of advanced space flights usually
connected with high and/or unknown risks. These roles are shared with
other animals but the squirrel monkey has been preferred when the use of
a small-sized, easily managed primate was indicated. It is remarkable how
these wild animals from South America can be trained to serve in some of
the most sophisticated and stressful laboratory and field experiments. The
squirrel monkey was originally introduced into aerospace research in 1958
by Robert B. Voas, who recognized intuitively the great value of this primate in animal space flight. The following account is written in recognition
of the contributions of this small primate to aerospace medical research.*

* Opinions or conclusions contained in this report are those of the author and do not necessarily reflect the views or endorsement of the United States Navy Department.

I. Space Flight Experiments

A. Army—Navy Bio-Flights 1 and 2

In the early years of space flight two squirrel monkeys served as passengers in the Army—Navy Bio-Flights 1 and 2 (Graybiel *et al.*, 1959; Hixson *et al.*, 1960). Both were ballistic missile flights to altitudes of 300 miles and distances of 1500 miles; the monkeys were riding piggyback on a "noninterference" basis in the nose cones of Jupiter military missiles not originally designed for biological space experiments. Consequently, the animals had to tolerate high acceleration (up to 15 *G*) and deceleration (up to 45 *G*) forces. While the nose cone with the first animal (Old Reliable) could not be recovered, the flight with squirrel monkey Baker as passenger (May 28, 1959) was a complete success. The animal was recovered and is still in good health on exhibit at the Aerospace Medical Institute in Pensacola, Florida; the nose cone with the biocapsule used in this flight is on permanent display at the Smithsonian Institution in Washington, D.C.

FIG. 1. Biocapsule used in Baker space flight with armored and padded animal couch, oxygen supply, and carbon dioxide absorber as well as electronic equipment for telemetry.

These two bio-flights are well documented (Graybiel *et al.*, 1959) in every detail. In retrospect, it is amazing how all major difficulties of bio-flights were recognized and mastered by a very small crew of scientific workers. A 30-pound, 750-cubic-inch biocapsule contained the squirrel monkey and provided (1) protection against shock and temperature extremes, (2) life support for 1 day, and (3) electronic equipment for in-flight telemetry of vital information (Fig. 1). The quality of these early biosignals (EKG, body temperature, and respiration rate) has hardly been equaled since. For the first time, the reaction of a primate to the in-flight stresses of acceleration, weightlessness of over 10 minutes, and deceleration was monitored in-flight and found well within the tolerance of the primate organism. At a time when no human space flight experience was available, the electrocardiograms (Graybiel *et al.*, 1959; Burch and Gerathewohl, 1960) which showed tachycardia during accelerated flight, return to normal during weightless flight, and recurrence of tachycardia during re-entry were viewed with apprehension and a keen eye to possible human application under similar space flight conditions. The confidence in the flight results from one of the smallest primates was a factor in the initiation of the Mercury program and thus an important contribution to an eventual landing on the moon.

B. PREPARATION FOR LONG-DURATION BIO-SPACE FLIGHT

Since the animal flights mentioned above, we have witnessed a most successful and exciting series of astronaut flights. In the future these manned flights will be increased in duration as experience is gradually collected. A long-term animal flight of about 6 months or a year in duration is considered a possible means of solving many of the vexing questions of long-term habitat in the absence of gravitational forces much faster than gradual escalation of manned flight can. Preparations for such a flight using squirrel monkeys as experimental animals have been described by Beischer (1966) and Thach (1966) and will be characterized here briefly. An attempt will be made in the animal flights to simulate later manned flight conditions as closely as possible. It has been proposed that the animals should not be restrained since free movement in work and play during the entire orbital time is essential. The animals will be required to pass through a certain work cycle which, in connection with food rewards, could be used to collect physiological and psychological information. Since companionship in long isolation is considered beneficial, two or more animals should be used. Recovery of the animals for physiological and pathological examination will be mandatory.

Ground-based experiments with squirrel monkeys were performed in preparation for the 6-month orbital flight. An egg-shaped capsule con-

FIG. 2. Biocapsule by Ling-Temco-Vought, Dallas, Texas, in ground-based experiment at Naval Aerospace Medical Institute, Pensacola, Florida. Two squirrel monkeys can live in this capsule for 3 months.

structed by Ling-Temco-Vought, Astronautics Division, Dallas, Texas, housed the animals and their life support system with the exception of the gas supply (Fig. 2); the total weight of this capsule at launch with two squirrel monkeys will be less than 400 pounds. An atmosphere of a nitrogen — oxygen mixture at 16 lb pressure has been provided. A liquid, low-residue diet, originally developed for rats (Schwarz BioResearch, Inc., Orangeburg, New York) was fed to the monkeys which reduced the daily excretion to about 3 gm, compared to 15 gm under normal solid food conditions. However, certain nutritional deficiencies of this diet have not yet been corrected and feeding must be limited to about 4 months. The animals were conditioned to perform certain tasks that produced physiological as well as behavioral information in addition to data from implanted sensors and television. The electrocardiogram, for instance, was monitored by training the animals to hold instrumented levers for a prolonged period of time; at the same time thermistors embedded in these levers measured the palm temperature.

Other experiments concern the activity of squirrel monkeys in severe isolation. The first two inhabitants of the Ling-Temco-Vought capsule showed a high level of activity for a few weeks followed by a gradual decrease to little movement. This behavior may present a problem in prolonged space flight and needs more extensive study. Circadian rhythms during extreme isolation in the space capsule under different conditions of illumination were also investigated. In a shift from a 12-hour light and 12-hour dark schedule to a continuous light schedule both animals settled rather quickly into a 26-hour day routine with a widened activity span.

These few examples characterize the approach and the difficulties of long-term experiments with the animals completely isolated from the experimenter. Preparation for long-term animal flight is made still more difficult by the extended run time of each experiment but parallel experiments can relieve this difficulty to a certain degree. The preparations for long-term flights in progress at present have uncovered many problems of general interest concerning support and management as well as measurement techniques and behavior of animals in long-term severe confinement in restricted areas.

II. Laboratory Experiments under Unusual Environmental Conditions

A. ANATOMY, HISTOLOGY, PHYSIOLOGY, AND PSYCHOLOGY OF THE NORMAL SQUIRREL MONKEY

Animal space flights are necessarily preceded by extensive laboratory experiments and tests. The reaction of animals under several kinds of stress expected in flight is compared with the animals' normal functions and behavior. In the case of the squirrel monkey only a scant store of knowledge of the clinically normal animal was available at the outset of its use in space flight, and a considerable risk was taken in selecting a non-laboratory-bred and -raised animal for space experimentation. However, in searching for an appropriate subject the squirrel monkey was the only readily available primate small enough to fill the size requirement, that proved to be easily tamed and quite resistant under laboratory conditions. The following data represent some of the information collected in immediate connection with the preparation for space flight. Much other data reported throughout this volume will be of value for the same purpose.

Anatomy. Table I lists values on weight and length of selected organs of the squirrel monkey (Beischer and Furry, 1964). Edwards and Fogg-Amed

TABLE I

WEIGHTS AND LENGTH OF ORGANS OF 10 PERUVIAN SQUIRREL MONKEYS WITH AN AVERAGE BODY WEIGHT OF 663.4 GM AND BODY LENGTH OF 27.2 CM[a]

Organ	Weight (gm)	Organ	Weight (gm)	Organ	Length (cm)
Brain	21.4 ± 2.2	Kidney		Esophagus	7.3 ± 1.6
Pituitary	0.06	Right	1.8 ± 0.2	Stomach	6.3 ± 1.4
Heart	3.3 ± 0.5	Left	1.8 ± 0.3	Duodenum	5.9 ± 1.0
Lungs	5.0 ± 1.0	Adrenal		Small Intestine	90.7 ± 13.0
Spleen	1.6 ± 0.8	Right	0.15 ± 0.1	Cecum	3.9 ± 1
Liver	18.1 ± 4.3	Left	0.15 ± 0.1	Colon	8.3 ± 1.4
Pancreas	1.5 ± 0.3	Testes			
		Right	1.4 ± 0.4		
		Left	1.2 ± 0.5		
		Ovary			
		Right	0.13		
		Left	0.10		

[a] Abstracted from Tables 2 and 3 of Beischer and Furry (1964).

(1965a,b) made a careful study of the musculoskeletal anatomy of the thorax and brachium as well as antebrachium, including comparisons with data in the literature on other platyrrhines and nonplatyrrhine forms, and offered a hypothesis on the phylogeny of *Saimiri* and its relatives. The study suffers from the fact that only one animal was dissected and it appears questionable if this animal was healthy before necropsy.

Histology. Furry (1964) has started a systematic histopathological evaluation of the squirrel monkey. In his evaluation of major organs he found numerous acute and chronic lesions in apparently normal animals. Such inflamatory and degenerative lesions may lead to a false interpretation of the effects of experimental stresses. There is then an obvious need for a laboratory colony of squirrel monkeys to be brought up to a health level that is comparable to other laboratory animals, and for "normal" values to be collected on such a colony.

Physiology. Some data used in preparation for long-duration space flights are summarized in Table II. Most of these data have been accumulated in work with squirrel monkeys at the Naval Aerospace Medical Institute in Pensacola, Florida. The data represent in essence data for the planning engineer. Closer ranges of the normal functions and behavior are usually set for the individual test animal in connection with a specific stress situation using the animal as its own control.

Hematological and biochemical determinations in a colony of healthy, normal squirrel monkeys are given in this volume in the tables of A. E. New from the Animal Support Laboratory Veterinary Services, Naval Aerospace Medical Institute, Pensacola, Florida (see Appendix). These values

TABLE II

PHYSIOLOGICAL DATA FOR SQUIRREL MONKEY AS USED IN PLANNING FOR
SPACE FLIGHTS

Weight		
Adult male	800 – 1100 gm	NAMI colony
Adult female	500 – 850 gm	NAMI colony
Food consumption		
CIBA diet pellets	28 gm/kg	Beischer and Furry (1964)
Purina chow (3.9 kcal/gm)	25-30 gm/kg	NAMI colony
Oxygen uptake	800 ml/kg/hr	Malinow and Wagner (1966)
Water consumption	100 ml/kg/day	Beischer and Furry (1964)
	70-80 ml/kg/day	NAMI colony
Heart rate	250-300 beats/minute	Beischer and Furry (1964); NAMI colony
Respiratory rate	40-60/minute	Beischer and Furry (1964); NAMI colony
Body temperature	96-101°F	Beischer and Furry (1964); NAMI colony

should be compared with the hematogram observed by Garcia and Hunt (1966). (See Chapter 14.)

Psychology. "Normal" behavioral data are also of great interest, and the study of Thach (1966) gives some values for two severely confined monkeys in specific situations. For the investigation of the long-term effect of the gravity-free state on squirrel monkeys, it will be necessary to study a variety of aspects of the behavior of these animals in a simulator with all stresses of space flight present but being operated at 1 G. The extensive data on general learning factors and influences on performance in squirrel monkeys reviewed by Rumbaugh (see Chapter 10) provide the background for carrying out such basic work under space flight conditions.

B. Effects of High Gravitational Stress

Launch and recovery, including impact, impose unidirectional mechanical forces on animals used in space flight. These forces can be simulated in the laboratory on a centrifuge, and the stress on the animals studied. The results of such studies using the squirrel monkey have not only given the information needed in space flight operation but have also rendered valuable contributions to an understanding of cardiac physiology in a force-dominated environment with possible application on human exposure to acceleration and accidental impact.

Monkeys restrained in preparation for the Able-Baker flight (Graybiel *et al.*, 1959) were tested on a centrifuge that was programmed to simulate the acceleration and deceleration forces of the Jupiter missile on which the animals would be piggyback riding. The restrained animals, subjected in an "eyeball in" position to the sequence of forces with a maximum of 30 G simulating reentry forces, showed no adverse effect. Exposure of the monkeys to 100 G for a few seconds only was also tolerated well without aftereffects.

In preparation for satellite flight we exposed unrestrained squirrel monkeys in a wire cage mounted to an animal centrifuge to a force of 10 G for 1 minute. The animals vocalized frequently during exposure and stayed in their spread-eagle position for a few minutes after exposure. Their first movements were ataxic, but full coordination was soon restored.

Spoendlin *et al.* (1965) studied the cause of ataxia in squirrel monkeys exposed on the centrifuge to 5.43 and 10.92 G for periods of 1 – 10 minutes. In very careful electron microscopic observations these authors found no anatomical alterations in the vestibular organs of the inner ear of the immediately sacrificed animals. Macula utriculi and sacculi were found intact with the otoliths in place. The report is a rich source of information on the synaptic ultrastructure in the maculae of squirrel monkeys. An unusually large variety and number of synaptic accessory structures (bars, membranes) were observed in the vestibular sensory epithelium. The question was raised whether or not these striking structures are possibly related to the functional importance of the gravity receptors in the squirrel monkey for which acrobatic skill is important to survival.

Recently Igarashi and Nagaba (1968) exposed squirrel monkeys to extremely high linear acceleration. A peak of 500 G reached in these experiments was survived by the animals and represents the highest acceleration force to which a primate has ever been exposed in an experimental situation. The experiments were performed on the Space Flight Acceleration Profile Simulator at Space/Defense Corporation, Birmingham, Michigan. The selected well-restrained animals were exposed to a ventral-dorsal directed force of increasing intensity. After an exposure of 1 minute at the 60 G level otoconia dislocation from the macula was observed. At this level and at higher levels no structural changes of the semicircular canal cristae or the organ of Corti were noticed. From 200 G for 1 minute and up to a peak of 450 G, transformation of mitochondria in the nerve chalice and increased numbers of lysosomes were observed and considered by the authors as prodromal signs of cell death. Ataxia in the monkeys increased with high-G levels and reached severe conditions at 500 G (Fig. 3). It dimin-

FIG. 3. Severe ataxic posture of a squirrel monkey after exposure to 200 G for 1 minute. Note stretched fingers indicating attempt to regain balance. Igarashi and Nagaba (1968).

ished usually after a short time. In cases in which ataxia was observed for 1 month the cause is expected to be located in the higher nervous system and not in peripheral organ.

The study of the inner ear represents only part of an extensive effort to characterize the effects of high-G forces on the squirrel monkey. Pinc and associates (Pinc and Barr, 1963; Mehelas and Pinc, 1965; Pinc and Life, 1966; Life and Pinc, 1966) have used the Space/Defense Corporation Simulator to study the limits of tolerance of this small primate in an effort to shed new light on possible survival of man in escape from air and space craft and in crash of fast-moving vehicles. The most amazing result of these experiments was the very high resistance of some squirrel monkeys to severe accelerative forces. Animals survived 430 G at an average exposure time of 120 seconds. The general condition of animals exposed to peak G for 20 seconds was very good. Aside from the acceleration force, survival depended on the dwell time at maximum G, the direction of the forces in regard to the body axes, and on body weight. Clinical observations and pathological findings indicated increasing damage with higher G force, longer dwell time, exposure in the ventral-dorsal direction as compared with the lateral direction, and with higher body weight. Translocation of tissue at low forces may lead to circulatory and respiratory difficulties which are readily reversed. At higher G levels beyond 300 G, mechanical failures of tissue began to appear. Separation of cranial suture lines may lead to extrusion of brain tissue and play a role in deaths of some animals at peak G forces. The original reports should be consulted for a wealth of information on physiological, pathological, and histochemical observations collected in connection with high-G exposure.

A recent study of Pinc and Life (1966) of the role of the autonomic nervous system and hypoxia in the cardiac control of squirrel monkeys exposed to 200 plus G_x for 200 seconds deserves special mentioning in connection with the bradycardia of accidental impact of airmen and astronauts as well as drivers of automotive vehicles. The authors demonstrated that the intrinsic response of the heart to high acceleration was a fall of the heart rate. Blocking of the parasympathetic nervous system by atropine moderated the fall in heart rate. In this case the sympathetic nervous system exerts also its positive chronotropic action. Profound positive changes in cardiac performance and increased survivability were found in hyperoxygenated monkeys that did not experience the extreme bradycardia normally experienced as an intrinsic response of the heart to high acceleration forces.

The acceleration experiments are a typical example of the practical contributions that a small, readily available primate can make to the study of stresses to which man cannot readily be exposed on an experimental basis.

C. Effects of the Forces of a Rotating Environment on the Vestibular Organ

Squirrel monkeys have been used repeatedly in the study of orientation and disorientation in exotic force environments. Similar to man, these animals become motion sick under certain conditions, and "canal sickness" can be easily elicited experimentally in the "slow rotation room" (Meek *et al.*, 1962). The investigation of the physiological effects of a rotating environment plays a role in connection with the generation of a directed force (artificial gravity) in a satellite in the gravity-free state. The effective stimulus, a Coriolis acceleration, is generated whenever the animal rotates its head out of the plane of rotation of the room. The signs of illness exhibited by squirrel monkeys are similar to those seen in man and include drowsiness, salivation, retching, and vomiting. The animals have been used in studies of threshold adaptation and aftereffects of the sickness as well as in the clarification of the etiology and final control of canal sickness. In this latter respect, the squirrel monkey with its high sensitivity to the stimulus of Coriolis acceleration is the animal of choice for experiments that cannot be carried out on man.

All present experience points to the conclusion that in the squirrel monkey, as in man, the sickness experienced in a slowly rotating room depends upon normal vestibular functions. Johnson *et al.* (1962) demonstrated that squirrel monkeys following bilateral labyrinthectomy showed a complete insensitivity to Coriolis acceleration in rotation, and an absence of canal sickness. Animals subjected to unilateral labyrinthectomy after 6 months recovered their sensitivity to canal sickness.

Suppression of semicircular canal function by streptomycin sulfate had effects similar to surgical labyrinthectomy. Igarashi *et al.* (1966) investigated the ototoxic effects of this drug, and their clinical and pathological findings in squirrel monkeys deserve interest in connection with the application of the drug in man. Findings prior to sacrifice of the animals included increase of the caloric threshold, ataxia, and loss of susceptibility to the effects of Coriolis forces observed as absence of canal sickness. Pathological findings showed moderate to severe damage to the cristae of the semicircular canals and also to the organ of Corti. Very slight abnormal findings were reported on the maculae of utricle and saccule. The drug has a place in selective suppression of canal functions in squirrel monkeys and probably also in man, with a clear warning of the danger of injury to the organ of Corti. The squirrel monkey has a definite place beside the guinea pig in future investigation of ototoxic drugs.

D. Effects of High-Intensity Noise on the Organ of Corti

Very effective methods have been described recently by Engström *et al.* (1966) to demonstrate the arrangement of cochlear sensory cells by phase contrast photomicrographs. Changes produced by intense noise exposure can be registered and plotted in the form of cochleograms. Figure 4 shows a preparation of the organ of Corti of a squirrel monkey exposed repeatedly to high-intensity noise. Series of monkeys exposed to pure tones and white noise as well as to the intense noise of gun shot, helicopter rotor, and tail-pipe blast of jet aircraft showed a certain pattern of damage to the inner ear sensory cells. The appearance of osmiophillic granules of considerable size in the uppermost parts of the hair cells was the most conspicuous evidence of damage (Ades *et al.*, 1962).

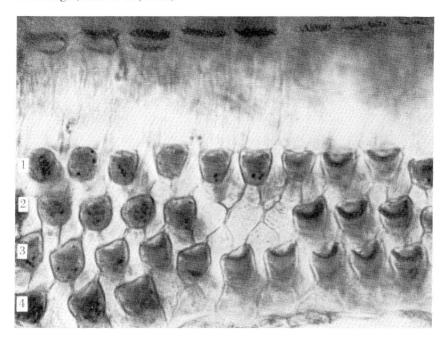

FIG. 4. Surface preparation of organ of Corti, 1½ coil from base. Phase contrast micrograph. This squirrel monkey had been exposed to sinusoidal tones with a frequency of 4000 cps for 2 hours during 3 consecutive days and sacrificed 45 days after the last exposure. There were scattered cells lost in this region and the micrograph gives a good picture of the phalangeal scar replacing two destroyed cells. Further down the loss was more extensive. It can be observed that there are four rows of cells (1, 2, 3, and 4) in the left third of the specimen. Magnification 1480 ×. Engström *et al.* (1966).

E. Structure and Function of the Inner Ear Sensory Organs

The problems characterized in the last three sections have stimulated extensive basic research in the field of vestibular end organs. It was in the main part the work of Igarashi, Engström, Ades, and their colleagues that enriched our knowledge on the anatomy and fine structure of the inner ear of the squirrel monkey. The interested reader should consult the original literature which is copiously illustrated by excellent photomicrographs.

Igarashi (1964, 1966) described a standard technique for temporal bone preparation and gave, in a study of horizontal serial sections, the inner ear anatomy of the squirrel monkey on a microscopic basis.

Igarashi and Yoshinobu (1965) compared the dimensions of the cochlear organ of the squirrel monkey with the human organ (human dimensions in parentheses) as follows: diameter of cochlea basal turn 3.7 mm (6.2 mm); length of basal membrane 22 mm (32 mm); turns in cochlea 2¾−3 (2½−2¾). Engström *et al.* (1966) reported a sensory cell count in the organ of Corti of a squirrel monkey and gave the total number of sensory cells in the left ear as 10,095 and in the right ear as 10,148. The cytoarchitecture of the organ of Corti is illustrated by Engström *et al.* (1964, 1966) and by Igarashi and Yoshinobu (1965). The excellent method of phase contrast photomicrography (Fig. 4) allows studies of the normal cells and of pathologically changed cochlear sensory cells.

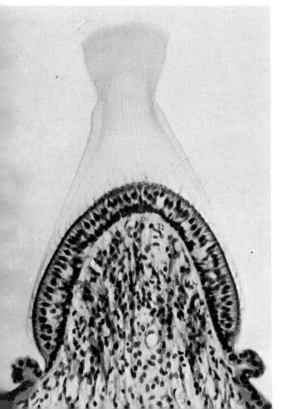

FIG. 5. View of normal semicircular canal crista from a squirrel monkey. Specimen was fixed (intravital cardiac perfusion) with Heidenhain−Susa fixative and decalcified by 5% trichloroacetic acid solution. Igarashi (1966).

Otolith End Organ. The architecture of the otolith end organs in the squirrel monkey (utricle and saccule) is described by Igarashi (1965b). It is confirmed that, except for the existence of otoconia, both otolith and semicircular canal end organs have almost similar components (Fig. 5). A similar excitatory mechanism can be expected at the level of the hair cells even though the otolith organs register in the main part unidirectional acceleration and the semicircular canals angular acceleration. Selective unilateral saccular end organ surgical destruction resulted only in a temporal unbalance of the afflicted squirrel monkeys (Igarashi, 1965a). Animals subjected to bilateral labyrinthectomy showed unsteadiness of gait which persisted for 6 weeks with only gradual improvement. These experiments stress the reliance of the squirrel monkey in its orientation on well-functioning semicircular canals with the otolith organs playing a secondary role.

F. Effects of High and Low Environmental Oxygen Partial Pressure and Ambient Pressure

Cook and Leon (1960) studied the survival of squirrel monkeys in hyperoxia and hypoxia. The critical oxygen levels between which the animals survived for a prolonged period of time appeared to be 95 mm Hg oxygen on the hypoxic side and 624 mm Hg oxygen on the hyperoxic side. These data, however, have limited value since the number of animals used in the experiments was very small and their original state of health doubtful.

Of much greater interest are experiments of Workman *et al.* (1962) in which squirrel monkeys were used in preparation for human exposure in the Sea Lab programs. The animals were pressurized to 7 atm corresponding to 200 ft equivalent depth of sea water. The oxygen partial pressure was 160 mm Hg (total gas pressure 5320 mm Hg) which corresponds to 3% oxygen in the helium – oxygen mixture. After 12 days' exposure no significant blood biochemical or pathological changes of vital organs were observed. These findings played a decisive role in the decision to expose human subjects to similar conditions and are milestones in the eminently successful Sea Lab program.

Squirrel monkeys also fulfilled a valuable function in the investigation of explosive decompression to near vacuum. The danger of such a decompression lingers for astronauts in space flight simulators and during actual space flight. If life is spared in such an accident, the rate of recovery of physiological and psychological functions is of paramount interest. Along with dogs (Bancroft and Dunn, 1965) and chimpanzees (Koestler, 1965), squirrel monkeys have served as experimental animals to estimate the time of consciousness, collapse, and survival. Bancroft and Dunn (1965) decompressed the animals in an oxygen atmosphere from 30,000 ft to above

120,000 ft (approximately 1 mm Hg absolute) in less than 1 second. After a
stay in vacuum for up to 90 seconds, the animals were recompressed first
with oxygen and later with air. The monkeys lost consciousness in less than
5 seconds. Both tonic and clonic seizures progressed to flaccid paralysis,
and subcutaneous emphysema and swelling occurred during exposure.
Animals that recovered after the longer exposure times exhibited stagger-
ing and disorientation for a longer period. Short-term interference with vision and hearing was noted. However, it was concluded by Rumbaugh and
Ternes (1965) that if life is spared, restoration of normal functions is promising and to be expected in full measure. These authors have conducted
learning-set performance tests before and after exposure of squirrel monkeys to vacuum and found no significant loss in learning-set performance
among survivors. They concluded that there was no behavioral basis for
inferring brain damage in any instance.

The most important result of these vacuum experiments with squirrel
monkeys and similar experiments with chimpanzees is the high survival
rate and the low apparent damage to the central nervous system of these
animals.

G. Effects of Cold and Heat

Animals in space flight depend on automatic regulation of the temperature in the capsule. It is of great interest to know the extremes of temperature that squirrel monkeys can tolerate in case of failure of the automatic
regulation. Chaffee *et al.* (1965, 1966) studied the cellular physiology and
biochemistry as well as organ mass of squirrel monkeys during prolonged
cold and heat exposure. The extremes of temperature at which 90% of the
animals survived exposure for 6 weeks are given as 14° – 16°C on the cold
side and 36° – 39°C for heat exposure. Controls were kept at 24°C.

In the cold the animals initially lost weight but regained it in the latter
part of the experiments. During the first 2.5 weeks the animals shivered
intermittently, and some showed stiff movements and a certain loss of coordination, but this condition improved with prolonged exposure. The food
intake increased considerably during cold exposure. Chemical analysis of a
number of oxidative enzyme systems usually showed no change during
cold adaptation, and only the activity of α-glycerophosphate dehydrogenase of brown fat homogenate and of liver mitochondria increased. An increase of the relative and absolute weight of centrally located organs
(heart, kidney, thyroid and adrenal glands, liver, pancreas, and brown fat)
was noted.

Squirrel monkeys were also rather sensitive to excessive heat and
showed extreme lethargy when subjected to 36° – 39°C. The fact that the
animals became gradually active again indicated acclimation to heat. The

weight change of internal organs was in general opposite to the change seen in cold animals. Even though they were eating less than the control animals, the monkeys in a hot environment gained weight. In most cases no change in the level of oxidative enzyme activity was observed. The heat-producing pathway of a α-glycerophosphate was probably suppressed to insure survival by lowered heat production in the hot environment. However, squirrel monkeys normally show a variety of gross behavioral adaptations to changes in environmental temperature; these behavior patterns have been discussed elsewhere in this volume by Thorington (Chapter 3) and Dumond (Chapter 4). A consideration of the monkey's utilization of these behavioral mechanisms under confined laboratory conditions may be of considerable importance.

H. EFFECTS OF STRONG MAGNETIC FIELDS

Magnetic fields are considered for a number of applications in space travel, including magnetic shielding against cosmic radiation and magneto-hydrodynamic propulsion. Since a certain amount of risk is involved in human exposure, a subhuman primate was chosen for systematic experimentation. Beischer and Knepton (1964, 1966) reported on the exposure of squirrel monkeys to magnetic fields of a strength up to 100,000 oersted. In different experiments two monkeys survived a 1-day-long exposure to such a strong magnetic field generated in a 4-inch core superconductive magnet. The electrocardiogram during magnetic field exposure was marked by a notched T-wave of high amplitude. The second maximum of the T-wave corresponds to the normal repolarization signal. The first maximum was newly identified as the electric potential generated by the blood flowing in the aorta at right angle to the strong magnetic field. This signal can possibly be used to determine the heart output by making the flow measurement with the entire animal in a strong magnetic field. Deep-core body temperature, respiration, and heart rate were not significantly abnormal during exposure. In necropsy of one of the animals no gross pathological abnormalities and no flagrant histopathological or histochemical changes were observed. The other animal has remained in good health several months after exposure.

The electroencephalogram of squirrel monkeys in a strong magnetic field is usually not different from the control. Occasionally, however, an unusually high beta activity is observed.

Performance of the conditioned monkeys in a reward situation with acoustical signals did not deviate significantly from the normal performance. However, in experiments with optical cues the monkeys did not perform their task at field strength higher than 60,000 oersted. This most interesting behavioral disruption is currently under more extensive investigations. In general, the survival of squirrel monkeys in very strong magnetic fields has given reassurance for future experimental exposure of man to medium intensity (10 — 20 kilo-oersted) magnetic fields.

III. Summary

Squirrel monkeys have played a remarkable role in the development of space flight. Use of the animal in the laboratory investigation of space flight-connected stresses, the preparation of a long-term bio-flight, and in an actual ballistic flight have been described based on widely scattered and not readily available references.

REFERENCES

Ades, H. W., Engström, H., and Hawkins, J. E., Jr. (1962). Structure of inner ear sensory epithelial cells, in relation to their function. Rep. NSAM-831, Naval School of Aviation Med., Pensacola, Florida.

Bancroft, R. W., and Dunn, J. E. (1965). Experimental animal decompression to a near vacuum environment. *Aerospace Med.* **36**, 720-725.

Beischer, D. E. (1966). Long-term performance of squirrel monkeys under space simulation conditions. Part I: Characteristics of approach and capsule. *NASA* **SP-115**, 273-275.

Beischer, D. E., and Furry, D. E. (1964). *Saimiri sciureus* as an experimental animal. *Anat. Record* **148**, 615-624.

Beicher, D. E., and Knepton, J. C., Jr. (1964). Influence of strong magnetic fields on the electrocardiogram of squirrel monkeys (*Saimiri sciureus*). *Aerospace Med.* **35**, 939-944.

Beischer, D. E., and Knepton, J. C., Jr. (1966). The electroencephalogram of the squirrel monkey (*Saimiri sciureus*) in a very high magnetic field. Rep. NAMI-972, Naval Aerospace Med. Inst., Pensacola, Florida.

Burch, G. E., and Gerathewohl, S. J. (1960). Observations on heart rate and cardiodynamics during weightlessness. *Aerospace Med.* **31**, 661-669.

Chaffee, R. R. J., Allen, J. R., Brewer, M., Horvath, S. M., Mason, C., and Smith, R. E. (1965). Cellular physiology of cold- and heat-exposed squirrel monkeys (*Saimiri sciurea*). *J. Appl. Physiol.* **21**, 151-157.

Chaffee, R. R. J., Horvath, S. M., Smith, R. E., and Welsh, R. S. (1966). Cellular biochemistry and organ mass of cold- and heat-acclimated monkeys. *Federation Proc.* **25**, 1177-1184.

Cook, S. F., and Leon, H. F. (1960). Survival of C-57 mice and squirrel monkeys in high and low pressures of oxygen. Rep. AFMDC-TR-60-21, Air Force Missile Develop. Center, Holloman Air Force Base, New Mexico.

Edwards, W. E., and Fogg-Amed, E. (1965a). The musculoskeletal anatomy of the thorax and brachium of a squirrel monkey (*Saimiri*). Rep. ARL-TR-65-8, 6571st Aeromed. Res. Lab., Holloman Air Force Base, New Mexico.

Edwards, W. E., and Fogg-Amed, E. (1965b). The musculoskeletal anatomy of the antebrachium of a squirrel monkey (*Saimiri*). Rep. ARL-TR-65-9, 6571st Aeromed. Res. Lab., Holloman Air Force Base, New Mexico.

Engström, H., Ades, H. W., and Hawkins, J. E., Jr. (1964). Cytoarchitecture of the organ of Corti. *Acta Oto-Laryngol.* Suppl. 188, 92-99.

Engström, H., Ades, H. W., and Andersson, A. (1966). "Structural Pattern of the Organ of Corti." Almqvist & Wiksell, Uppsala.

Furry, D. E. (1964). Histopathologic evaluation of a laboratory primate: The squirrel monkey *(Saimiri sciureus)*. Rep. NSAM-902, Naval School of Aviation Med., Pensacola, Florida.

Garcia, F. G., and Hunt, R. D. (1966). The hematogram of the squirrel monkey *(Saimiri sciurea)*. *Lab. Animal Care* **16,** 50-51.

Graybiel, A., Holmes, R. H., and Beischer, D. E., Champlin, G. E., Pedigo, G. P., Hixson, W. C., Davis, T. R. A., Barr, N. L., Kistler, W. G., Niven, J. I., Wilbarger, E., Stullken, D. E., Augerson, W. S., Clark, R., and Berrian, J. H. (1959). An account of experiments in which two monkeys were recovered unharmed after ballistic space flight. *Aerospace Med.* **30,** 871-931.

Hixson, W. C., Paludan, C. T., and Downs, S. W., Jr. (1960). Primate bio-instrumentation for two Jupiter ballistic flights. *IRE, Trans. Med. Electron.* **7,** 318-325.

Igarashi, M. (1964). The inner ear anatomy of the squirrel monkey. Monograph No. 8. Naval School of Aviation Med., Pensacola, Florida.

Igarashi, M. (1965a). Histopathological findings after experimental saccular destruction in the squirrel monkey. *Laryngoscope* **75,** 1048-1061.

Igarashi, M. (1965b). Architecture of the otolith end organ: With some functional considerations. Rep. NAMI-952, Naval Aerospace Med. Inst., Pensacola, Florida.

Igarashi, M. (1966). A standard technique for temporal bone preparation. Monograph No. 13. Naval Aerospace Med. Inst., Pensacola, Florida.

Igarashi, M., and Nagaba, M. (1968). Vestibular end organ damage in squirrel monkeys after exposure to intensive linear acceleration. *NASA* **SP-152,** 63-81.

Igarashi, M., and Yoshinobu, T. (1965). Comparative cochlear reconstruction in mammals. Rep. NSAM-931, Naval School of Aviation Med., Pensacola, Florida.

Igarashi, M., McLeod, M. E., and Graybiel, A. (1966). Clinical pathological correlations in squirrel monkeys after suppression of semicircular canal function by streptomycin sulfate. *Acta Oto-Laryngol.* Suppl. 214, 1-28.

Johnson, W. H., Meek, J. C., and Graybiel, A. (1962). Effects of labyrinthectomy on canal sickness in squirrel monkey. *Ann. Otol., Rhinol., Laryngol.* **71,** 289-298.

Koestler, A. G. (1965). The effect on the chimpanzee of rapid decompression to a near vacuum. *NASA, Contractor Rept.* **CR-329.**

Life, J. S., and Pinc, B. W. (1966). Parasympathetic control of heart rate in acceleratively stressed monkeys. *Preprint, 37th Aerospace Med. Assoc. Meeting, Las Vegas, Nevada,* pp. 144-154 and 189-190.

Malinow, M. R., and Wagner, R. (1966). Oxygen uptake in squirrel monkeys *(Saimiri sciurea)*. *Lab. Animal Care,* **16,** 105-108.

Meek, J. C., Graybiel, A., Beischer, D. E., and Riopelle, A. J. (1962). Observations of canal sickness and adaptation in chimpanzees and squirrel monkeys in a "Slow Rotation Room." *Aerospace Med.* **33,** 571-578.

Mehelas, J. N., and Pinc, B. W. (1965). The response of squirrel monkeys to high accelerative forces. *NASA Contractor Rept.* **CR-236.**

Pinc, B. W., and Barr, N. L. (1963). Some responses of squirrel monkeys to high G-brief duration acceleration profiles. *Aerospace Med.* **34,** 752-757.

Pinc, B. W., and Life, J. S. (1966). Role of the autonomic nervous system and hypoxia in the cardiac control of squirrel monkeys exposed to $200+g_x$ for 200 seconds. Nonr-4952(00) Final Rept. Space/Defense Corporation, Birmingham, Michigan.

Rumbaugh, D. M., and Ternes, J. W. (1965). Learning-set performance of squirrel monkeys after rapid decompression to vacuum. *Aerospace Med.* **36,** 8-12.

364 Dietrich E. Beischer

Spoendlin, H. H., Schuknecht, H. F., and Graybiel, A. (1965). Ultrastructure of the otolith organs in squirrel monkeys after exposure to high levels of gravitoinertial force. *Aerospace Med.* **36,** 497-503.

Thach, J. S., Jr. (1966). Long-term performance of squirrel monkeys under space simulation conditions. Part II: Behavioral technique. *NASA* **SP-115,** 276-282.

Workman, R. D., Bond, G. F., and Mazzone, W. F. (1962). Prolonged exposure of animals to pressurized normal and synthetic atmospheres. Rept. 374, Vol. XXI, No. 5. U.S. Naval Med. Res. Lab., Submarine Base, New London, Groton, Connecticut.

CHAPTER **13**

Use of the Squirrel Monkey in Pharmacology

Harley M. Hanson

I. Introduction

In this chapter my aim is not to consider the pharmacology of the squirrel monkey per se in the sense of medical management but rather to explore the role that the squirrel monkey is presently playing in pharmacological research and, hopefully, to point out areas where the squirrel monkey might advantageously be used.

Infrahuman primates have been used in isolated instances for the study of various drugs almost as long as pharmacology has been a recognized discipline. However, the total use of primates in pharmacological studies when compared to the usage of other animals has always been extremely small. For example, in a survey of the experimental reports in 9 journals publishing pharmacological studies* in 1960, of 47 species cited as being

*Journal of Pharmacology and Experimental Therapeutics, Archives Internationales de Pharmacodynamie et de Therapie, Toxicology and Applied Pharmacology, Psychopharmacologia, Proceedings of the Society for Experimental Biology and Medicine, Acta Pharmacologica et Toxicologica, British Journal of Pharmacology and Chemotherapy, Journal of Pharmacy and Pharmacology, Journal of Applied Physiology.

used, primates accounted for less than 1.3% of such citations, and squirrel monkeys were not reported as being used at all. It should be noted, however, that even in the most scholarly journals many authors did not classify primates other than by the term "monkey" until recently, and some of the species used had to be identified on the basis of weight and other data given. A similar survey of the articles appearing in the same journals in 1965 indicated that the use of primates had not materially changed (1.6% of 2210 citations) but squirrel monkeys accounted for 10.8% of the infrahuman primate total. These data would seem to suggest that the squirrel monkey is gaining greater recognition as a useful experimental animal but that the overall use of primates in pharmacological research remains constant. (The rat incidentally, by this method of counting, was by far the most popular experimental animal for both years.)

In 1963, an article appeared entitled "The Use of the Squirrel Monkey in Behavioral and Pharmacological Experiments" (Kelleher *et al.*, 1963). The authors cited only two references for pharmacological studies, both in the behavioral area; there were, of course, other studies available for squirrel monkeys at that time. In a sense, however, this article and the references cited are representative of the general level of primate utilization by the scientific community. It is apparent that as a result of limited utilization of squirrel monkeys, a large body of information is not available for analysis, and much of our discussion of uses of this species will have to be in terms of possibilities rather than accomplishments.

There is, of course, no reason why with sufficient ingenuity the squirrel monkey could or should not be used for any pharmacological purpose for which rats, dogs, and cats are presently utilized. The problem of cost is of little concern, since at least at present rates in the northeastern United States, the cost of a squirrel monkey is approximately one-fifth that of a rhesus monkey, and certainly no more than the cost of a dozen rats. The reasons offered by pharmacologists for not using primates are many, common among which have been initial expense, difficulties in housing, and vagaries of supply. The preferred species for a particular area of research also depends, to a large extent, on the animal popular for that type of study at the time the basic research was completed. For example, most studies on gastric secretion have been done in the dog although there is no reason why other animals could not serve. For such reasons the growth of central nervous system research during the past 15 years, with its attendant anthromorpism overlapping with the emergence of a reliable supply of quality primates (a remarkable phenomenon of the 1950's), has resulted in the increased frequency of the adoption and to some degree the acceptance of primates, particularly rhesus monkeys, as a standard animal for central nervous system research. To a degree it would appear that the suppliers of experimental animals have determined the direction a research area takes.

II. Special Considerations

As is discussed elsewhere, a basic problem presented by the use of any wild-born primate in the laboratory is the ever-present, and in the case of the squirrel monkey, almost certain infestation by a variety of parasites. In the past squirrel monkeys received from commercial vendors quite deservedly had the reputation of being heavily infested with intestinal parasites, and this turned some investigators to other species, e.g., the "safer" rat, cat, or dog. However, with appropriate application of anthelminthics (see Chapter 14), this problem, with good husbandry, can be permanently solved. When the squirrel monkey becomes routinely available in a relatively parasite-free state, it is to be expected that its use in pharmacological investigation will increase.

A. SEX DIFFERENCES

Speaking only from our own experience, we find no sex differences in the squirrel monkey that can be shown to have effects on the pharmacological studies we have carried out. On a statistical basis, however, the females in our laboratory seem to withstand pharmacological "stresses" more successfully than males, i.e., they live longer when employed in a routine testing program. The fact that the females are generally smaller than the males also makes them somewhat more desirable for experiments when the compounds to be studied are in extremely short supply and even a few milligrams of compound saved makes a difference. The decreased risk of injury to the experimenter from a smaller animal that is more easily handled cannot be discounted.

B. RACIAL DIFFERENCES

When attention was first paid to the types of *Saimiri* we noted that there were representatives of both common "races" in our colony (see Chapter 1). We have never noticed any differences between them in terms of response to drugs, although it is pertinent to note that to demonstrate such differences large samples (hundreds) from each population would have to be tested in a standard situation. A similar comment could also be made about the apparent lack of sex differences noted above. No differences have yet been demonstrated—but then no one has yet actually tried to demonstrate such differences.

C. ROUTES OF DRUG ADMINISTRATION

Any of the usual routes of drug administration can be followed with the squirrel monkey. The intramuscular, subcutaneous, and intraperitoneal routes offer no particular problems—the rather small muscle mass of the squirrel monkey, however, necessitates relative care in the selection of the site for intramuscular injection. The muscles of the posterior aspect of the thigh (hamstring muscles) have been found to be satisfactory for intramuscular dosing. A slightly lateral placement of the needle will ensure missing the sciatic nerve. Intraperitoneal dosing as in most other species is most successful if a short, relatively blunt, large-gauge needle is used for injection to prevent the perforation of the intestine. A little-appreciated fact is that absorption from the peritoneal cavity is excellent, and insoluble compounds injected as a suspension are often well absorbed. The possibility of accidentally injecting the dose into the intestine where many compounds are not absorbed is one that should be weighed carefully before selecting this route.

Intravenous injections are somewhat difficult with the squirrel monkey; we have found that injection into the superficial saphenous veins with a small-gauge needle is most satisfactory, and with practice can be done routinely. It might be noted that very acidic or basic solutions sometimes produce injury making further injections into a particular vein difficult if not impossible. Oral dosing in those situations allowing it because of its ease and surity, is almost to be considered the route of choice. For oral dosing to be effective the squirrel monkey must be food-deprived 12—18 hours predosing. If the stomach is not relatively free of food at the time of drug administration, absorption is surprisingly poor—in many cases approximately *twice* the normal dose of many compounds must be given to produce a given effect.

To administer an oral dose the mouth is held open with a gag (a metal rod the size and shape of a pencil) and an appropriate tube (male urinary catheter no. 8 French) is passed over the gag, down the esophagus into the stomach. A compound then can be injected via the catheter into the stomach either as a solution or a suspension. Literally thousands of doses have been given in this fashion in our laboratory without any complications. It is most convenient, although not absolutely necessary, to have the monkey restrained in an upright posture while this procedure is taking place. A "chair" found most useful for this purpose in our laboratory is shown in Fig. 1. The monkey is restrained only by the neck (note the movable plate that fastens it into the chair). The large nonperforated plastic top of the chair protects the operator from any interference from the animal's feet. Since the animal is controlled by the fixed collar, intravenous, intraperitoneal, or intramuscular doses can be given by the simple expedient of grasping the hind limbs of the animal and exerting moderate traction out and downward. Other restraint chairs designed for other purposes have also been reported (e.g., Carmichael and MacLean, 1961; Kelleher and Morse,

FIG. 1. Squirrel monkey "seated" in simple restraint chair. The animal is held only by the neck allowing complete freedom to the limbs.

1964) (see also the "trough" method described in Chapter 14). The particular chair pictured, if desired, can also be equipped with a lever and appropriate feeding devices for operant conditioning studies. Shock is deliverable via the metal neck plate and the seat (perch) of the chair.

Kelleher *et al.* (1963) describe a method of maintaining monkeys on the end of leash in order to facilitate handling. In our experience this method, while useful when no more than a small number of animals are to be managed, is excessively time-consuming and the risk of the chain tangling and strangling the animal is excessive. If chaining is desirable we have found that stainless steel ball chains make a most satisfactory collar, which is strong, resistant to water, and does not abrade the animal's neck. As has been noted elsewhere in this book a pair of heavy leather gloves (with gauntlets) offers adequate protection and with proper caging allows an animal to be captured and handled at will. Individual caging is of course necessary if this system is to be followed.

In our laboratory squirrel monkeys are individually housed in cages 10 ×

14 × 18 inches which not only facilitates catching the animals and allows uninterrupted feeding, but also, and perhaps most importantly, allows unhindered recovery when a high dose of a depressant or toxic agent has been administered. It should be kept in mind that an unconscious or sedated animal is unable to protect itself; in a group cage it is invariably stepped on by its cage mates, perhaps resulting in death.

III. Selected Data

A. OBSERVED BEHAVIOR

The earliest reported pharmacological experiment with the squirrel monkey that we have been able to discover utilized the animals for a comparison of the effects of thiopropazate and chlorpromazine on observed behavior (Stone et al., 1960). A group of animals was given various oral doses of the two compounds and their behavior evaluated and rated, i.e., "no effect," "depressed," or "markedly depressed" with an appropriate delineation of typical behavior of the animal at each rating level. By using appropriate statistics, these observational data were compared with similar data collected in the dog and the rhesus monkey. These values are shown in Table I. With regard to sedation, it is interesting to note that the squirrel monkey, at least in this situation, appears approximately twice as sensitive to the effects of thiopropazate and half as sensitive to chlorpromazine as the other two species.

A study using similar (though somewhat more refined) observational techniques was reported by Schaper et al. (1960) from the laboratories of C. Janssen (Beerse, Belgium). Using eight squirrel monkeys, these investigators were able to show clear dose-related effects with four doses of haloperidol and haloperidide. The doses were administered according to a Latin-square design over a period of 8 weeks. The animals were observed by three judges under blind conditions and rated for the degree of sedation, catalepsia, general activity, and excitation. On the basis of these data the two compounds were considered to be equiactive.

It is interesting to note that both these groups of investigators adopted the squirrel monkey for essentially the same purpose at approximately the same time although one set of researchers was in the United States and the other in Belgium. A second set of papers describing experiments that used squirrel monkeys in a similar fashion to study other compounds (piperacetazine and dehydrobenzperidol) was later issued (Knapp et al., 1962; Janssen et al., 1963).

Since these first studies there has been a marked absence of published studies using observed behavior in the squirrel monkey for the comparison

TABLE I
TRANQUILIZING EFFECTS OF THIOPROPAZATE, AND CHLORPROMAZINE[a]

| | Oral $ED_{50} \pm$ S.E. (mg/kg)[b] | |
Species	Thiopropazate	Chlorpromazine
Squirrel monkey	0.455 ± 0.108	9.80 ± 0.84
Rhesus monkey	0.875 ± 0.235	4.74 ± 0.75
Dog	$1.22 \ \pm 0.52$	2.36 ± 0.85

[a] Data derived from Stone et al., 1960.
[b] ED_{50} = Estimated dose necessary to produce 50% of the maximally possible observable effect.

of pharmacological agents. It is difficult to determine why such studies should be unpopular but perhaps the increased interest in the study of the more clearly defined conditioned behaviors is a factor. Observation studies in *Saimiri*, however, seem to have a definite value for the simple rapid comparison of pharmacological agents when carefully done, and it is possible such studies will increase.

B. OPERANT BEHAVIOR STUDIES

The adoption of operant conditioning methodology by pharmacologists and in particular by the pharmaceutical industry in the middle and late 1950's for the study of the then just popular tranquilizers was a natural match for the then just emerging squirrel monkey "as a laboratory primate." A qualitative study* that is a good example of this early use of the squirrel monkey was published by Cook and Kelleher (1961, 1962). Monkeys were trained to lever-press for food on a multiple fixed-interval fixed-ratio schedule of reinforcement. In the presence of stimulus 1, a 10-minute fixed interval (FI 10) was in effect and the first lever response after 10 minutes was rewarded with food. In the presence of stimulus 2, a 30-response fixed ratio (FR 30) was in effect, i.e., every thirtieth response was rewarded. Following each food reinforcement all stimuli were removed for $2\frac{1}{2}$ minutes and the experiment stopped (time out). These conditions alternated throughout a test session. A representative control performance is shown in the top of Fig. 2, as a "cumulative record" (cumulative work curve). In the FI-10 components, indicated in the figure by a, as is typical with this schedule the monkeys did not respond for $3-6$ minutes and then responded at an increasing rate until the reward was delivered (indicated by the resetting of the recorder pen). In the "time out" components (b and

*In contrast to quantitative studies yielding dose-response relationships.

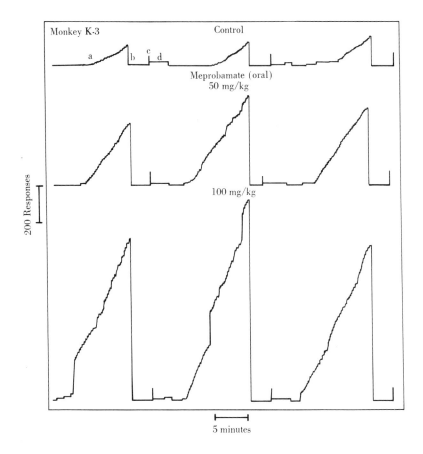

FIG. 2. Effects of meprobamate on behavior maintained by a multiple schedule of positive reinforcement including FI 10 (a), FR 30 (b), and time out (b,d) components. The main effect of the drug was to increase responding in the FI components. (Figure reproduced by permission of The New York Academy of Sciences from Cook and Kelleher, 1962.)

d) no responding occurred. In the fixed ratio component (as at c) the monkeys responded at a high rate.

The effects of meprobamate (50 and 100 mg/kg p.o.) produced significant increases in responding only during the FI components. Discrimination between conditions remained intact. The high dose tested was reported to produce depression and ataxia. *d*-Amphetamine produced very similar patterns of response as is shown in Fig. 3 although with this compound stimulation was noted. Figure 4 shows data collected with chlorpromazine. It will be noted that chlorpromazine markedly depressed the fixed-interval performance but left the FR behavior relatively intact.

It was concluded that these experiments showed that this method can be used to demonstrate differences between drugs such as meprobamate and chlorpromazine. It must be noted, however, that the effects shown are equally demonstrable with other species such as rats, and our primary interest in these experiments is that they were among the first executed with squirrel monkeys. Later quantitative studies with the same technique were published presenting dose — response curves for d-amphetamine and chlorpromazine (Kelleher and Morse, 1964) along with some interesting manipulations of the basic test situation.

Studies comparing more than a few compounds in groups of squirrel monkeys trained on operant schedules have never been numerous. Apparently the first to be reported was by Hanson (1961) (more fully presented in Vernier, 1961) who compared the effects of amitriptyline, imipramine, and chlorpromazine in squirrel monkeys trained to lever press to avoid electric shock. This avoidance technique was later more fully exploited to study the effects of several other compounds (Hanson et al., 1966). A group of 11 monkeys was highly trained to lever-press on a modified Sidman avoidance schedule (RS-4, SS-5) in standard operant-conditioning chambers. Each lever-press postponed electric shocks delivered through the grid floor for 40 seconds. If a response that would terminate it was not made during or following a shock, additional shocks were delivered at 4-second intervals.

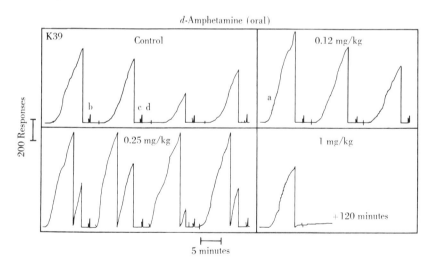

FIG. 3. Effects of d-amphetamine on behavior maintained by a multiple schedule of positive reinforcement including FI 10 (a), FR 30 (b), and time out (b,d) components. (Figure reproduced by permission of The New York Academy of Sciences from Cook and Kelleher, 1962.)

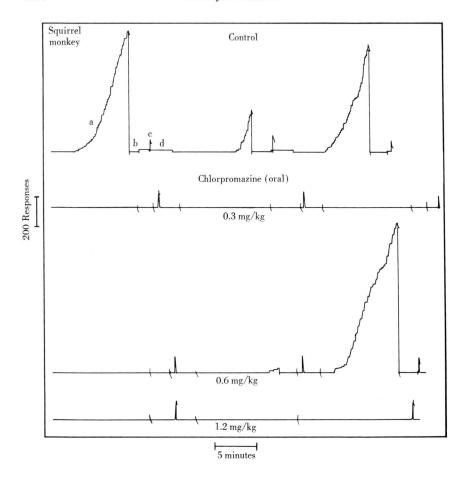

FIG. 4. Effects of chlorpromazine on behavior maintained by a multiple schedule of positive reinforcement including FI 10 (a), FR 30 (b), and time out (b,d) components. (Figure reproduced by permission of The New York Academy of Sciences from Cook and Kelleher, 1962.)

Under normal conditions the animals steadily lever-pressed for several hours taking very few shocks. Cumulative oral doses of seven different compounds were administered during 7-hour test sessions; the first dose was given 30 minutes presession and the remaining doses at 90-minute intervals. The data collected are shown in Fig. 5. The maximal number of shocks deliverable under the conditions of the experiment was 200. Doses necessary to produce a shock incidence of 100 per hour (ED_{50}) were estimated from linear functions fitted to these data. These values are shown in Table II. Table III, adapted from Cole and Edwards (1964), compares the

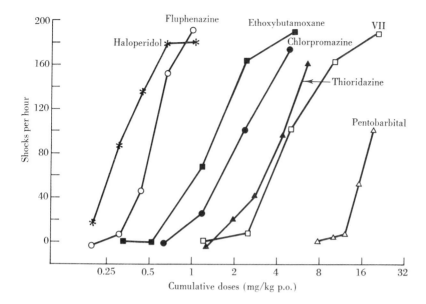

FIG. 5. Effects of cumulative doses of several depressant agents on the number of shocks delivered to a group of 11 squirrel monkeys lever pressing to avoid shock on a modified Sidman avoidance schedule (RS40, SS-5). The maximum number of shocks possible was 200. (Figure from Hanson et al., 1966.)

TABLE II
ESTIMATES OF ANTIAVOIDANCE POTENCY[a]

Compound	SI 100[b] mg/kg p.o.	Potency relative to chlorpromazine	Relative potency confidence limits
Haloperidol	0.33	6.74	5.50−8.26
Fluphenazine	0.48	4.57	3.58−5.82
Ethoxybutamoxane	1.40	1.58	1.24−2.02
Chlorpromazine	2.20	1.00	−
Thioridazine	3.83	0.58	0.47−0.70
VII[c]	4.75	0.46	0.37−0.58
Pentobarbital	19.59	0.11	0.09−0.14

[a] Data from Hanson et al., 1966.
[b] Estimated dose necessary to produce an incidence of 100 shocks per hour.
[c] β-3-Chloro-5-(3-dimethylaminopropylidene)-dibenzo(a,e) cycloheptatriene hydrochloride.

doses of the phenothiazines effective in monkeys with the doses used in a drug study with humans by the Psychopharmacology Service Center. The squirrel monkey doses compare well with the human doses on a milligram

TABLE III
COMPARISON OF CLINICAL DOSES WITH EFFECTIVE SQUIRREL MONKEY DOSES[a]

Compound	Squirrel monkey dose mg/kg	Human dose mg/kg
Chlorpromazine	2.20	9.36
Thioridazine	3.83	10.0
Fluphenazine	0.48	0.9

[a] From Cole and Edwards, 1964.

per kilogram basis suggesting the squirrel monkey has approximately the sensitivity of man.

A more complex schedule was found useful for studying another class of drugs also possessing depressant properties; two of the compounds were reported in the previous study. The data are summarized in Fig. 6 (Hanson *et al.*, 1967). A group of four squirrel monkeys trained to lever-press for food in a standard operant conditioning chamber were used. A multiple schedule alternated 10-minute periods of VI 1 (milk rewards were delivered randomly in time if a lever-press was made) concurrent FR 10, VR 15 shock (milk rewards were delivered for each tenth response, shocks were given on the average for every fifteenth response), and S^{Δ} (no rewards or punishments were delivered). The three conditions were appropriately "signaled" by colored lights and clicking sounds. The three conditions alternated in order for 10-minute periods. Under normal (control) conditions the monkeys lever-pressed steadily during the period when only food was given (VI 1, indicated by the horizontal line in the first row of Fig. 6) and at very low rates during the other two conditions. The six compounds were administered 30 minutes preceding a 3-hour test session. As can be seen in the figure, pentobarbital, meprobamate, and chlordiazepoxide all increased lever-responding under all three conditions of the experiment, while chlorpromazine clearly only depressed responding. Scopolamine and *d*-amphetamine increased responding in S^{Δ} but decreased the number of responses made in the period when responses were punished. Other of our data not presently published support the idea that this or a similar procedure in squirrel monkeys is useful in discriminating between these classes of depressant agents. It is instructive to compare the effective doses of pentobarbital (5.0 − 10.0 mg/kg p.o.) and chlorpromazine (0.625 − 2.0 mg/kg p.o.) in this test situation with the data in Table II. The SI_{100}'s reported were 19.59 mg/kg for pentobarbital and 2.20 mg/kg for chlorpromazine. The procedure involving the more complex schedules is clearly generally more sensitive but the relationship between the compounds is approximately the same.

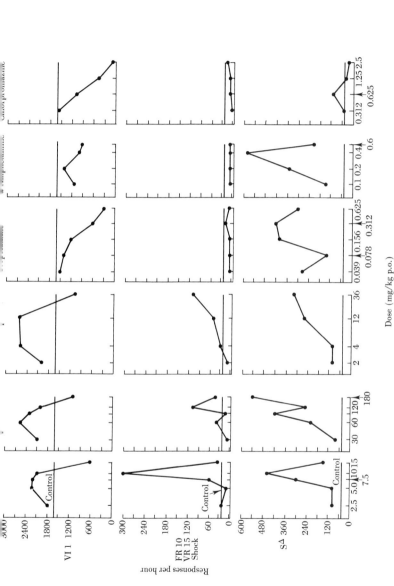

Dose (mg/kg p.o.)

FIG. 6. Dose−response relationships yielded by each of the components of a multiple schedule. VI programmed only positive rewards; FR 10 VR15 shock programmed both rewards and shocks (conflict); in S△ no contingencies were programmed. (Figure from Hanson *et al.*, 1967, copyright 1967 by the Society for the Experimental Analysis of Behavior, Inc.)

Feldman and Green (1966) reported that chlordiazepoxide at 20 mg/kg p.o. affected fixated behavior in squirrel monkeys. This somewhat complex situation consisted in training the animals in a choice situation for food reward, and then randomly rewarding with food or punishing with electric shock all responses, with the added contingency of punishing nonresponse. Under these conditions the animals responded in a stereotyped fashion (always choosing one alternative) for many trials, even when a soluble problem was programmed although eventually they "get over" this "fixation." Chlordiazepoxide given during this relearning phase decreased the time for the response to be made to the positive stimulus and increased eating behavior.

The preceding experiments yielded reasonably regular dose — response relationships, but gave little attention to the problem of duration of action of a compound. Figure 7 presents data collected in our laboratory during 19- to 20-hour test sessions with a single highly trained squirrel monkey. The animal had been previously trained to lever-press to avoid shock while restrained in a test stand similar to the one shown in Fig. 1. The type of tracing shown, while sensitive to artifacts of the recording device, illustrates clearly the importance of two factors: (1) magnitude of a pharmacological response (which always has a ceiling, sometimes imposed by the recording apparatus) and (2) the duration of the pharmacological response. The data are presented in the form of a bar graph, each bar representing 5 minutes, and the height of a particular bar representing the number of lever responses made during that 5-minute period. *d*-Amphetamine was injected intramuscularly after approximately 7 hours of the session had elapsed (indicated by the arrows) and then an additional 12 hours of data collected. It can be seen that the squirrel monkey under these conditions makes lever responses at a fairly stable rate over a long period, and there is a definite tendency for a slow decline in responding to occur with the passage of time. The various doses of amphetamine injected resulted in an almost immediate enhancement in responding more or less in relation to dose. A dose of 1 mg/kg i.m. was an excessive dose and resulted in all responding being eliminated for several hours; the eventual level of responding recorded, however, surpasses anything recorded at any other dose. The duration of the effects of the compound even at the lowest doses was in excess of 6 hours which is not an unusual duration for many compounds.

The data reviewed, which unfortunately at this date are only fragmentary in nature, clearly indicate that the squirrel monkey can be useful in the study of compounds affecting the central nervous system. Based on preliminary data gathered in our laboratories on chimpanzees, rhesus and stumptailed macaques, and capuchins, it seems that squirrel monkeys are unusually sensitive to this class of compounds compared to other primates;

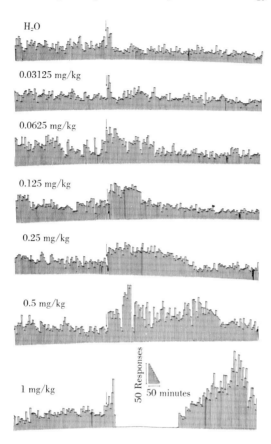

FIG. 7. Avoidance responding during extended avoidance sessions by a single monkey. *d*-Amphetamine markedly reversed the slow decline in performance occurring with time.

my guess would be that in the central nervous system area in general only man is more sensitive. The lack of systematic data hampers the evaluation of *Saimiri* as a research tool—it appears at this time, however, that the place of the squirrel monkey in this research area is secure.

C. Gastrointestinal Studies

The dog is usually thought of as the "standard" test animal for studies of the gastrointestinal system, although as early as 1932 green and rhesus monkeys were used for this type of investigation (Ferguson, 1932; Ferguson *et al.*, 1934). Studies of gastric secretion in the squirrel monkey were first reported by Brodie and Marshall (1963a,b) who studied gastric functioning by implanting modified Thomas gastric cannulae in the stomachs of male

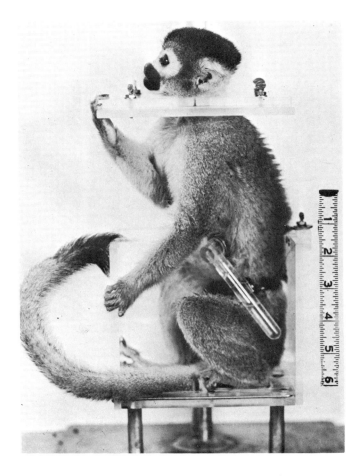

FIG. 8. Monkey prepared with gastric fistula for collection of stomach contents.

squirrel monkeys. Following recovery the animals were conditioned to a restraining chair, and the gastric contents were collected in a plastic tube attached to a Lucite connector fitted to the cannula (Fig. 8). Gastric contents were also collected using the same system in unrestrained animals remaining in their home cages. The effects of histamine, methacholine, and atropine on secretion were studied. The data collected are shown in Table IV. Histamine significantly increased free and total acid concentration. Atropine sulfate decreased the volume of juice collected at all doses tested; however, acidity was decreased only when the cumulative dose was increased to 48 mg/kg.

TABLE IV
DRUG EFFECTS ON SQUIRREL MONKEY GASTRIC CONTENTS[a,b]

Drug (base wt)	Cum. dose	Volume (ml)	Concentration					
			Free acid (meq/liter)	Total acid (meq/liter)	Pepsin (PU[b] × 10⁻⁴/ml)	Chloride (meq/liter)	Sodium (meq/liter)	Potassium (meq/liter)
Saline (1 mg/2 hour) i.p.	1.0	4.5	61.6	80.8	640.9	142.6	51.1	13.9
	2.0	4.0	64.0	82.4	678.2	149.8	53.6	12.6
	3.0	3.5	62.3	80.1	656.6	149.5	59.4	11.5
Histamine (0.1 mg/kg/hour s.c.)	0.2	5.9	90.0[c]	111.0[c]	495.9	154.3[c]	29.6[c]	14.2
	0.4	4.3	92.9[c]	109.2[c]	581.2	153.9[c]	29.4	12.9
	0.6	3.2	99.0[c]	116.3[c]	580.9	164.3[c]	33.9[c]	11.2
Methacholine (mg/kg) s.c.	0.25	5.4	31.0[c]	53.2[c]	699.6	114.7	50.8	17.7[c]
	1.0	4.0	19.7[c]	36.8[c]	554.5[c]	112.4[c]	64.5	16.5
	2.0	3.7	20.2[c]	34.3[c]	460.7[c]	113.7[c]	62.5	12.9
Atropine (mg/kg) i.p.	8.0	2.3[c]	62.7	84.8	422.2[c]	151.6	60.0	10.3
	16.0	1.7[c]	55.3	81.5	585.0	164.3[c]	79.8[c]	7.9[c]
	48.0	1.1[c]	36.7[c]	64.1	725.1	162.1[c]	d	d

[a] Collected at 2-hour intervals.
[b] Adapted from Brodie and Marshall (1963a).
[c] Significant difference from control value $P < 0.05$.
[d] Sample too small for analysis.

Compared to the doses of atropine needed to produce a similar effect in dogs and rats, the squirrel monkey appears to be singularly insensitive to atropine, a standard compound in gastrointestinal studies. It is worthy of note, however, that these investigators later concluded a report of a survey of the gastric contents of representatives from seven families of primates with the statement, "from the viewpoint of spontaneous acid secretion for physiological and pharmacological studies, the squirrel monkey appeared to be the most useful primate" (Brodie and Marshall, 1963b).

Studies of gastric functioning are also possible in the anesthetized squirrel monkey employing extraluminal contractile force transducers sutured onto the serosal layer of the gastric antrum and using recently developed techniques (Jacoby and Brodie, 1967). Representative data are shown in Fig. 9 (data supplied by H. I. Jacoby of the Merck Institute for Therapeutic

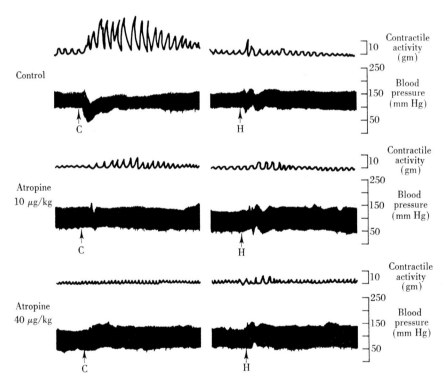

FIG. 9. Effects of carbachol (C) 1 μg/kg i.v. and histamine (H) 4 mg/kg i.v. on contractile activity of the gastric antrum (top tracing). Femoral arterial blood pressure second tracing. Pentobarbitol 32 mg/kg i.p. was used as anesthesia. (Figure supplied by H. I. Jacoby, Merck Institute for Therapeutic Research.)

Research). The top tracing of each set indicates the activity of the circular muscle of the antrum under control conditions following intravenous administration of carbachol and histamine. The increased amplitude of contractions of the stomach produced by carbachol were reduced by $10\mu g/kg$ of atropine and completely blocked by $40\mu g/kg$ i.v. of atropine. The effects of histamine (4 mg/kg i.v.) shown to the right of the figure indicated that this compound, as in the dog when similarly studied, produced only a minimal effect on the gastric antrum. The doses of atropine administered did somewhat attenuate the effects of histamine on the stomach but did not eliminate it. The blood pressure recordings shown indicate the expected blockade of the depressor effects of carbachol by atropine. Histamine produced only minimal effects on blood pressure which is in contrast to the effects producible by this agent in dogs. Gastric motility studied by means of a small balloon placed in the stomach via a gastric fistula was reported by Yankell and Marshall (1967) for the study of the spasmogenic properties of insulin and the spasmolytic actions of atropine.

Although the unexpected insensitivity of the squirrel monkey to atropine does not appear to particularily recommend this species as a "standard" for pharmacological studies of the gastrointestinal system, it is possible that its more humanlike pattern of secretion, and its other advantages of size, etc., may bring it to the forefront of this research area.

D. CARDIOVASCULAR STUDIES

To remedy the shortage of reported drug—cardiovascular data for *Saimiri* my colleague at the Merck Institute for Therapeutic Research, M. L. Torchiana, performed some preliminary experiments with the squirrel monkey. The basic protocol was the same as that found useful during years of this type of experimentation with dogs; the drugs studied are standards and were selected to allow the "evaluation" of this species. Since these data are not available elsewhere the method will be described fully.

Squirrel monkeys of either sex (500—800 gm) were anesthetized with vinbarbital (37—50 mg/kg injected into the saphenous vein). Tracheal cannulae were inserted to maintain an adequate airway and rectal temperatures were monitored and maintained at 38°C by means of a heat lamp. Femoral arterial pressure and the electrocardiogram (lead II) were monitored via appropriate transducers and recorders. Drugs were injected via a cannulated femoral vein, at 10-minute intervals. Increasing doses of epinephrine (0.5—4.0 μg/kg), methacholine (0.25—4.0 μg/kg), norepinephrine (0.125—4.0 μg/kg) and histamine (1.0—8.0 μg/kg) were studied in groups of four animals. In other experiments the blood pressure and heart rate responses to epinephrine (1.5 μg/kg) and norepinephrine (1.0 μg/kg) were recorded before and after the administration of mecamylamine (0.5 mg/kg), a ganglionic blocking agent, propranolol (0.5 mg/kg), a β-adrenergic blocking agent, and dibenzyline (1.0 mg/kg), an α-adrenergic blocking agent. For comparative purposes electrocardiograms were recorded in four unanesthetized animals previously conditioned to "sit" in a restraining stand.

In 10 anesthetized animals the average mean blood pressure was 97 mm Hg with a standard deviation of ±16; the average heart rate was 266 ± 44 per minute. In the unanesthetized monkeys the average heart rate recorded in 50 observations over a 2-hour period was 310 ± 46 per minute. Both of these heart rate measurements compare well with the value reported by Scheckel and Pazery (1962).

The responses obtained to increasing doses of norepinephrine, epinephrine, and methacholine are shown in Fig. 10. The dose, estimated from the dose–response line, required for a rise of 50 mm Hg (pressor dose$_{50}$) was 1.1 μg/kg for norepinephrine and 1.6 μg/kg for epinephrine. Methacholine evoked a depressor response; the depressor dose$_{50}$ was 2.0 μg/kg. The doses used and the responses obtained in the squirrel monkey are in the same range as those found under similar conditions in the dog and cat. The response to histamine, however, differed and was biphasic, consisting of an initial depressor followed by a pressor phase of approximate equal magnitude; in doses up to 8.0 μg/kg the maximum change obtained was ±20 mm Hg.

A chronotropic dose–response to the injected sympathomimetic agents was not consistently obtained; in some animals epinephrine and norepinephrine produced a slight increase in rate (tachycardia) and in others bradycardia or a biphasic response was obtained. The lack of a dose-related chronotropic response could be attributed in part to the high heart rate in this species; similar observations have been made in the anesthetized rat.

In animals given the ganglionic blocking agent, mecamylamine, mean arterial pressure decreased to 85–58 mm Hg and heart rate to 225–172 per minute. Following the ganglionic blocking agent there was an increase in the acute pressure change to epinephrine and norepinephrine but the maximum pressure attained was lower than during the control phase of the experiments (Table V, Group I). Due to lower heart rate after mecamylamine, the positive chronotropic response to epinephrine and norepinephrine was more evident. Following the administration of propranolol, a β-receptor antagonist, the chronotropic response to these sympathomimetics was blocked, demonstrating as in other species the presence of β-adrenergic receptors in the heart. The pressor response to epinephrine and norepinephrine was also reduced following propranolol which is believed to be due

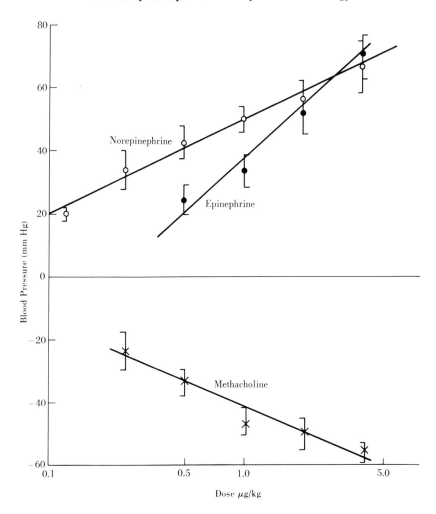

FIG. 10. Blood pressure response in groups of four squirrel monkeys to increasing doses of norepinephrine, epinephrine, and methacholine. The vertical lines indicate the standard error of the mean. (Figure supplied by M. L. Torchiana, Merck Institute for Therapeutic Research.)

to a depression of vascular responsiveness or to the diminished myocardial response which under other conditions could contribute to the total response to these agents.

Following the administration of an α-adrenergic blocking agent, dibenzyline (Table V, Group II) there was an unmasking of the β-receptor agonist

TABLE V

EFFECT OF STANDARD ADRENERGIC BLOCKING AGENTS ON THE RESPONSES TO
EPINEPHRINE AND NOREPINEPHRINE IN THE ANESTHETIZED SQUIRREL MONKEY

Group no. monkey no., and agent	Epinephrine (1.5 γ/kg)				Norepinephrine (1.0 γ/kg)			
	Pressure (mm Hg)		Heart rate		Pressure (mm Hg)		Heart rate	
	Initial	Change	Initial	Change	Initial	Change	Initial	Change
Group I								
Pretreatment Control								
1	78	+40	280	+20	88	+45	290	+20
1	73	+50	280	+30	68	+57	278	+32
2	95	+69	172	+118	93	+64	185	+90
2	92	+81	170	+110	85	+59	230	+52
Average	85	+60	225	+70	85	+59	230	+52
Mecamylamine (0.5 mg/kg)								
1	39	+73	192	+106	37	+75	192	+73
1	32	+81	170	+95	34	+71	170	+88
2	92	+77	165	+125	67	+94	165	+110
2	69	+103	162	+126	73	+90	160	+106
Average	58	+84	172	+113	53	+83	172	+94
Propranolol (0.5 mg/kg)								
1	32	+41	158	+30	32	+29	156	+4
2	59	+64	144	+26	67	+53	150	+10
Average	46	+53	151	+28	50	+41	154	+7
Group II								
Pretreatment Control								
3	87	+22	246	+34	87	+33	250	+28
3	85	+22	248	+30	97	+30	250	+22

4	93	+30	300	−5	95	+32	288	+12
4	105	+30	300	+8,−4	109	+35	304	+12
Average	93	+26	274	+18,−1	95	+33	273	+19

Dibenzyline (1.0 mg/kg)

3	78	−9	290	+10,−5	65	+26	284	+6
3	62	+8,−11	266	+16	60	+32	264	+10
4	89	+4,−16	320	+2,−6	88	+24	308	+4
4	85	−17	310	+6	85	+24	318	+7
Average	77	+3,−13	295	+9,−3	75	+27	294	+7

Group III
Pretreatment Control

5	82	+33	254	+28,−14	81	+34	244	+30
5	93	+34	240	+42	97	+31	248	+40
6	85	+45	242	−4,+14	87	+58	245	−67
6	85	+58	236	+10,20	90	+59	247	−77
Average	86	+43	243	+19,−5	89	+46	246	−19

Saline

5	101	+32	242	+53	98	+40	240	+42
5	95	+40	238	+42	95	+42	240	+40
6	90	+52	215	+20	87	+65	230	+6,−60
6	91	+56	220	+12,−25	87	+60	222	−60
Average	94	+45	229	+32,−6	92	+52	231	+22,−30

Saline

5	97	+30	240	+50	95	+43	262	+20,−17
6	88	+57	210	+16,−16	82	+65	210	+5,−50
Average	93	+44	225	+33,−8	89	+54	236	+13,−34

properties of epinephrine as shown by the reversal of the pressor response and a slight decrease in the pressor response to norepinephrine.

It was concluded that the vascular responsiveness of the squirrel monkey to these agents, with the exception of histamine, was qualitatively similar to that obtained in the dog or cat. The animals were found to tolerate the anesthesia well, to yield excellent blood pressure recordings, and to be sufficiently "robust" to be used for 4 or more hours of study. An "aberrant" response to histamine was noted previously in experiments reviewed on gastric function; the effects seen in this system seem consistent with a general lack of activity of histamine in *Saimiri*. This difference is of interest and requires further study for its elucidation; comparison with other subhuman primates would be of particular value.

E. Biochemical Studies

With few exceptions the investigators doing pharmacological research in squirrel monkeys have used this animal as a chronic preparation, and rarely have considered it a readily available inexpensive *primate* for acute studies. Two recently published papers suggest that not only are such studies possible but perhaps indicate the path they may take.

Ordy *et al.* (1966) studied concurrent changes in hypothalamic and cardiac catecholamine levels after administration of ether, fluothane, chlorpromazine, haloperidol, or reserpine, and a "stress" state produced by isolation or by periodic electric shocks. Ninety-six animals were used in the study. Control norepinephrine levels in the hypothalamus were found to be about 1.75 $\mu g/gm$. It was found that a 1-hour exposure to electric shock depleted norepinephrine; a similar effect was noted 4 hours after fluothane anesthesia. Pretreatment with chlorpromazine and haloperidol effectively inhibited electric shock-induced depletion of catecholamines in both the heart and the hypothalamus. There were significant correlations between the changes measured in hypothalamic and cardiac norepinephrine levels after the anesthetics, tranquilizers, stress, and inhibition of the stress treatments.

Cram *et al.* (1965) reported that γ-chlordane given daily for 7 days at a dose of 10 mg/kg resulted in a 2- to 6-fold increase in the activity of the hepatic microsomal enzymes that metabolize benzpyrene, zoxazolamine, hexobarbital, and *p*-nitrobenzoic acid, and in the appearance of significant metabolic activity for the metabolism of aminopyrine. Also significantly enhanced by γ-chlordane was the ability of hepatic microsomes to oxidize NADPH and bind carbon monoxide. These effects were considered similar to those previously observed in mice, rabbits, and rats.

Ellison *et al.* (1966), utilizing a carbon-14 tag on the α-position of the side chain of (+)amphetamine studied the metabolic fate of this compound in the rat, dog, and squirrel monkey. It was found that the rat metabolizes the drug through ring hydroxylation while in the squirrel monkey oxidative deamination is the primary pathway. In the dog either pathway can be utilized. Hippuric acid was the major metabolite found in the urine of the monkey.

Studies such as these are important first steps toward the accumulation of sufficient "base-line" data to support the widespread use of the squirrel monkey for metabolic studies. When sufficient base-line data become available, we might expect investigators to be "forced" to use this species in order to compare their work with that already published. Until such a time, however, it seems to me that the opportunity to do basic biochemical studies using primates (or primate tissue) in a routine fashion is bound to be appealing.

F. TOXICITY STUDIES

With the increasing emphasis on toxicological investigations, particularly with new drugs, it seems natural that the squirrel monkey would be selected as a test animal. Almost all major laboratories involved with toxicity testing have at least investigated the utility of squirrel monkey but generally speaking little routine use is made of this species. One notable exception is Consultox Laboratories, Limited, London, which has developed a very successful program. As yet, however, there have been few published investigations, and no body of normative data is presently available. One of the few published investigations is that of Lu *et al.* (1965) who studied the effects of infusions of sodium fluoride on EEG, blood pressure, and respiration in squirrel monkeys. The infusions were continued until death occurred. Squirrel monkeys were found to be approximately two times more sensitive to the lethal effects of this compound compared to rhesus monkeys and rats. It was suggested that this sensitivity may have been due to the heavy infestation of intestinal parasites discovered at autopsy. The value of this type of study at this time would seem questionable and little is to be gained without comparative data.

Special studies of the ototoxic effects of single doses of sodium salicylate were made in a group of 12 squirrel monkeys by Myers and Bernstein (1965). These investigators gathered audiograms by a conditioning procedure (shuttle box) before and after administration of a single subcutaneous dose of salicylate. A reversible hearing loss (17—36 decibels) correlated with plasma salicylate levels was reported. No abnormalities of the inner ear were demonstrated. A series of studies with squirrel monkeys investigating various aspects of the auditory system have been carried out by Igarashi *et al.* (1966). Of particular interest is the study of canal function studied by the threshold caloric test, emesis in the "slow rotation" room and ataxia during and following a series of doses of streptomycin sulfate. It was found that the compound injured the hair cells of the organ of Corti as readily as those of the cristae. These findings were felt to be of importance for application to man.

Some factors militating against the use of the squirrel monkey as a standard test animal at this point are (1) the relative lack of normative data in certain areas, hopefully to be rectified during the next decade; (2) the inherent smallness of all physiological samples, requiring development of more efficient test procedures; (3) the previous acceptance of the rhesus monkey as a laboratory standard. This last consideration, possibly the most telling, we suspect will be attenuated in time if for no other reason than the increasing expense of the rhesus as supply becomes more difficult.

At present, the role of the squirrel monkey in toxicology seems particularly suited to specialty studies, for example ototoxicity, specific organ toxicity, and behavioral toxicity. Development of *Saimiri* use in this area will probably be gradual; however, the increasing interest and demand for preclinical testing in primates will undoubtedly find an outlet in studies with the squirrel monkey.

IV. Summary and Conclusions

We have seen that pharmacological research with the squirrel monkey is in its infancy, the first pharmacological publication citing *Saimiri* being dated 1960, and the total number of studies available for analysis being less than 25. It is also true, however, that much data are awaiting publication and that the immediate development of the use of this species is probably a victim of the inevitable delay in the scientific reporting process.

Presently the most actively reported area of pharmacological research using squirrel monkeys deals with the effects of agents acting on the CNS, and research in this area is expected to expand. It is possible that for this type of study the squirrel monkey is already approaching the status of a standard animal.

Pharmacologists interested in the cardiovascular and gastric systems, as mentioned earlier, could well afford to devote some of their efforts toward investigations of this species. The squirrel monkey would rather dramatically allow routine drug studies to be done in a primate, and in one that appears to be a fairly satisfactory human "model." Obviously the potential for this type of study has just been scratched.

Finally, the area of toxicological testing, which is receiving ever more emphasis in our society, seems to be naturally matched to the squirrel monkey. However, as yet there have been relatively few adoptions of this species and essentially no studies published. As in all other areas of pharmacological study it seems that the squirrel monkey is on the threshold of discovery. It can be expected that while the eventual general use of *Saimiri* by pharmacologists is most probable, the process will be by a regrettable slow "bootstrapping" process, as basal data slowly accrete. It would hardly seem necessary to add that the future of this species in the pharmacology laboratory will be greatly influenced by the quality as well as quantity of animals available.

REFERENCES

Brodie, D. A., and Marshall, R. W. (1963a). Fasting gastric content of the squirrel monkey (*Saimiri sciurea*). *Am. J. Physiol.* **204**, 681-685.
Brodie, D. A., and Marshall, R. W. (1963b). Gastric content of fasted primates: A survey. *Science* **141**, 174-175.
Carmichael, M., and MacLean, P. D. (1961). Use of the squirrel monkey for brain research with description of the restraining chair. *Electroencephalog. Clin. Neurophysiol.* **13**, 128-129.
Cole, J. O., and Edwards, R. E. (1964). Prediction of clinical effects of psychotropic drugs from animal data. *Ciba Found. Symp., Animal Behaviour Drug Action, 1964* p. 286-297.
Cook, L., and Kelleher, R. T. (1961). The interaction of drugs and behavior. *In* "Neuro-Psychopharmacology" (E. Rothlin, ed.), Vol. 2, pp. 77-92. Elsevier, Amsterdam.
Cook, L., and Kelleher, R. T. (1962). Drug effects on the behavior of animals. *Ann. N. Y. Acad. Sci.* **96**, 315-335.
Cram, R. L., Juchau, M. R., and Fouts, J. R. (1965). Stimulation by chlordane of hepatic drug metabolism in the squirrel monkey. *J. Lab. Clin. Med.* **66**, 906-911.
Ellison, T., Gutzuit, L., and VanLoon, E. J. (1966). The comparative metabolism of *d*-amphetamine-C^{14} in the rat, dog, and monkey. *J. Pharmacol. Exptl. Therap.* **152**, 383-387.
Feldman, R. S., and Green, K. F. (1966). Effects of chlordiazepoxide on fixated behavior in squirrel monkeys. *J. Psycho-Pharmacol.* **1**, 37-45.
Ferguson, J. H. (1932). The central nervous system in relation to the digestive functions. *Proc. Soc. Exptl. Biol. Med.* **30**, 328-330.
Ferguson, J. H., McGavran, J., and Smith, E. R. B. (1934). Pilocarpine and gastric anacidity in monkeys. *J. Physiol. (London)* **82**, 1-10.
Hanson, H. M. (1961). The effects of amitriptyline, imipramine, chlorpromazine and nialamide on avoidance behavior. *Federation Proc.* **20**, 396.
Hanson, H. M., Witoslawski, J. J., Campbell, E. H., and Itkin, A. G. (1966). Estimation of relative antiavoidance activity of depressant drugs in squirrel monkeys. *Arch. Intern. Pharmacodyn.* **161**, 7-16.
Hanson, H. M., Witoslawski, J. J., and Campbell, E. H. (1967). Drug effects in squirrel monkeys trained on a multiple schedule with a punishment contingency. *J. Exptl. Anal. Behavior* **10**, 565-569.

Igarashi, M., McLeod, M. E., and Graybiel, A. (1966). Clinical pathological correlations in squirrel monkeys after suppression of semicircular canal function by streptomycin sulfate. *Acta Oto-Laryngol.* Suppl. 214, 1-28.

Jacoby, H. I., and Brodie, D. A. (1967). Gastrointestinal actions of metoclopramide. *Gastroenterology* **52**, 676-684.

Janssen, P. A. J., Niemegeers, G. J. E., Schellekens, K. H. L., Verbruggen, F. J., and Van-Nueten, J. M. (1963). The pharmacology of dehydrobenzperidol, a new potent and short-acting neuroleptic agent chemically related to haloperidol. *Arzneimittel-Forsch.* **13**, 205-211.

Kelleher, R. T. and Morse, W. H. (1964). Escape behavior and punished behavior. *Federation Proc.* **23**, No. 4, Part 1, 808-817.

Kelleher, R. T., Gill, C. A., Riddle, W. C., and Cook, L. (1963). On the use of the squirrel monkey in behavioral and pharmacological experiments. *J. Exptl. Anal. Behavior* **6**, 249-262.

Knapp, D. L., Stone, G. C., Hambourger, W. E., and Drill, V. A. (1962). Behavioral and pharmacological studies of piperacetazine, a potent tranquilizing agent. *Arch. Intern. Pharmacodyn.* **135**, 152-166.

Lu, F. C., Grewal, R. S., Rice, W. B., Graham, R. C. B., and Allmark, M. G. (1965). Acute toxicity of sodium fluoride for rhesus monkeys and other laboratory animals. *Acta Pharmacol. Toxicol.* **22**, 99-106.

Myers, E. N., and Bernstein, J. M., (1965). Salicylate ototoxicity. *Arch. Otolaryngol.* **82**, 483-493.

Ordy, J. M., Samorajski, T., and Schroeder, D. (1966). Concurrent changes in hypothalamic and cardiac catecholamine levels after anesthetics, tranquilizers, and stress in a subhuman primate. *J. Pharmacol. Exptl. Therap.* **152**, 445-457.

Schaper, W. K. A., Jageneau, A. H. M., Huggens, J., and Janssen, P. A. J. (1960). Der Einfluss von Haloperidol (R1625) und Haloperidide (R3201) auf das Allgemeinverhalten des Sudamerikanischen Totenkopffaffen (*Saimiri*). *Med. Exptl.* **3**, 169-176.

Scheckel, C. L., and Pazery, L. M. (1962). Blood pressure of monkeys (*Saimiri sciurea*). *Lab. Primate Newsletter* **1**, 18.

Stone, G. C., Bernstein, B. M., Hambourger, W. E., and Drill, V. A. (1960). Behavioral and pharmacological studies of thiopropazate, a potent tranquilizing agent. *Arch. Intern. Pharmacodyn.* **127**, 85-103.

Vernier, V. G. (1961). The pharmacology of antidepressant agents. *Diseases Nervous System* **22**, Suppl. 7, 7-13.

Yankell, S., and Marshall, R. W. (1967). Gastric motility in the squirrel monkey: methodology and preliminary results. *Symp. on Use of Subhuman Primates in Drug Evaluation, San Antonio, Texas, 1967.* Southwest Found. for Research and Education.

CHAPTER 14

The Laboratory Care and Clinical Management of *Saimiri* (Squirrel Monkeys)

C. Max Lang

I. Introduction

Nonhuman primates, particularly squirrel monkeys, are being used more and more in biomedical research; yet the literature contains relatively little information about the biology and management of these species of animals. For the successful conduct of experiments employing squirrel monkeys, some knowledge of their husbandry and of techniques for handling them is essential. One must also be familiar with the range of normal clinical and laboratory findings in these animals. In this discussion of the laboratory care and clinical management of *Saimiri*, every attempt has been made to include all pertinent information currently available, including that obtained by our own personal experience.

II. Laboratory Acclimatization

A. RECEIPT

Because of their general sensitivity to environmental stimuli, stress factors may soon lead to significant health problems in captive nonhuman primates. Until more scientific evidence is available, however, it is difficult, if not impossible, to differentiate precisely between the effect of stress and that of concurrent exposure to infection in the susceptibility of monkeys to disease.

The first and perhaps the most important stress factors to be considered are those of suddenly losing all freedom (in the trap and cage) and of being separated from the monkey's social group and from familiar surroundings. Additional stress factors are then introduced whenever the animals are caught, handled, or put into a cage with unfamiliar companions. The sustained stress involved in the establishment and stabilization of a dominance order may be of particular importance, although this factor is seldom considered unless overt injuries are observed.

Upon arrival in the laboratory, squirrel monkeys should be given a thorough physical examination and some means of identification (a tattoo on the abdomen, a beaded neck chain, or a waist belt); a permanent record should be started at this time. Even though squirrel monkeys are considered to be relatively resistant to tuberculosis (Fiennes, 1965), they are probably not immune and thus should be tested for tuberculosis by the palpebral intradermal injection of 0.05 ml of undiluted Koch's old tuberculin. Fecal material or material obtained by rectal swabs should be examined for intestinal parasites and cultured for bacterial growth. The mouth should be thoroughly examined for oral and dental lesions. The relative amount of wear shown by the teeth affords a rough estimate of the animal's age (juvenile, adult, or old adult). The dental formula (Hill, 1964) of the squirrel monkey is as follows:

$$I\frac{2-2}{2-2} \quad C\frac{1-1}{1-1} \quad PM\frac{3-3}{3-3} \quad M\frac{3-3}{3-3}$$

B. QUARANTINE

Upon arrival at the laboratory, squirrel monkeys should be given plenty of fresh water and food and quarantined in individual cages or large group pens. It has been our experience that monkeys can be observed more closely and given more individualized care if they are caged separately during quarantine. If the monkeys are placed in cages with an automatic watering system (Section II, C), it may be necessary to work the valve with the finger to show them the source of water. If they are dehydrated upon arrival, however, it is best to give them limited amounts of water in a bowl or pan until this condition is overcome.

The quarantine area should be kept quiet for several days until the monkeys have had a chance to become acclimatized to their surroundings and to the caretakers. The monkeys should be closely observed each day for anorexia and for signs of illness or diarrhea. Newly arrived monkeys should not be placed in the same room with an established colony until the investigator has assured himself that they are thoroughly acclimatized and free from disease. It is my opinion that squirrel monkeys should be kept in quarantine for a minimum of 30 days.

Squirrel monkeys should never be housed in the same room with other new world primates. Evidence suggests that *Saimiri* may be a natural host for *Herpesvirus tamarinus* (Melendez et al., 1966), which produces a fatal disease in marmosets and owl monkeys (Hunt and Melendez, 1966).

In the wild, the squirrel monkey's diet consists of fruit and nuts and vegetation supplemented with insects, including flies, butterflies, mosquitoes, and spiders (Hill, 1964; Fooden, 1964; DuMond and Cooper, 1965). The diet offered to squirrel monkeys newly arrived in the laboratory will depend upon their prior acclimatization. If the monkeys already have been acclimatized, i.e., held for a period by a dealer and gradually introduced to a laboratory diet, they can be given a commercial monkey diet such as those made by Purina and Wayne. If the monkeys have not been acclimatized, it is usually necessary to give them some peanuts and slices of orange or apple upon receipt and, over a period of days, induce them to eat a commercial diet by soaking it in milk. If the monkeys are not exposed to sunlight, it is essential that the diet contain vitamin D_3 in order to prevent rickets or osteomalacia (see Section III,C).

Young monkeys or old monkeys with worn teeth may not be able to chew the commercial diet. In such cases, excellent results have been obtained with semisynthetic diets suspended in agar and flavored with banana flavoring (see Section III,D).

C. CAGING

Definitive information on optimal and minimal cage sizes for squirrel monkeys is lacking. Although there are several methods of caging *Saimiri* in the laboratory, most investigators use small cages on a rack, each cage housing two monkeys (Fig. 1), or large, walk-in cages for groups of monkeys (Fig. 2). Monkeys that are to be kept for long periods and will not be caught often can easily be kept in a large group cage or pen. The latter, if chosen, should be large enough to allow entrance of a caretaker for selective capture of group members and thorough cage sanitation. If it is necessary to

FIG. 1. Squirrel monkey cages on a movable rack. Courtesy of Specialty Equipment Division, American Sterilizer Company.

FIG. 2. Group cage. Courtesy of Specialty Equipment Division, American Sterilizer Company.

catch the monkeys at regular intervals, it will be much easier to keep them in smaller cages. We have kept squirrel monkeys in cages 12 × 24 × 24 inches (two monkeys per cage) for periods up to 3 years with no apparent adverse effects. Squirrel monkeys will breed in captivity regardless of whether they are kept in small cages or in large group pens, although the relative influence of each condition, if any, on postconceptual reproductive success has not as yet been evaluated.

The small cages should be constructed of stainless steel wire to prevent excessive collection of fecal material and to give maximum exposure during the washing procedures. This type of cage can be obtained from Harford Metal Products, Aberdeen, Maryland; from Hoeltge, Incorporated, Cincinnati, Ohio; and from Specialty Equipment Company, Winston-Salem, North Carolina. The large group pens can be built as permanent structures or purchased from the above companies which supply such cages on wheels.

Water bottles or automatic watering systems which provide a constant supply of fresh, filtered water can be used successfully with either type of caging equipment. The automatic watering system should be maintained at a pressure of 2 — 4 lb per square inch. Higher pressures make it difficult for the monkey to drink, and lower pressures permit food particles and saliva to be siphoned back into the system. If an automatic watering system is being used, the valves should be checked daily to insure that they are functioning properly. Water bottles with nipples of varying types can also be used satisfactorily, but require daily washing, sterilizing, and filling.

Bantin (1966) feels that perches should be placed in the cages in order to prevent tail lesions; however, we have seen no tail lesions in monkeys kept in small cages without perches (two monkeys per cage) for periods up to 3 years. If perches are installed, wooden dowels or plastic or metal pipes (1 inch in diameter) are easier to clean than platforms and have been found highly acceptable (Feldman and Green, 1964; Clewe, 1965).

Unless the purpose of the experiment dictates otherwise, we have found it desirable to house squirrel monkeys of comparable age and sex together. Squirrel monkeys grouped together soon establish a social order. According to Ploog and MacLean (1963), penile display gives a better indication of hierarchy in the social structure of captive monkeys than does the outcome of rivalry for food. If the less dominant monkeys do not remain passive and quiet during display by the dominant animal, fighting usually ensues. This problem can sometimes be minimized by putting *all* the monkeys from one cage into a new cage when introducing a new member into the group.

III. Nutrition

A. GENERAL REQUIREMENTS

The nutritional requirements of the squirrel monkey are not known. Squirrel monkeys are susceptible to many infections, and it is almost impossible to determine whether the seriousness of these diseases results from the pathogenic capacity of the infective organism or from dietary inadequacies that reduce the resistance of the host. There is little doubt, however, that dietary inadequacies were partly responsible for the high death rates that occurred for several years in laboratory colonies of *Saimiri*. Malnourished monkeys are undoubtedly more susceptible to disease and to the effects of experimental variation. The possibility of malnutrition can be minimized by feeding commercial diets rather than nuts, fruits, and vegetables indiscriminately.

Although there are no definitive data concerning the optimal levels of protein and fat in the diets of squirrel monkeys, we use synthetic or semi-synthetic diets containing 25% protein and 8% fat. Casein (USP), the chief protein of milk, has high nutritive value and is an adequate source of protein in experimental diets. The fat (butter or vegetable oil) serves as a source of energy and also adds flavor to the diet; excessive amounts of fat, however, will cause severe diarrhea.

B. Vitamin C

The requirement for vitamin C has been documented in other species of primates (Ruch, 1959), but definitive information is lacking for the squirrel monkey. According to Lehner and Bullock (1967), however, signs of vitamin C deficiency have been noted in the squirrel monkey and corrected by the daily administration of 10 mg of ascorbic acid per kilogram of body weight. Squirrel monkeys on a synthetic diet devoid of ascorbic acid were inactive and anemic, lost weight and teeth, and had metaphyseal fractures and extensive subperiosteal hemorrhages.

Most of the commercially prepared diets for monkeys include ascorbic acid in a form claimed to be stable for a period of 90 days; in most cases, however, the investigator does not know when the food was manufactured. For singly caged monkeys, it is easy to ensure an adequate intake of vitamin C by the daily feeding of orange juice fortified with vitamin C; fresh green peppers (1 gm contains 1.2 mg of vitamin C); or oranges (1 gm contains 0.5 mg of vitamin C). If the monkeys are caged together, however, the weaker or less dominant ones may not get any of this preferred food unless it is administered in relatively large quantities and/or distributed widely in the cage.

The importance of vitamin C to wound healing and resistance to surgical stress in human beings is well recognized, and massive doses of ascorbic acid are given preoperatively. The same practice might well be made a routine procedure before operations performed on squirrel monkeys.

C. Vitamin D

It has long been recognized that many species of new world monkeys are particularly susceptible to diseases of the skeletal system. Recent studies indicate that vitamin D_2 is less active physiologically than vitamin D_3 in several species of new world monkeys. In a personal communication, Lehner (1967) has stated his belief that vitamin $D2$ is not utilized by these species or that dietary levels ordinarily considered to be adequate are too small to be effective in the absence of ultraviolet irradiation. In groups of squirrel monkeys fed diets containing as much as 10 IU of vitamin D_2 per gram but no vitamin D_3, rickets has been observed in young animals and osteomalacia in adults (Bullock and Bowen, 1966; Hunt et al., 1966 a,b, 1967).

Lehner (1967) has shown that this disease can be prevented by feeding as little as 2 IU of vitamin D_3 per gram of diet. Bantin (1966) has obtained equally good results by exposing the animals to ultraviolet light for 1 hour per day. He uses a lamp fitted with a special quartz glass that eliminates radiation harmful to the eyes. Most commercial diets, however, now contain vitamin D_3.

D. SPECIAL DIETS

Some research projects require that monkeys be fed synthetic or controlled diets. As basic ingredients for such a diet, we use casein (USP), dextrin or sucrose, butter or vegetable oil, Hegsted's salts mixture, and a complete vitamin fortification mixture. Cellulose flour (non-nutritive fiber) can be used to bring the ingredients up to 100%. Such a diet can be formed into refrigerator cookies and baked, or can be suspended in agar. Some of the heat-labile vitamins may be destroyed by cooking, however, and the cookies tend to crumble during storage. Hence, we have found it more satisfactory to add banana flavoring (3 ml per 100 gm) and Sucaryl* (10 ml per 100 gm) and suspend the ingredients in a 2½% solution of agar. After the agar is brought to a boil, the other ingredients are added and are thoroughly blended with a mixer. The mixture is then poured into a pan and allowed to cool. After cooling, it can be cut into squares, each containing a prescribed amount of the diet. The mixture should be prepared weekly and kept in a refrigerator between feedings to prevent drying. This form of diet, being soft, can also be used to feed monkeys unable to chew the harder diets.

A diet containing the ingredients shown in the tabulation is given in this form to infant squirrel monkeys not yet weaned and to sick or debilitated monkeys:

Ingredient	Quantity
Butter	100 gm
Casein	200 gm
Dextrin	640 gm
Hegsted's salts mixture	40 gm
Complete vitamin mixture	20 gm
Banana flavoring	6 tsp
Sucaryl	7 tbsp

Drugs such as anthelmintics or experimental agents can also be incorporated into the agar mixture.

* Abbott Laboratories, North Chicago, Illinois.

Liquid diets are sometimes required for various procedures. In such cases the ingredients listed can be mixed with water (1 ml per 2 gm of dry mixture) and mixed either in a blender or by hand. This diet should be stored in the refrigerator and kept no longer than 24 hours. Squirrel monkeys ranging in weight from 500 to 900 gm have been kept vigorous and in good health for 2 years on this diet, a total of 40 to 50 ml being given each day (Ellison and Riddle, 1961). This diet may also be made up in pellets for mechanical feeding in behavioral experiments (Riddle *et al.*, 1966).

IV. Handling and Restraint

With regular and gentle handling, squirrel monkeys soon become tame. Since they have an unreliable temperament, however, it is important to maintain suitable precautions against being bitten. The handler should

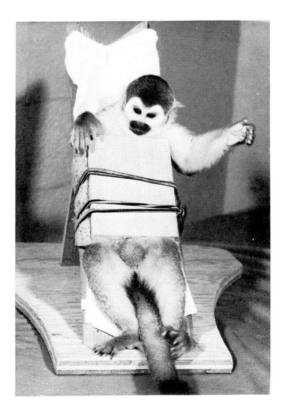

FIG. 3. Restraining chair.

wear gloves at all times, and when removing a monkey from a cage housing more than one animal, he should protect the forearm also. Scissor or hoop nets can be used to catch monkeys but usually are not necessary unless the monkeys are housed in a group pen. Transfer cages can be used to transport individual monkeys over short distances — for example, from the animal room to the laboratory. These cages are also useful for weighing monkeys. Manual force should never be used in handling squirrel monkeys as it will usually injure them. To prevent injuries, squirrel monkeys should be held gently but firmly around the lower abdomen.

For procedures such as intravenous feeding and blood collection, squirrel monkeys can be adequately restrained in a reclining trough (Fig. 3). This restraining device can be constructed with two $1 \times 4 \times 18$ inch boards, nailed together to form a V and mounted on a platform at a 40° angle; a towel can be used for padding. The animal is held in the trough by a block of wood tied around his abdomen and the trough. To prevent discomfort to the monkey and to hold him more firmly, a sponge at least 2 inches thick should be glued to the block. To prevent interference with experimental or clinical procedures it is necessary to secure the monkey's hind legs.

V. Anesthetics

Satisfactory anesthesia is necessary for humane treatment of the monkeys and for technical efficiency. Unfortunately, the use of anesthetics in experimental animals is beset by problems arising from both species and individual variations and temperament.

Phencyclidine,* given either orally or parenterally, is effective as an anesthetic in the squirrel monkey. Although intravenous administration greatly shortens the induction period, the effects otherwise are essentially identical to those produced by other parenteral routes of administration (Melby, 1965); hence, this drug is usually given intramuscularly. A dosage of 0.5 – 1.5 mg per kilogram (Melby, 1967) is usually satisfactory for parenteral administration. Higher doses result in excessive salivation, and the degree of muscle relaxation necessary for major surgery is not obtained at any safe dose. The lower dosage of phencyclidine can be used for initial sedation and followed by the administration of volatile or other parenteral anesthetics. Barbiturates and phencyclidine apparently have a synergistic effect; hence the total amount of the barbiturate anesthetic should be greatly reduced when it is used in combination with phencyclidine. In my

*Sernylan (Parke, Davis & Company, Detroit, Michigan).

experience, this potentiating effect varies widely among individual animals. For this reason, we use an ultrashort-acting barbiturate (thiamylal sodium* exclusively in order to maintain control over the level of anesthesia.

For procedures of short duration, thiamylal sodium can also be used alone. It is given intravenously as a 2% solution until the desired effect is obtained, the usual dosage being approximately 1.0 ml per kilogram. The anesthetic can be injected into the lateral coccygeal vein on the tail. After applying pressure proximal to the point of injection, a 25-gauge, $\frac{1}{2}$-inch needle is inserted in the middle third of the tail. For continuous injections, the syringe can be taped to the tail. Induction requires only about 60 seconds and the anesthesia lasts about $15-20$ minutes from the initial dose.

Another short-acting anesthetic that works very well in squirrel monkeys is methoxyflurane,† which can be administered with a nose cone. This inhalant anesthetic has a wide margin of safety, but we have found that it causes inversion of the T-waves in about 50% of *Saimiri*; consequently, it is not satisfactory when electrocardiograms are being made.

For procedures requiring longer periods of anesthesia, we have had excellent results with pentobarbital sodium.‡ This anesthetic may conveniently be given intraperitoneally with a wide margin of safety. The intraperitoneal dosage for squirrel monkeys is approximately 2.5 mg per 100 gm of body weight. Anesthesia is complete approximately $10-15$ minutes after the injections and lasts $2-6$ hours. We have also used amobarbital sodium§ (50 mg per kilogram) intraperitoneally to anesthetize squirrel monkeys. Anesthesia is complete approximately 15 minutes after the injection and lasts $3-4$ hours.

Barbiturates given in anesthetic doses depress basal metabolism so that less body heat is produced. According to Jones (1965, p. 157), vasodilation causes excessive heat loss during anesthesia. Since the squirrel monkey has a large surface area in relation to body mass, heat loss under prolonged anesthesia can be quite pronounced. If the monkey it to be anesthetized for more than 20 minutes, it should be wrapped in a towel or blanket to maintain normal body temperature. The monkey's temperature should be monitored continuously until it has regained consciousness.

In my opinion, a fasting period of 12 hours before the administration of an anesthetic is sufficient. In the squirrel monkey, prolonged fasting (18—

*Surital (Parke, Davis & Company, Detroit, Michigan).
†Metafane (Pitman-Moore, Indianapolis, Indiana).
‡Napental (The S. E. Massengill Company, Bristol, Tennessee).
§Amytal (Eli Lilly and Company, Indianapolis, Indiana).

24 hours) often causes hypoglycemia, with blood sugars as low as 25 mg per
100 ml. This consideration is especially important in monkeys with impaired carbohydrate metabolism (Lang, 1966; Davidson *et al.*, 1967).

VI. Collection and Withdrawal of Body Fluids

A. URINE

Adult squirrel monkeys usually pass 8—15 ml of urine per 24 hours. The
most convenient method to obtain urine samples is to place the monkey in
a squirrel monkey metabolism cage (Fig. 4) which is designed to collect all
urine and fecal excreta. The cage has a wire bottom, and beneath this a
funnel leading into the collecting flask; two strainers in the funnel prevent
the fecal material from becoming mixed with the urine. Five milliliters of
toluene should be placed in the collecting flask to act as a preservative and

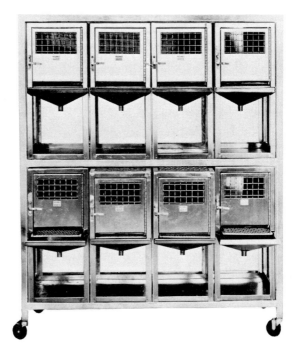

FIG. 4. Squirrel monkey metabolism cage. Courtesy of Specialty Equipment Division,
American Sterilizer Company.

to prevent evaporation of the urine. Fecal contamination of the urine can be minimized by washing the funnels at frequent intervals.

B. BLOOD

The jugular and femoral veins are the most accessible for bleeding. Approximately 5 — 10 ml of blood can be withdrawn from an adult squirrel monkey at any one time. Removal of the larger amount, however, may result in weakness or temporary unconsciousness, or even in the death of a monkey not in good health. A convenient rule of thumb is to withdraw not more than 1 ml of blood per 100 gm of body weight, even from healthy monkeys, and not to withdraw this amount more often than once a month. The hemogram of squirrel monkeys that are bled regularly should be followed closely, and the hematocrit should not be allowed to fall below 30 volumes percent. Monkeys that are bled frequently may require additional iron, given parenterally or as a dietary supplement.

Jugular venipuncture is advantageous for techniques involving multiple injections or collections during a relatively short period of time. Anesthesia is recommended for jugular venipuncture, as it is difficult to restrain the monkey adequately without it. My technique is to apply pressure in the jugular furrow at the thoracic inlet and use a $\frac{1}{2}$-inch, 20-gauge needle, with the point directed toward the head along the planes of the vein. To minimize the occurrence of hematomas, alternate veins should be used for multiple injections.

Femoral venipuncture is best suited for obtaining single blood samples or performing single injections. The femoral vein lies just medial to the femoral artery, which can be located by palpating the pulse. One can usually discern a small depression in the femoral triangle; the needle should be inserted in this depression. Immediately after withdrawal of the needle, pressure should be applied to the site of injection to prevent the formation of a hematoma.

C. VAGINAL FLUID

Among the techniques that may be used to collect vaginal fluid for diagnostic or cytological studies are: (1) inserting a cotton swab, glass rod, or a wire loop into the vagina and smearing the adherent fluid onto a glass slide; and (2) washing the vagina with distilled water or saline from a medicine dropper. Squirrel monkeys can be trained to stand at the front of their cages for the swabbing procedure by rewarding them with food. In my experience, however, vaginal washing provides the most accurate method for routine collection of vaginal fluids.

To prepare specimens for studies of vaginal cytology, we use the following technique: Approximately 1 ml of distilled water is instilled into the vagina with an eyedropper and then aspirated. A drop of the vaginal washing is diluted with 2 drops of distilled water on a microscope slide and allowed to dry at room temperature for 1 hour. After being placed for 1 hour in a fixative consisting of absolute ethyl alcohol and ether in equal parts, the slides are stained by the following modification of the Papanicolaou procedure (Lang, 1967a):

(1) Immerse the slides in three successive solutions of ethyl alcohol (90%, 70%, and 50%). (2) Rinse in water and dip in Harris' hematoxylin for 7 minutes. (3) Rinse in water until free of color. (4) Dip quickly in a 0.5% solution of hydrochloric acid and rinse again in water. (5) Place in a saturated solution of lithium carbonate for 2 minutes and rinse in water. (6) Immerse in three successive solutions of ethyl alcohol (50%, 70%, and 80%). (7) Stain for 3 minutes in OG-6.* (8) Rinse twice in a 95% solution of ethyl alcohol. (9) Stain in EA-36* for 3 minutes. (10) Immerse in three dishes of a 95% solution of ethyl alcohol. (11) Dehydrate and clear by dipping in a 100% solution of ethyl alcohol. (12) Dip in a dish of exylene. (13) Mount.

Light microscopy can be used to examine the vaginal smears for the presence of red blood cells, the ratio of basophilic to acidophilic cells, and the percentage of nucleated cells.

The daily collection of vaginal fluid over a period of time may produce a vaginal infection in some monkeys; this is indicated by large numbers of neutrophils in the smear. We have been able to clear up these infections by adding Chloromycetin† to the distilled water used in the washing (25 mg per milliliter).

D. Semen

Semen can be collected from the squirrel monkey by the use of an electroejaculator (Lang, 1967b). The volume of ejaculate usually obtained is about 0.1 ml. The average sperm count in my series was $295,000 \pm 13,000$, $79 \pm 2\%$ of the spermatozoa being live. There appeared to be no relation between the total count or percentage of live spermatozoa and the length of time the monkeys were kept in the laboratory. Similar results have also been reported by Bennett (1967).

---

*Paragon C & C Company, Inc., 2540 Beamont Avenue, New York, New York.
†Chloramphenicol (Parke, Davis & Company, Detroit, Michigan).

VII. Infusion Techniques

A. PERORAL

Squirrel monkeys, like most primates, are wary of strange tastes and will not readily accept medicines or experimental compounds given by mouth. Direct instillation of unaccepted fluids into the stomach is not traumatic and requires little effort. In the approach we have used, the monkey's arms and legs are held securely by an assistant while the investigator grasps the back of the head with one hand as if he were holding a baseball. With the other hand an infant feeding tube, no. 5 French, lubricated with a water-soluble lubricant, is passed gently into a nostril. The animal will be observed to swallow as the tube reaches the pharynx, and the tube is then advanced into the esophagus. Coughing and violent activity result if the tube enters the trachea. An alternative technique involving oral passage of a stomach tube is described by Hanson (Chapter 13).

Squirrel monkeys have been intubated daily for several months without any unfavorable side effects. It has been my experience that they will usually vomit if given more than 5 ml by this method.

B. PARENTERAL

Parenteral injections may be given by any of the common routes. Subcutaneous injections are easily given in the loose skin of the abdominal region. Intravenous injection is usually accomplished by techniques similar to those described for blood collection (Section VI,B). For injections by the intraperitoneal route, the needle can be inserted in the abdomen lateral to the midline. It should be directed slightly anteriorly and care should be taken to insert the needle far enough above the pelvis to avoid the urinary bladder and far enough below the diaphragm to avoid injection into the liver.

Because of the high density of muscle, only small volumes can be injected intramuscularly. The most common site for this injection is the heavy musculature of the rear limb. The needle should be introduced in such a manner as to avoid striking any bony structures, and after the needle is inserted, aspiration should always be done to make certain that a blood vessel has not been entered.

VIII. Prophylactic, Diagnostic, and Therapeutic Measures

A. GENERAL

One often hears the statement that squirrel monkeys collapse and die within hours. It is my experience, however, that clinical observation will reveal indications of poor health before most illnesses reach their terminal stages. The clinical signs of illness include dehydration, rough hair coat, and depressed activity. General observation, however, is never an adequate substitute for complete clinical diagnostic procedures. This fact cannot be overemphasized since definitive treatment cannot be given without a proper diagnosis.

Clinical values for the squirrel monkey are fragmentary. The hematological values found by Garcia and Hunt (1966) in 59 squirrel monkeys of Peruvian origin (see Chapter 1) are listed in Table I. Without more observations from additional animals and a complete statistical analysis it is difficult to comment on the normality of these findings. Garcia and Hunt stated that monkeys with hemoglobin values of 8.2 gm per 100 ml and hematocrits of 25 volumes percent showed no clinical signs of anemia, and that no explanation could be found for the high eosinophil values (40% in some monkeys). In my opinion, these figures should not be equated with normal values, although they can serve as a valuable working guide. Other investigators who have reported the hematological values found in squirrel monkeys did not use sufficient numbers of animals for statistical analysis (Beischer and Furry, 1964; Ponder *et al.*, 1928; Workman *et al.*, 1962).

TABLE I

TABULATION OF HEMATOLOGICAL ANALYSIS OF 59 SQUIRREL
MONKEYS (*Saimiri sciureus*)[a,b]

Observations	Mean	Range
Erythrocytes (10^6/mm³)	7.31	5.5 – 9.49
Hemoglobin (gm %)	12.9	8.2 – 15.4
Hematocrit	38.6	25 – 45
Mean cell volume (cubic micron)	53.1	43.9 – 69.5
Mean cell hemoglobin (micromicrograms)	17.8	14.6 – 22.4
Mean cell hemoglobin concentration (%)	33.6	30.9 – 37.4
Reticulocytes (per 100 RBC)	0.97	0 – 3.5
Sedimentation rate (mm/hr uncorrected)	1.4	0 – 12
White blood cells (10^3/mm³)	10.4	4.5 – 23.8
Neutrophils (per 100 WBC)	40.7	8 – 76
Band cells (per 100 WBC)	0.75	0 – 7
Lymphocytes (per 100 WBC)	48.6	18 – 81
Eosinophils (per 100 WBC)	6.2	0 – 40
Basophils (per 100 WBC)	0.2	0 – 3
Monocytes (per 100 WBC)	3.4	0 – 15

[a] Garcia and Hunt, 1966.
[b] All values based on a total of 118 observations with the exception of the reticulocyte count and the sedimentation rate which were based on 72 observations.

The normal rectal temperature for a squirrel monkey ranges from 102.9° to 104.9° F, the average being 103.3° F (Bantin, 1966). The average pulse rate in healthy animals is 248 per minute, with a range of 184—296, and the average respiratory rate is 70 per minute, with a range of 40—180. One should always recognize, however, that restraint of the animal may cause these values to be above the usual range (see also Chapter 11). Even well-tamed squirrel monkeys respond unfavorably to manipulation.

B. Preventive Medicine

There is no substitute for a good program of preventive medicine. The following prophylactic measures can and should be applied to almost any colony in any laboratory.

(1) Before new monkeys are allowed out of quarantine, three negative tuberculin tests should be obtained (Section II,A). Tuberculin tests should be given every 6 months thereafter. (2) Only necessary personnel should be permitted in the animal quarters. (3) Handlers should wash hands and equipment before and after handling each group of monkeys. (4) Asepsis should be practiced in minor as well as major surgical procedures. (5) A visual appraisal should be made of each animal at least twice a day. Monkeys with diarrhea or other signs of illness should be thoroughly examined for the presence of parasites and pathogenic bacteria. Monkeys suspected of disease should be isolated. (6) Each animal should be weighed at least once a month. Comparative body weights often give a clue to the presence of disease or of dietary or social problems. (7) The monkey room should be cleaned every day and the cages washed at least once a week.

Many investigators routinely administer antibiotics to squirrel monkeys. In my opinion, this procedure is unwarranted and may even be harmful. Such indiscriminate treatment may result in resistant strains of organisms or mask signs of illness until the infection is well established.

C. Dental Hygiene

Dental hygiene is quite important in squirrel monkeys. Their teeth often become abscessed, and if this condition is not corrected it may result in a draining fistula from the maxillary sinus beneath the eye. In my experience, worn canine teeth predispose to abscess formation. Because dental plaques lead to gingival and peridontal disease, we make it a practice to scale the teeth of squirrel monkeys at regular intervals, i.e., every 1 to 2 months or when the animals are caught for experimental procedures.

D. Gastrointestinal Illnesses

Diarrhea is probably the most common clinical sign of gastrointestinal illness in the squirrel monkey. Changes in diet and environment seem to be the most common causes rather than bacterial infections. It is my opinion that monkeys with severe diarrhea should be maintained solely on intravenous fluids until clinical material can be evaluated and an etiological diagnosis made. Oral feeding should not be resumed for at least 24 hours after the animal has resumed normal activity.

Since dehydration results in the loss of electrolytes and several of the B vitamins as well as a loss of body water, treatment must include restoration of the former factors. For corrective fluid therapy we usually give a saline solution containing 5% dextrose. Dextrose given intravenously provides an immediate source of carbohydrate fuel. Strongly hypertonic solutions of dextrose, however, should not be used in dehydrated monkeys because they dehydrate the tissues further (by attracting intracellular fluid into the extracellular spaces) and place an additional excretory burden on the kidneys. For the dextrose to be totally utilized, no more than 0.5 gm per kilogram should be administered in an hour. In my experience, more rapid administration of dextrose results in glycosuria. It is important that glycosuria due to dextrose overloading not be confused with glycosuria due to impaired carbohydrate metabolism (Lang, 1966; Davidson *et al.*, 1967).

Several fractions of the vitamin B complex should also be given in supportive treatment of diarrhea; it is particularly important to include thiamine, which is poorly conserved by the body tissues (Jones, 1965, p. 907). We prefer injectable vitamin B complex with vitamin C* (0.5 ml intramuscularly, given in one dose).

If the diarrhea is severe or if the administration of intravenous fluid is prolonged, protein replacement must be initiated. The most commonly used amino acid source is a protein hydrolyzate. The intravenous route has proven to be quite satisfactory unless the injection is made too rapidly in which case it may lead to reactions characterized by chills, nausea, and vomiting. The nausea, which has been attributed to the glutamic acid content of the hydrolyzate, can be minimized by decreasing the rate of injection.

In order to establish a positive nitrogen balance and to promote rapid recovery, we give 2 gm of protein hydrolyzate† per kilogram of body weight daily. It is estimated that, in order to stimulate maximal tissue repair and recovery, the intravenous infusion should contain twice as much dextrose as protein hydrolyzate (Jones, 1965, p. 841). The provision of dextrose decreases or eliminates the necessity for the body to convert protein into carbohydrate for energy production.

*Bejectal with vitamin C (Abbott Laboratories, North Chicago, Illinois).
†Aminosol (Abbott Laboratories, North Chicago, Illinois).

If the animal has a very profuse diarrhea, the peristaltic action of the intestinal tract may be decreased by 1 tablespoon of Taka-diastase* and 1 drop of paregoric (USP) mixed in 5 ml of water and administered by way of a stomach tube.

Endoparasites that have been found in squirrel monkeys include cestodes, acanthocephalans, trematodes, and nematodes (see Chapter 2). Thibenzole† (100 mg per kilogram) is quite effective against nematodes of the families Trichostrongylidae and Strongyloididae. Perhaps the most severe endoparasitic infections in *Saimiri* are caused by the acanthocephalan *Prosthenorchis elegans*, which produces mechanical damage to the intestinal mucosa; in these cases, perforation and peritonitis sometimes occur when bacteria from the intestines gain access to the submucosal tissue (Takos and Thomas, 1958).

In laboratories, cockroaches (*Blattella germanica*) are potential intermediate hosts for the acanthellas, *P. elegans*, which cause endoparasitic infections when swallowed by the final host (Takos and Thomas 1958). Although there is no known treatment for this parasite, it has been my experience that the squirrel monkey will eliminate them over a period of time if means of reinfestation are eliminated by proper sanitation.

E. RESPIRATORY ILLNESSES

Although squirrel monkeys, at least when in captivity, are mildly susceptible to *Mycobacterium tuberculosis*, clinical tuberculosis is relatively rare and when it occurs is more often abdominal or generalized than pulmonary (Hill, 1964, p. 300).

The most common organisms isolated from squirrel monkeys with respiratory infections are *Klebsiella pneumoniae* and *Pasteurella multocida*. However, respiratory infections are not usually a problem if the monkeys are kept in a suitable environment. If the relative humidity falls below 35%, continual sneezing and sniffing will be noted among squirrel monkeys (Bantin, 1966). Since this condition might predispose the monkey to respiratory diseases, the relative humidity should be kept at 50±5%.

The novice investigator examining routine sections of the lungs taken at necropsy would think that all squirrel monkeys are affected with severe respiratory disorders. In performing a necropsy, the trachea should be tied before the thoracic cavity is opened to prevent collapse of the alveoli and present a more accurate histology. *Filaroides gordius* are frequently found in sections of the lung (see Chapter 2). Since they apparently cause little damage, however, they do not seem to be a matter of concern.

*Parke, Davis & Company, Detroit, Michigan.
†Merck Sharp and Dohme, West Point, Pennsylvania.

TABLE II

THERAPEUTIC AGENTS EFFECTIVE IN SQUIRREL MONKEYS

Drug	Trade name	Indication	Total dosage per day	Method of administration
For peroral administration				
Oxytetracycline (USP)	Terramycin[a]	Gastrointestinal infections	50–100 mg/kg	Given in two to four divided doses or in drinking water
Neomycin sulfate and polymixin B sulfate	Daribiotic[b]	Gastrointestinal infections	2 mg/kg	Given in two to four divided doses or in drinking water
Furazolidone	Furoxone[c]	Gastrointestinal infections	5– 10 mg/kg	Given in two to four divided doses
Thiabendazole	Thibenzole[d]	Anthelmintic	100 mg/kg	Given in one dose
Demethylchlor tetracycline	Declomycin[e]	Respiratory infections	10– 20 mg/kg	Given in two to four divided doses
For intramuscular injection				
Oxytetracycline (USP)	Terramycin[a]	Respiratory infections, septicemia, wounds	25 mg/kg	Given in two to four divided doses
Chloramphenicol	Chloromycetin[f]	Respiratory infections, septicemia, wounds	15– 25 mg/kg	Given in four divided doses

Penicillin-dihycrostreptomycin	—	Respiratory infections, septicemia	5,000–10,000 units/kg (penicillin) and 10–20 mg/kg (dihydrostreptomycin)	Given in one dose
Dihydrostreptomycin sulfate	—	Septicemia, wounds	10– 20 mg/kg	Given in two divided doses
Vitamin B complex and vitamin C	Bejectal-C[g]	Dehydration	0.5 ml/kg	Given in one dose
For topical application				
Nitrofurazone, NF	Furacin ointment[b]	Wounds	—	Locally
Scarlet red	Scarlet oil[b]	Wounds (antiseptic, epithelial growth stimulant, and protective dressing)	—	Locally

[a] Pfizer Laboratories, New York, New York.
[b] The S. E. Massengill Company, Bristol, Tennessee.
[c] Eaton Laboratories, Norwich, New York.
[d] Merck Sharp & Dohme, West Point, Pennsylvania.
[e] Lederle Laboratories, Pearl River, New York.
[e] Parke, Davis & Company, Detroit, Michigan.
[f] Abbott Laboratories, North Chicago, Illinois.
[g] Pitman-Moore Company, Indianapolis, Indiana.

F. CHEMOTHERAPY

Unless chemotherapy is based on an accurate clinical and etiological diagnosis, it will probably do more harm than good. For this reason we have not recommended specific chemotherapeutic agents to be used in various disease states. Where indicated by clinical and laboratory studies, the therapeutic agents listed in Table II have proved valuable in my experience. For systemic treatment to be effective, it is important that adequate blood levels of the chemotherapeutic agent be maintained. One should keep in mind that this is best accomplished by divided doses administered throughout the day rather than by large single doses.

We have found that overdosage or prolonged treatment with oral antibiotics can produce chronic diarrhea in squirrel monkeys, probably by altering the normal bacterial flora of the intestine. Matanic (1967) has suggested the possibility that squirrel monkeys are sensitive to penicillin-di-hydrostreptomycin. It is my opinion, however, that such reactions are due to gross overdosage rather than to a specific sensitivity.

G. DIAGNOSTIC TESTS

Only a few diagnostic procedures have been adapted to the squirrel monkey. There is a definite need to develop other diagnostic tests that can be used in biomedical research employing squirrel monkeys as well as in the clinical evaluation of their illnesses.

The *glucose tolerance test* has been adapted for use in the squirrel monkey (Lang, 1966). Following a 12-hour fast, blood samples are obtained and, immediately afterward, glucose (4 gm per kilogram of body weight) is administered through a stomach tube. Additional blood samples are obtained at 1 hour and 4 hours following the administration of glucose. In the normal monkey, the maximum level (50 mg per 100 ml above the fasting blood sugar level) is reached at 1 hour; at the end of 4 hours, the blood sugar should return to the fasting level or below.

Another diagnostic test that has been standardized for the squirrel monkey is the *tolbutamide test* (Davidson *et al.*, 1967). This test is carried out under methoxyflurane anesthesia (Section V) in monkeys that have fasted for 12 hours. Thirty minutes after the induction of anesthesia, sodium tolbutamide (50 mg per kilogram) is given by way of the external jugular vein. Blood glucose determinations are then performed on three blood samples drawn from the contralateral jugular vein at 10-minute intervals. The normal response to this test is a fall in blood sugar.

We have used halogenated phthalein dyes* for the *study of liver func-*

*Bromsulphalein (BSP) (Hynson, Westcott, and Dunning, Baltimore, Maryland).

tion in the squirrel monkey. The dosage is 10 mg per kilogram of body weight injected intravenously. The dye solution should be injected slowly, care being taken to prevent perivascular infiltration which may cause tissue sloughing. Twenty minutes after the injection is completed, a blood sample is removed from a different location and immediately heparinized. We consider BSP retention of less than 5% at 20 minutes to be within the normal range for squirrel monkeys.

IX. Summary

In this chapter we have attempted to review all available information pertinent to the laboratory care and clinical management of *Saimiri*. Our knowledge in this area is indeed fragmentary, and it is my hope that the information presented here will serve as a stimulus to the acquisition of more definitive information on the care and treatment of these valuable research animals.

REFERENCES

Bantin, G. C. (1966). Establishment of a squirrel monkey colony. *J. Inst. Animal Tech.* **17**, No. 2, 66-73.

Beischer, D. E., and Furry, D. E. (1964). *Saimiri sciureus* as an experimental animal. *Anat. Record* **148**, No. 4, 615-624.

Bennett, J. P. (1967). Semen collection in the squirrel monkey. *J. Reprod. Fertility* **13**, 353-355.

Bullock, B. C., and Bowen, J. A. (1966). Rickets and osteomalacia in squirrel monkeys (*Saimiri sciureus*). *Federation Proc.* **25**, 533.

Clewe, T. H. (1965). Squirrel monkey perching habits. *Lab. Primate Newsletter* **4**, No. 1, 7.

Davidson, I. W., Lang, C. M., and Blackwell, W. L. (1967). Impairment of carbohydrate metabolism of the squirrel monkey. *Diabetes* **16**, 395-401.

DuMond, F. V., and Cooper, R. W. (1965). Reproduction in semifreeranging *Saimiri sciureus*. *Lab. Primate Newsletter* **4**, No. 1, 1-4.

Ellison, T., and Riddle, W. C. (1961). Commercial liquid diet for animals in behavioral studies. *J. Exptl. Anal. Behavior* **4**, 370.

Feldman, R. S., and Green, K. F. (1964). A perch for squirrel monkeys. *Lab. Primate Newsletter* **3**, No. 3, 9.

Fiennes, R. N. (1965). Incidence of TB in squirrel monkeys and marmosets. *Lab. Primate Newsletter* **4**, No. 1, 10.

Fooden, J. (1964). Stomach contents and gastro-intestinal proportions in wild-shot Guianan monkeys. *Am. J. Phys. Anthropol.* [N.S.] **22**, 227-231.

Garcia, F. G., and Hunt, R. D. (1966). The hematogram of the squirrel monkey (*Saimiri sciureus*). *Lab. Animal Care* **16**, 50-51.

Hill, W. C. O. (1964). "Primates. Comparative Anatomy and Taxonomy," Vol. IV, Part A. Edinburgh Univ. Press, Edinburgh.

Hunt, R. D., and Melendez, L. V. (1966). Spontaneous Herpes-T infection in the owl monkey (*Aotus trivirgatus*). *Pathol. Vet. (Basel)* **3**, 1-26.

Hunt, R. D., Garcia, F. G., and Hegsted, D. M. (1966a). Vitamin D requirement of New World monkeys. *Federation Proc.* **25**, 545.

Hunt, R. D., Garcia, F. G., and Hegsted, D. M. (1966b). Vitamin D deficiency in New World monkeys. *Lab. Primate Newsletter* **5**, No. 3, 12-13.

Hunt, R. D., Garcia, F. G. and Hegsted, D. M. (1967). A comparison of Vitamin D_2 and D_3 in New World primates, I. Production and regression of osteodystrophia fibrosa. *J. Lab. Animal Care* **17**, No. 2, 222-234.

Jones, L. M. (1965). "Veterinary Pharmacology and Therapeutics." Iowa State Coll. Press, Ames, Iowa.

Lang, C. M. (1966). Impaired glucose tolerance in the squirrel monkey (*Saimiri sciureus*). *Proc. Soc. Exptl. Biol. Med.* **122**, 84-86.

Lang, C. M. (1967a). The estrous cycle of the squirrel monkey (*Saimiri sciureus*). *J. Lab. Animal Care* **17**, 172-179.

Lang, C. M. (1967b). A technique for the collection of semen from squirrel monkeys (*Saimiri sciureus*) by electro-ejaculation. *J. Lab. Animal Care* **17**, 218-221.

Lehner, N. D. M. (1967). Personal communication.

Lehner, N. D. M., and Bullock, B. C. (1967). Ascorbic acid deficiency in the squirrel monkey. *Federation Proc.* **26**, No. 2, 306.

Matanic, B. (1967). Possible sensitivity of squirrel monkeys to Combiotic. *Lab. Primate Newsletter* **6**, No. 1, 12.

Melby, E. C. (1965). Phencyclidine for analgesia and anesthesia in simian primates. *J. Am. Vet. Med. Assoc.* **147**, 1068-1072.

Melby, E. C. (1967). Personal communication.

Melendez, L. V., Hunt, R. D., Garcia, F. G., and Trum, B. F. (1966). A latent Herpes-V infection in *Saimiri sciureus* (Squirrel Monkey). *Symp. Zool. Soc. London* **17**, 393-397.

Ploog, D. W., and MacLean, P. D. (1963). Display of penile erection in squirrel monkey (*Saimiri sciureus*). *Animal Behaviour* **11**, 32-39.

Ponder, E., Yeager, J. F., and Charipper, H. A. (1928). Studies in Comparative hematology, II. Primates. *Quart. J. Exptl. Physiol.* **19**, 181-195.

Riddle, W. C., Rednick, A. B., Catania, A. C., and Tucker, S. J. (1966). Complete squirrel monkey diet in tablet form. *J. Exptl. Anal. Behavior* **9**, No. 6, 670.

Ruch, T. C. (1959). "Diseases of Laboratory Primates." Saunders, Philadelphia, Pennsylvania.

Takos, M. J., and Thomas, L. J. (1958). The pathology and pathogenesis of fatal infections due to an acanthocephalid parasite of marmoset monkeys. *Am. J. Trop. Med. Hyg.* **7**, 90-94.

Workman, R. D., Bond, G. F., and Mazzone, W. F. (1962). Prolonged exposure of animals to pressurized normal and synthetic atmospheres. Rept. No. 374, Vol. XXI, No. 5. U. S. Naval Med. Res. Lab., Submarine Base, New London, Groton, Connecticut.

Base-line Blood Determinations of the Squirrel Monkey (*Saimiri sciureus*)

Albert E. New

The following data are tabulated biochemical and hematological results from squirrel monkeys (*Saimiri sciureus*) maintained at the Naval Aerospace Medical Institute. The animals utilized in the acquisition of data were purchased as acclimated monkeys from Tarpon Zoo, Tarpon Springs, Florida. The monkeys were wild caught from the vicinity of Leticia, Colombia in South America. The initial group of 70 squirrel monkeys when received ranged in weight from 420 to 570 gm and were placed in isolation for conditioning at NAMI for 60 days. They were housed in galvanized cages (12 × 18 × 16 inches), two animals per cage, in conventional windowless animal quarantine rooms. The room temperature was maintained at 76 ± 2°F and the lighting period was from 7:30 A.M. to 9:30 P.M. each day. The monkeys were fed Purina monkey chow (15% protein) *ad libitum*. Approximately 30 gm of either apple, orange, or banana were fed to each animal daily. Water was available from an automatic pipeline system.

Upon arrival at the Institute the squirrel monkeys were examined for disease, weighed, sexed, and aged according to dental eruption.* The age range based on their permanent dentention was from 12 to 48 months. During the conditioning period the monkeys were weighed weekly, tuberculin tested with first-strength KOT, intrapalpebrally at the beginning and ending of the 30 days. They were treated twice at 21-day intervals with thiabendazole (Merck and Company, Inc., Rahaway, New Jersey) for removal of *Strongyloides sp.* and *Oesophagostomum sp.* No effort was made to treat parasitic infections of *Acanthocephaliasis, Filariasis, Trypanosomiasis* or malaria. Two of the monkeys died within the first 20 days of quarantine. Necropsies complete with bacterial cultures and histopathological examinations established the absence of an infectious disease as the cause of death. A third animal died in restraint while a blood sample

*See Chapter 7.

was being obtained. The remaining 67 animals (36 males and 31 females) were clinically healthy and were utilized for this study. Blood samples were obtained in the morning prior to the morning feeding. One and one-half ml of blood was collected atraumatically from the external jugular vein. Blood was withdrawn from each animal on two occasions for completion of the study.

TABLE I

BIOCHEMICAL DETERMINATIONS IN THE
SQUIRREL MONKEY (*Saimiri sciureus*)

Constituent	Method of determination	Number of subjects	Mean	Standard deviation	Observed range
Sodium (meq/liter)	Flame photometry	67	159.7	6.1	144.0 – 173.0
Potassium (meq/liter)	Flame photometry	67	5.6	1.2	3.5 – 9.5
Calcium (meq/liter)	Stanbio, AZO Cal	67	5.1	0.3	4.2 – 5.8
Chloride (meq/liter)	Schales and Schales	48	113.6	5.2	103.0 – 118.0
Inorganic phosphorus (mg/100 ml)	Fiske-subarrow	67	5.3	1.4	3.2 – 9.2
Alkaline phosphatse (mmole units/liter)	Bessy-Lowery-Brock	66	21.8	10.7	6.0 – 49.0
Glutamic oxalacetic transaminase (units/ml)	Reitman-Frankel, 37°C	67	138.1	61.7	56.0 – 384.0
Glutamic pyruvic transaminase (units/ml)	Reitman-Frankel, 37°C	64	117.2	74.9	38.0 – 470.0
Lactic dehydrogenase (units/ml)	Berger and Broida, Sigma Tech. Bull. No. 500	32	381.9	110.9	230.0 – 760.0
Bilirubin, total (mg/100 ml)	Evelyn Malloy	38	0.2	0.3	0.0 – 1.9
Blood urea nitrogen (mg/100 ml)	Diacetyl monoxime	67	20.7	6.2	11.4 – 42.2
Nonprotein nitrogen (mg/100 ml)	Micro-Kjeldahl	32	28.8	8.6	12.0 – 49.6
Cholesterol (mg/100 ml)	Liebermann-Burchard	67	199.1	34.2	116.0 – 272.0
Glucose (mg/100 ml)	Somogyi	67	72.3	19.7	35.0 – 148.0
Uric acid (mg/100 ml)	Caraway	67	1.0	0.4	0.2 – 2.1

Constituent	Method of determination	Number of subjects	Mean	Standard deviation	Observed range
Red blood cells (10⁶/mm³)	Coulter counter	67	8.3	0.6	7.1 − 10.9
Hemoglobin (gm %)	Cyanmet hemoglobin	67	14.8	0.8	12.9 − 17.0
Packed cell volume (%)	Micro hematocrit	67	46.9	2.4	43.0 − 56.0
Mean corpuscular volume (μ^3)		67	57.1	3.8	41.4 − 62.7
Mean corpuscular hemoglobin (pg)		67	18.1	1.1	13.9 − 20.1
Mean corpuscular hemoglobin concentration (%)		67	31.7	1.1	29.2 − 34.8
White blood cells (10³/mm³)	Coulter counter	67	8.2	2.4	3.4 − 14.8
Lymphocytes (per 100 WBC)		67	51.9	13.7	19.0 − 82.0
Neutrophiles (per 100 WBC)		67	41.2	13.8	13.0 − 79.0
Band Cells (per 100 WBC)		67	0.1	0.4	0.0 − 2.0
Eosinophils (per 100 WBC)		67	5.3	5.2	0.0 − 22.0
Monocytes (per 100 WBC)		67	1.2	1.3	0.0 − 6.0
Basophiles (per 100 WBC)		67	0.3	0.7	0.0 − 4.0

TABLE III
SERUM PROTEIN DETERMINATIONS IN THE
SQUIRREL MONKEY (*Saimiri sciureus*)

Constituent	Number of subjects	Mean	Standard deviation	Observed range
Total Protein (gm%)	67	7.3	0.6	6.0 − 8.5
Albumin (%)	50	62.1	5.6	44.2 − 74.6
Globulin fractions				
Alpha 1 (%)	50	1.7	1.2	0.0 − 4.3
Alpha 2' (%)	50	3.8	1.3	1.2 − 6.1
Alpha 2 (%)[a]	50	6.5	1.7	3.5 − 10.5
Alpha 2'' (%)	50	4.1	1.2	1.9 − 6.7
Beta (%)	50	6.4	1.4	3.5 − 9.1
Gamma (%)	50	15.3	3.7	9.2 − 34.1

[a]Squirrel monkeys reflect three fractions in the alpha 2 region by cellulose acetate electrophoresis.

419

SUPPLEMENTARY BIBLIOGRAPHY ─────────────────

Alexander, M. F. (1965). Arousal effects on activity and response time in the squirrel monkey (*Saimiri sciureus*). *Dissertation Abstr.* **26**, 1769-1770.

Azrin, N. H., Hake, D. F., and Hutchinson, R. R. (1965). Elicitation of aggression by a physical blow. *J. Exptl. Anal. Behavior* **8**, 55-57.

Azrin, N. H., Holz, W. C., and Hake, D. (1962). Intermittent reinforcement by removal of a conditioned aversive stimulus. *Science* **136**, 781-782.

Azrin, N. H., Holz, W. C., Hake, D. F., and Ayllon, T. (1963). Fixed ratio escape reinforcement. *J. Exptl. Anal. Behavior* **6**, 449-456.

Azrin, N. H., Hutchinson, R. R., and Hake, D. (1963). Pain induced fighting in the squirrel monkey. *J. Exptl. Anal. Behavior* **6**, 620.

Azrin, N. H., Hutchinson, R. R., and Hake, D. (1967). Attack, avoidance, and escape reactions to aversive shock. *J. Exptl. Anal. Behavior* **10**, 131-148.

Azrin, N. H., Hutchinson, R. R., and McLaughlin, R. (1965). The opportunity for aggression as an operant reinforcer during aversive stimulation. *J. Exptl. Anal. Behavior* **8**, 171-180.

Azrin, N. H., Hutchinson, R. R., and Sallery, R. D. (1964). Pain-aggression toward inanimate objects. *J. Exptl. Anal. Behavior* **7**, 223-228.

Baldwin, J. D. (1967). A study of the social behavior of a semifree-ranging colony of squirrel monkeys (*Saimiri sciureus*). Ph.D. Thesis, The Johns Hopkins University, Baltimore, Maryland.

Banks, K. L., and Bullock, B. C. (1967). Naturally occurring secondary amyloidosis of a squirrel monkey (*Saimiri sciureus*). *J. Am. Vet. Med. Assoc.* **151**, 839-842.

Barney, G. H., Macapinlac, M. P., Pearson, W. N., and Darby, W. J. (1967). Parakeratosis of the tongue—A unique histopathologic lesion in the zinc-deficient squirrel monkey. *J. Nutr.* **93**, 511-517.

Bates, M. (1944). The *Saimiri* monkey as an experimental host for the virus of yellow fever. *Am. J. Trop. Med.* **24**, 83-89.

Bates, M. and Roca-Garcia, M. (1945). Laboratory studies of the *Saimiri-Haemagogus* cycle of jungle yellow fever. *Am. J. Trop. Med.* **25**, 203-216.

Bates, M., and Roca-Garcia, M. (1946). Experiments with various Colombian marsupials and primates in laboratory cycles of yellow fever. *Am. J. Trop. Med.* **26**, 437-453.

Bates, M., and Roca-Garcia, M. (1946). An experiment with neurotropic yellow fever virus in *Saimiri* and *Haemagogus* mosquitos. *Am. J. Trop. Med.* **26**, 607-612.

Benjamin, R. M., and Burton, H. (1968). Projection of taste nerve afferents to anterior opercular-insular cortex in squirrel monkey (*Saimiri sciureus*). *Brain Res.* **7**, 221-231.

Benjamin, R. M., Emmers, R., and Blomquist, A. J. (1968). Projection of tongue nerve afferents to somatic sensory area I in squirrel monkey (*Saimiri sciureus*). *Brain Res.* **7**, 208-220.

Brinkman, D. C., and Burch, G. R. (1964). Methoxyflurane anesthesia in primates. *Allied Vet.* **36**, 39; see *Lab. Primate Newsletter* **3**, No. 4, 18 (1964).

Brinster, R. L. (1967). Lactate dehydrogenase activity in human, squirrel monkey and rhesus monkey oocytes. *Exptl. Cell Res.* **48**, 643-645.

Brown, G. M., Grota, L., and Reichlin, S. (1968). Uniquely high resting plasma cortisol levels in the squirrel monkey and responsiveness to emotional stress. *Federation Proc.* **27**, 210.

Brown, G. M., Schalch, D. S., and Reichlin, S. (1967). Growth hormone response to stress in the squirrel monkey. *Federation Proc.* **26**, 585.

421

422 **Supplementary Bibliography**

Brown, L. T. (1967). Further studies of the attentional response of humans and squirrel monkeys to visual pa'terns. *Perceptual Motor Skills* **25**, 397-406.

Brown, L. T., and O'Donnell, C. R. (1966). Attentional response of humans and squirrel monkeys to visual patterns varying in three physical dimensions. *Perceptual Motor Skills* **22**, 707-717.

Buddington, R. W., King, F. A., and Roberts, L. (1967). Emotionally and conditioned avoidance responding in the squirrel monkey following septal injury. *Psychon. Sci.* **8**, No. 5, 195-196.

Bush, D. F., Heinrich, B., and Woodburne, L. S. (1967). Training of squirrel monkeys to perform a pulling-in task. *Lab. Primate Newsletter* **6**, No. 4, 16-18.

Butcher, E. O., and Mitchell, O. G. (1967). Structure and secretory mechanism of rodent and primate palatine glands. *J. Dental Res.* **46**, 672-674.

Campos-Ortega, J., and Glees, P. (1967). The visual subcortical connections in the squirrel monkey (*Saimiri sciureus*). *J. Physiol.* **191**, 93-95.

Campos-Ortega, J. A., and Glees, P. (1967). The subcortical distribution of optic fibers in *Saimiri sciureus* (squirrel monkey). *J. Comp. Neurol.* **131**, 131-142.

Capps, M. J., and Ades, H. W. (1968). Auditory frequency discrimination after transection of the olivocochlear bundle in squirrel monkeys. *Exptl. Neurol.* **21**, 147-153.

Carlisle, H. J. (1966). Heat intake and hypothalamic temperature during behavioral temperature regulation. *J. Comp. Physiol. Psychol.* **61**, No. 3, 388-397.

Carregal, E. J. A. (1968). Response of respiratory neurons to changes in ventilation. *Federation Proc.* **27**, No. 2.

Carregal, E. J. A., and Williams, B. (1967). Effects of etonitazene upon respiratory neurons. *Experientia* **23**, 57-59.

Carregal, E. J. A., Williams, B., and Biozis, L. (1967). Respiratory centers in the dog and squirrel monkey: A comparative study. *Resp. Physiol.* **3**, 333-348.

Castell, R. (1967). Die soziale Reorganisation nach der Zusammenfurhrung von Totenkopfaffenkolonien. *In* "Progress in Primatology" (D. Starck, R. Schneider, and H. J. Kuhn, eds.), pp. 272-277. Fischer, Stuttgart.

Castellanos, H., and McCombs, H. L. (1968). The reproductive cycle of the new world monkey. Gynecologic problems in a breeding colony. *Fertility Sterility* **19**, 213-227.

Catania, A. C., Deegan, J. F., and Cook, L. (1966). Concurrent fixed-ratio and avoidance responding in the squirrel monkey. *J. Exptl. Anal. Behavior* **9**, 227-231.

Chacko, L. W. (1954). The lateral geniculate body in the New World monkeys. *J. Anat. Soc. India* **3**, 62-74.

Chaffee, R. R. J., Cassuto, Y., and Horvath, S. M. (1965). Studies on the effects of cold acclimation on myoglobin levels in sparrows, mice, hamsters, and monkeys. *Can. J. Physiol. Pharmacol.* **43**, 1021-1025.

Chaffee, R. R. J., Horvath, S. M., Allen, J. R., Brewer, M., and Mason, C. F. (1965). Studies on chemical thermoregulation in primates. *Federation Proc.* **24**, No. 2, Part 1, 148.

Clemente, C. D., Chase, M. H., Sauerland, E. K., Nakamura, Y., and Goldberg, L. (1967). Cortical inhibition of bulbar and spinal monosynaptic reflexes in the cat and squirrel monkey. *Federation Proc.* **26**, 434.

Clewe, T. H. (1966). Regular occurrence of diabetes insipidus during pregnancy in the squirrel monkey (*Saimiri sciureus*). *Am. Zoologist* **6**, No. 3, 226.

Clewe, T. and DuVal, W. (1966). Sore tails in squirrel monkeys produced by perches. *Lab. Primate Newsletter* **5**, No. 4, 8.

Colborn, G. L. (1966). The gross morphology of the coronary arteries of the common squirrel monkey. *Anat. Record* **155**, No. 3, 353-368 (No. 101a); also *Anat. Record* **151**, 337 (1965).

Colborn, G. L. (1967). Observations on the cervix uteri of the squirrel monkey. *J. Morphol*, **122**, 81-88.

Colborn, G. L. (1968). The atrioventricular conducting system of the squirrel monkey. *Anat. Record* **160**, 333.

Colborn, G. L., and Lang, C. M. (1967). The cervix uteri of the squirrel monkey. *Anat. Record*, **157**, 230.

Cooper, R. W. (1968). Small species of primates in biomedical research. *Lab. Animal Care* **18**, No. 2, Part 2, 267-279.

Cowey, A. (1964). Projection of the retina on to striate and prestriate cortex in the squirrel monkey, *Saimiri sciureus*. *J. Neurophysiol*. **27**, 366-393.

Cross, H. A., and Brown, L. T. (1965). Discrimination reversal learning in squirrel monkeys as a function of number of acquisition trials and prereversal experience. *J. Comp. Physiol. Psychol*. **59**, No. 3, 429-431.

Cross, H. A., Fickling, R. M., Carpenter, J. B., and Brown, L. T. (1964). Discrimination reversal performance in squirrel monkeys as a function of prereversal experience and overlearning. *Psychon. Sci*. **1**, 353-354.

Cutt, R. A., Keels, E. W., Litvin, M., and Wolfson, R. J. (1966). Implanted electrodes for electronystagmography in the squirrel monkey. *J. Appl. Physiol*. **21**, 715,717.

Daniel, M. D., Karpas, A., Melendez, L. V., King, N. W., and Hunt, R. D. (1967). Isolation of herpes-T virus from a spontaneous disease in squirrel monkeys (*Saimiri sciureus*). *Arch. Ges. Virusforsch*. **22**, 324-331.

Daniel, M. D., King, N. W., Hunt, R. D., and Melendez, L. V. (1967). Herpes T virus isolation from a natural disease in squirrel monkeys (*Saimiri sciureus*). *Federation Proc*. **26**, No.2, 421.

Davidson, I. W. F., and Blackwell, W. L. (1968). Changes in carbohydrate metabolism of squirrel monkeys with chromium dietary supplementation. *Proc. Soc. Exptl. Biol. Med*. **127**, 66-70.

Davis, N. C. (1930). The transmission of yellow fever. Experiments with the woolly monkey (*Lagothrix lagotricha* Humboldt), the spider monkey (*Atelus ater*, F. Cuvier) and the squirrel monkey (*Saimiri sciureus* Linnaeus). *J. Exptl. Med*. **51**, 703-720.

Davis, N. C. (1931). The transmission of yellow fever. Further experiments with monkeys of the New World. *Am. J. Trop. Med. Hyg*. **11**, 113-125.

Davis, N. C., and Shannon, R. C. (1929). Studies on South American yellow fever. III. Transmission of the virus to Brazilian monkeys. Preliminary observations. *J. Exptl. Med*. **50**, 81-85.

Deane, L. M. (1964). Animal reservoirs of *Trypanosoma cruzi* in Brazil. *Rev. Brasil Malariol. Trop*. **16**, No. 1, 27-48.

Deane, L. M., and Damasceno, R. G. (1961). Tripanosomideos de mamíferos da Região Amazonica. II. Tripanosomas de macacos da Zona do Salgado, Estado do Pará. *Rev. Inst. Med. Trop. Sao Paulo* **3**, 61-70.

Deane, L. M., Deane, M. P., and Neto, J. F. (1965). Studies on transmission of simian malaria and on a natural infection of man with *Plasmodium simium* in Brazil. *Bull. World Health Organ*. **35**, 805-808.

Deane, L. M., Deane, M. P., and Neto, J. F. (1966). A naturally acquired human infection by *Plasmodium simium* of howler monkeys. *Trans. Roy. Soc. Trop. Med. Hyg*. **60**, No. 4, 563-564.

Deane, L. M., Neto, J. F., Silveira, I. P. S. (1966). Experimental infection of a splenectomized squirrel monkey, *Saimiri sciureus*, with *Plasmodium vivax*. *Trans. Roy. Soc. Trop. Med. Hyg*. **60**, No. 6, 811-812.

de la Iglesia, F. A., and Porta, E. A. (1967). Ciliated biliary epithelial cells in the livers of non-human primates. *Experientia* **23**, No. 49, 1-7.

de la Iglesia, F. A., Porta, E. A., and Hartroft, W. S. (1967). Effects of dietary protein levels on the *Saimiri sciureus*. *Exptl. Mol. Pathol.* **7**, 182-195.

Denniston, R. H., and MacLean, P. D. (1961) Erection display in male-male and male-female interaction in the squirrel monkey, *Saimiri sciureus*. (Motion picture, 15 minutes) *Am. Zoologist* **1**, No. 4, 83.

Dietschy, J. M., and Wilson, J. D. (1968). Cholesterol synthesis in the squirrel monkey: Relative rates of synthesis in various tissues and mechanisms of control. *J. Clin. Invest.* **47**, 166-174.

Doty, R. W., Kimura, D. S., and Mogenson, G. J. (1964). Photically and electrically elicited responses in the central visual system of the squirrel monkey. *Exptl. Neurol.* **10**, 19-51.

Drach, G. W., and Bowen, J. (1966). Nephrocalcinosis in the squirrel monkey. *Surg. Forum* **17**, 501-503.

DuMond, F. V. (1967). Semi-free-ranging colonies of monkeys at Goulds Monkey Jungle. *Intern. Zoo Yearbook* **7**, 202-207.

Egozcue, J. (1967). Position of the centromere in the marked acrocentric chromosomes of primates. *Folia Primat.* **7**, 238-242.

Egozcue, J., Vilarasau de Egozcue, M., and Hagemenas, F. (1967). The chromosomes of two species of *Saimiri: Saimiri madeirae juruanus* and *Saimiri boliviensis nigriceps*. *Mammal. Chromo. Newsletter* **8**, No. 1, 14.

Ellison, T., Gill, C. A., and Riddle, W. C. (1964). A restraining table for small laboratory primates. *Am. J. Vet. Res.* **25**, 872-873.

Epple, G., and Lorenz, R. (1967). Vorkommen, morphologie und funktion der sternaldruse bei den platyrrhini. *Folia Primat.* **7**, 98-126.

Fabio, R. (1967). Cytoarchitecture of the frontal lobe of the squirrel monkey. *J. Comp. Neurol.* **130**, No. 2, 87-108.

Faust, E. C. (1935). Notes on helminths from Panama. III. Filarial infection in the marmosets, *Leontocebus geoffroyi* (Pucheron) and *Saimiri orstedii orstedii* (Reinhardt) in Panama. *Trans. Roy. Soc. Trop. Med. Hyg.* **28**, 627-634.

Faust, E. C. (1967). Athesmia (Trematoda: Dicrocoeliidae) Odhner, 1911 liver fluke of monkeys from Colombia, South America, and other mammalian hosts. *Trans. Am. Microscop. Soc.* **86**, 113-119.

Fentress, J. C., and Doty, R. W. (1966). Protracted tetanization of the optic tract in squirrel monkeys. *Federation Proc.* **25**, 573.

Fernandez, C., Butler, R., Knoishi, T., Honrubia, V., and Tasaki, I. (1962). Cochlear potentials in rhesus and squirrel monkey. *J. Acoust. Soc. Am.* **34**, 1411-1417.

Fisher, G. L., Pfaffmann, C. and Brown, E. (1965). Dulcin and saccharin taste in squirrel monkeys, rats, and men. *Science* **150**, 506-507.

Fooden, J. (1961). Urinary amino acids of non-human primates. *Zoologica* **46**, 167-180.

Furry, D. E., Lowery, R. T., and Beischer, D. E. (1963). Laboratory maintenance of squirrel monkey. *Lab. Primate Newsletter* **2**, No. 3, 1-2.

Fry, W., Kelleher, R. T., and Cook, L. (1960). A mathematical index of performance on fixed-interval schedules of reinforcement. *J. Exptl. Anal. Behavior* **3**, 193-199.

Fussel, E. N., Roussel, J. D., and Austin, C. R. (1967). Use of the rectal probe method for electrical ejaculation of apes, monkeys and a prosimian. *Lab. Animal Care* **17**, No. 5, 528-530.

Ganchrow, J., and Fisher, G. L. (1968). Two behavioral measures of squirrel monkeys' (*Saimiri sciureus*) taste for four concentrations of five sugars. *Psychol. Rept.* **22**, 503-511.

Garner, E. (1967). *Dipetalonema gracile* infection in squirrel monkeys (*Saimiri sciureus*). *Lab. Animal Dig.* **3**, No. 2, 16-17.

Garnham, P. C. C., and Gonzales-Muga-Buru, L. (1962). A new trypanosome in *Saimiri* monkeys from Colombia. *Rev. Inst. Med. Trop. Sao Paulo* **4**, 79-84.

Gergen, J. A. (1964). Actions of hippocampus on subcortical neurones in the squirrel monkey. *Physiologist* **7**, 142.

Gergen, J. A., and MacLean, P. D. (1961). Hippocampal seizures in squirrel monkeys. *Electroencephalog. Clin. Neurophysiol.* **13**, 316-317.

Gergen, J. A., and MacLean, P. D. (1964). The limbic system: Photic activation of limbic cortical areas in the squirrel monkey. *Ann. N. Y. Acad. Sci.* **117**, No. 1, 69-87.

Gergen, J. A., and Reynolds, J. C. (1962). Unit and slow potential responses in hippocampus of squirrel monkey (*Saimiri sciureus*). *Federation Proc.* **21**, No. 2, 354.

Glasser, J. E., Weiner, I. M., and Lack, L. (1965). Comparative physiology of intestinal taurocholate transport. *Am. J. Physiol.* **208**, No. 2, 359-362.

Glickstein, M., Calvin, W., and Doty, R. W. (1966). Laminar structure of the dorsal lateral geniculate body of *Saimiri* and *Tupaia*. *Anat. Record* **154**, 348.

Godlewski, H. G., and Bourne, G. H. (1967). Distribution of neutral polysaccharides and activities of phosphorylase and glycogen synthetase in cheek pouch mucosa regions in hamsters and mouth mucosa of squirrel monkeys. *Folia Histochem. Cytochem.* **5**, 15-26.

Goodman, M. (1967). Deciphering primate phylogeny from macromolecular specificities. *Am. J. Phys. Anthropol.* **26**, No. 2, 255-275.

Gossette, R. L., and Feldman, J. (1968). An examination of the sensitivity of successive discrimination reversal (SDR) measures to differences in motivational level with squirrel monkeys. *Psychon. Sci.* **11**, 157-158.

Graybiel, A., Igarashi, M., and McLeod, M. E. (1965). Clinical pathological correlations in squirrel monkeys after suppression of semicircular canal function by streptomycin sulfate. *NASA Contractor Rept. No. NASA-CR-68007*, 1-37.

Grzimek, H. C. B. (1967). Reichtum aus verstummelten Indianern. *Das Tier 7*, No. 1, 4-10.

Hafleigh, A. S., and Williams, C. A. (1966). Antigenic correspondence of serum albumins among the primates. *Science* **151**, 1530-1535.

Hafner, E., and Woodburne, L. S. (1964). Breeding *Saimiri sciureus*. *Lab. Primate Newsletter* **3**, No. 4, 15-16.

Hake, D. F., Azrin, N. H., and Oxford, R. (1967). The effects of punishment intensity on squirrel monkeys. *J. Exptl. Anal. Behavior* **10**, 95-107.

Hanson, H. M. (1963). Laboratory note on *Saimiri sciurea*. *Lab. Primate Newsletter* **2**, No. 1, 1-3.

Harlow, H. F., Uehling, H., and Maslow, A. H. (1932). Comparative behavior of primates: I. Delayed reaction tests on primates from the lemur to the orang-utan. *J. Comp. Psychol.* **13**, 313-343.

Herd, J. A., Morse, W. H., Kelleher, R. T., and Jones, L. G. (1968). Arterial blood pressure in the squirrel monkey during behavioral experiments. *Federation Proc.* **27**, 743.

Hildebrand, M. (1967). Symmetrical gaits of primates. *Am. J. Phys. Anthropol.* **26**, No. 2, 119-130.

Hill, W. C. O. (1936). Notes on malaria and tetanus in monkeys. *J. Comp. Pathol. Therap.* **49**, 274-278.

Hind, J. E., Anderson, D. J., Brugge, J. F., and Rose, J. E. (1967). Coding of information pertaining to paired low-frequency tones in single auditory nerve fibers of the squirrel monkey. *J. Neurophysiol.* **30**, 794-816.

Holmes, A. W., Devine, J. A., Nowakowski, E., and Deinhardt, F. (1966). The epidemiology of a herpes virus infection of New World monkeys. *J. Immunol.* **90**, 668-671.

Hopf, S. (1967). Ontogeny of social behavior in the squirrel monkey. *In* "Progress in Primatology" (D. Starck, R. Schneider, and H. -J. Kuhn, eds.) pp. 255-262. Fischer, Stuttgart.

Horrocks, L. A. (1967). Composition of myelin from peripheral and central nervous systems of the squirrel monkey. *J. Lipid Res.* **8**, 569-576.

Huser, H. -J., and Olberding, B. A. (1967). Neutrophil alkaline phosphatases in blood cells of primates. *Nature* **214**, 1043-1044.

Hutchinson, R. R., Azrin, N. H., and Hake, D. F. (1966). An automatic method for the study of aggression in squirrel monkeys. *J. Exptl. Anal. Behavior* **9**, 233-237.

Hutchinson, R. R., Azrin, N. H., and Renfrew, J. W. (1968). Effects of shock intensity and duration on the frequency of biting attack by squirrel monkeys. *J. Exptl. Anal. Behavior* **11**, 83-88.

Iijima, K., and Bourne, G. H. (1968). Histochemical studies on distribution of esterases, monoamine oxidase and dephosphorylating enzymes in area postrema of squirrel monkey. *Acta Histochem.* **29**, 349.

Iijima, K., Bourne, G. H., and Shantha, T. R. (1967). Histochemical studies on the distribution of enzymes of glycolytic pathways in the area postrema of the squirrel monkey. *Acta Histochem.* **27**, 42-54.

Iijima, K., Shantha, T. R., and Bourne, G. H. (1967). Histochemical studies on the distribution of some enzymes of the glycolytic pathways in the olfactory bulb of the squirrel monkey (*Saimiri sciureus*). *Histochemie* **10**, 224-229.

Iijima, K., Shantha, T. R., and Bourne, G. H. (1967). Enzyme-histochemical studies on the hypothalamus with special reference to the supraoptic and paraventricular nuclei of squirrel monkey (*Saimiri sciureus*). *Z. Zellforsch,* **79**, 76-91.

Ishii, T., Murakami, Y., and Gacek, R. R. (1967). Histochemical study of the acetylcholinesterase activity in the inner ear of the squirrel monkey. *Acta Oto-Laryngol.* **64**, 267-279.

Jacobs, G. H. (1968). Functional roles for different classes of cells in the lateral geniculate nucleus of the squirrel monkey. *Federation Proc.* **27**, 518.

Jacobs, G. H., and DeValois, R. L. (1965). Chromatic opponent cells in squirrel monkey lateral geniculate nucleus. *Nature* **206**, 487-489.

Jacobson, S. (1967). Dimensions of the dendritic spine in the sensorimotor cortex of the rat, cat, squirrel monkey and man. *J. Comp. Neurol.* **129**, 49-58.

Jones, M. L. (1962). Mammals in captivity—primate longevity. *Lab. Primate Newsletter* **1**, No. 3, 3-14.

Jones, M. L. (1967). Outstanding American zoo primates. *Am. Assoc. Zool. Parks and Acquariums Newsletter* **8**, No. 6, 12-13.

Jurgens, U., Maurus, M., Ploog, D., and Winter, P. (1967). Vocalization in the squirrel monkey (*Saimiri sciureus*) elicited by brain stimulation. *Exptl. Brain Res.* **4**, 114-117.

Kelemen, G. (1965). Non-experimental aural pathology in squirrel monkeys (*Saimiri sciureus*) and marmosets. *Acta Oto-Laryngd.* **61**, 237-254.

Kelleher, R. T., Fry, W., and Cook, L. (1964). Adjusting fixed-ratio schedules in the squirrel monkey. *J. Exptl. Anal. Behavior* **7**, 69-77.

King, F. A., Roberts, L., and King, R. L. (1963). Visual and auditory learning in squirrel monkeys with restricted lesions of frontal occipital cortex. *Federation Proc.* **22**, 514.

King, N. W., Hunt, R. D., Daniel, M. D., and Melendez, L. V. (1967). Overt herpes-T infection in squirrel monkeys (*Saimiri sciureus*). *Lab. Animal Care* **17**, 413-423.

Kirchshofer, R. (1963). Einige bemerkenswerte Verhaltensweisen bei Saimiris im Vergleich zu verwandten Arten. *Z. Morphol. Anthropol.* **53**, 77-91.

Klüver, H. (1936). The study of personality and the method of equivalent and non-equivalent stimuli. *Character Personality* **5**, 91-112.

Klüver, H. (1951). Functional differences between the occipital and temporal lobes. *In* "Cerebral Mechanisms in Behavior" (L.A. Jeffress, ed.), pp. 147-182. Wiley, New York.

Knepton, J. C., and Beischer, D. E. (1966). Effects of very high magnetic fields on the electroencephalogram of the squirrel monkey (*Saimiri sciureus*). *Aerospace Med.* **37**, 287 (abstr.).

Kubota, K., Hayama, S., and Iwamoto, M. (1966). Comparative anatomical and neurohistological observations on the tongue of the squirrel monkey (*Saimiri sciurea*). *Primates* **7**, No. 3, 381-390.

Lang, C. M. (1967). Effects of psychic stress on atherosclerosis in the squirrel monkey (*Saimiri sciureus*). *Proc. Soc. Exptl. Biol. Med.* **126**, 30-34.

Latta, J., Hopf, S., and Ploog, D. (1967). Observation on mating behavior and sexual play in the squirrel monkey (*Saimiri sciureus*). *Primates* **8**, 229-246.

Layton, L. L., Greer, W. E., Greene, F. C., and Yamanaka, E. (1963). Passive transfer of human atopic allergies to catarrhine and platyrrhine primates of suborder Anthropoidea. *Intern. Arch. Allergy Appl. Immunol.* **23**, 176-187.

Lehner, N. D. M., Bullock, B. C., Clarkson, T. B., and Lofland, H. B. (1966). Biological activity of vitamins D_2 and D_3 fed to squirrel monkeys. *Federation Proc.* **25**, 533.

Lehner, N. D. M., Bullock, B. C., Clarkson, T. B., and Lofland, H. B. (1967). Biological activities of vitamins D_2 and D_3 for growing squirrel monkeys. *Lab. Animal Care* **17**, No. 5, 483-493.

Leppi, T. J. and Spicer, S. S. (1966). The histochemistry of mucins in certain primate salivary glands. *Am. J. Anat.* **118**, No. 3, 833-860.

Lofland, H. B., St. Clair, R. W., MacNintch, J. E., and Pritchard, R. W. (1967). Atherosclerosis in New World Primates. *Arch. Pathol.* **83**, 211-214.

Macapinlac, M. P., Barney, G. H., Pearson, W. N., and Darby, W. J. (1967). Production of zinc deficiency in the squirrel monkey (*Saimiri sciureus*). *J. Nutr.* **93**, 499.

Machida, H., Perkins, E., and Hu, F. (1967). The skin of primates. XXXV. The skin of the squirrel monkey (*Saimiri sciurea*). *Am. J. Phys. Anthrop.* **26**, 45-54.

MacLean, P. D., and Ploog, D. W. (1960). Cerebral loci involved in penile erection. *Federation Proc.* **1**, Part 1, 19.

MacLean, P. D., Denniston, R. H., and Dua, S. (1963). Further studies on cerebral representation of penile erection: Caudal thalamus, midbrain, and pons. *J. Neurophysiol.* **26**, 273-393.

MacLean, P. D., Dua, S., and Denniston, R. H. (1962). A mapping of cerebral structures involved in seminal discharge and genital scratching. *Trans. Am. Neurolo. Assoc.* **87**, 136-139.

MacLean, P. D., Dua, S., and Denniston, R. H. (1963). Cerebral localization for scratching and seminal discharge. *Arch. Neurol.* **9**, 485-497.

MacLean, P. D., Robinson, B. W., and Ploog, D. W. (1959). Experiments on localization of genital function in the brain. *Electroencephalog. Clin. Neurophysiol.* **11**, 617.

MacLean, P. D., Robinson, B. W., and Ploog, D. W. (1960). Circulatory effects of limbic stimulation, with special reference to the male genital organ. *Physiol. Rev.* **40**, Suppl. 4, 105-112.

MacNintch, J. E., Middleton, C. C., Clarkson, T. B., St. Clair, R. W., and Lofland, H. B. (1966). The effects of changing environment on serum cholesterol levels in squirrel monkeys. *Federation Proc.* **25**, No. 388, 1124.

Maisel, H., and Goodman, M. (1965). Comparative electrophoretic study of vertebrate lens proteins. *Am. J. Opthalmol.* **59**, No. 4, 697-704.

Malinow, M. R. (1965). Atherosclerosis in subhuman primates. *Folia Primatol.* **3**, 277-300.

Malinow, M. R., Maruffo, C. A., and Perley, A. M. (1966). Experimental atherosclerosis in squirrel monkeys (*Saimiri sciurea*). *J. Pathol. Bacteriol.* **92**, 491-510.

Malinow, M. R., Perley, A., and McLaughlin, P. (1968). The effect of pyridinolcarbamate on aortic and coronary atherosclerosis in squirrel monkeys (*Saimiri sciurea*). *J. Atherosclerosis Res.* **8**, 455-461.

Manocha, S. L., and Bourne, G. H. (1966). Histochemical mapping of succinic dehydrogenase and cytochrome oxidase in the pons and mesencephalon of squirrel monkey (*Saimiri sciureus*). *Exptl. Brain Res.* **2**, 230-246.

Manocha, S. L., and Bourne, G. H. (1966). Histochemical mapping of succinic dehydrogenase and cytochrome oxidase in the spinal cord, medulla oblongata and cerebellum of squirrel monkey (*Saimiri sciureus*). *Exptl. Brain Res.* **2**, 216-229.

Manocha, S. L., and Bourne, G. H. (1966). Histochemical mapping of monoamine oxidase and lactic dehydrogenase in the pons and mesencephalon of squirrel monkey (*Saimiri sciureus*). *J. Neurochem.* **13**, No. 11, 1047-1056.

Manocha, S. L., and Bourne, G. H., (1967). Histochemical mapping of succinic dehydrogenase and cytochrome oxidase in the diencephalon and basal telencephalic centers of the brain of squirrel monkey (*Saimiri sciureus*). *Histochemie* **9**, 300-319.

Manocha, S. L., Shantha, T. R., and Bourne, G. H. (1967). Histochemical mapping of the distribution of monoamine oxidase in the diencephalon and basal telencephalic centers of the brain of squirrel monkey (*Saimiri sciureus*). *Brain Res.* **6**, 570-586.

Manocha, S. L., Shantha, T. R., and Bourne, G. H. (1967). Histochemical studies on the spinal cord of squirrel monkey (*Saimiri sciureus*). *Exptl. Brain Res.* **3**, 25-39.

Martin, W. C, (1833). Notes on the dissection of a squirrel monkey (*Callithrix sciureus*, Geoffr.). *Proc. Zool. Soc. London* 88-90.

Maruffo, C. A., and Cramer, D. L. (1967). Congenital renal malformations in monkeys. *Folia Primatol.* **5**, No. 4, 305-311.

Maruffo, C. A., and Portman, O. W. (1968). Nutritional control of coronary artery atherosclerosis in squirrel monkey. *J. Atherosclerosis Res.* **8**, 237.

Massopust, L. C., Jr., and Wolin, L. R. (1965). Visual cortex of the squirrel monkey. *Anat. Record* **151**, 464-465.

Massopust, L. C., Wolin, L. R., and Kadoya, S. (1968). Evoked responses in the auditory cortex of the squirrel monkey. *Exptl. Neurol.* **21**, 35-40.

Maurus, M. (1967). A new telestimulation technique for the study of social behavior of the squirrel monkey. *In* "Progress in Primatology" (D. Starck, R. Schneider, and H. J. Kuhn, eds.) p. 287. Fischer, Stuttgart.

McBroom, P. (1966). Neurophysiology. Nerve cells and Parkinsonism. *Sci. News,* **90**, No. 24, 492.

Melendez, L. V., Daniel, M. D., Hunt, R. D., and Garcia, F. G. (1968). An apparently new herpes-virus from primary kidney cultures of the squirrel monkey (*Saimiri sciureus*). *Lab. Animal Care* **18**, 374-381.

Meltzer, D., Maxey, G. C., and Merkler, N. L. (1966). Sequential amatching in the squirrel monkey. *Psychol. Rept.* **19**, 859-867.

Middleton, C. C. (1966). Acanthocephala (*Prosthenorchis elegans*) infection in squirrel monkeys (*Saimiri sciureus*). *Lab. Animal Digest* **2** No. 2, 10-13.

Middleton, C. C., and Lofland, H. B. (1965). Aggravation of atherosclerosis in squirrel monkeys (*Saimiri sciureus*) by diet. *Federation Proc.* **24**, No. 2, Part 1, 311.

Middleton, C. C., Clarkson, T. B., Lofland, H. B. (1967). Diet and atherosclerosis of squirrel monkeys. *Arch. Pathol.* **83**, 145-153.

Middleton, C. C., Clarkson, T. B., Lofland, H. B., and Pritchard, R. W. (1963). Naturally occurring atherosclerosis in the squirrel monkey (*Saimiri sciurea*). *Circulation* **28**, No. 4, Part 2, 665-666.

Middleton, C. C., Clarkson, T. B., Lofland, H. B., and Pritchard, R. W. (1964). Atherosclerosis in the squirrel monkey. *Arch. Pathol.* **78**, 16-23.

Middleton, C. C., Rosal, J., Clarkson, T. B., Newman, W. P., and McGill, H. C. (1967). Arterial lesions in squirrel monkeys. *Arch. Pathol.* **83**, 352-358.

Minette, H. P., and Shaffer, M. F. (1968). Experimental leptospirosis in monkeys. *Am. J. Trop. Med. Hyg.* **17**, No. 2, 202-212.

Mitoma, C., and Scholler, J. (1967). Durations of action of hexobarbital, zoxazolamine, and carisoprodol in rhesus and squirrel monkeys. *Life Sci.* **6**, 2087-2092.

Myers, E. N., and Schuknecht, H. F. (1965). Multiple traumatic surgical procedures on the oval windows of conditioned squirrel monkeys. Limitations of functional middle ear surgery in small animals. *Pract. Oto-rhino-laryng.* **27**, 239-248.

Nieuwendijk, J. G. (1967). Doodshoofdaapjes. *Artis* **12e**, No. 5, 170-176.

Paronetto, F., and Koffler, D. (1967). Autoimmune proliferative glomerulonephritis in monkeys. *Am. J. Pathol.* **50**, No. 5, 887-897.

Parsons, J. (1751-1752). An account of a very small monkey, communicated to Martin Falkes, Esq; LL.D. and President of the Royal and Antiquarian Societies, London. *Phil. Trans. Roy. Soc. London* **47**, 146-150.

Payne, P. R., and Wheeler, E. F. (1967). Comparative nutrition in pregnancy. *Nature* **215**, 1134-1136.

Pennypacker, H. S., and Cook, W. A. (1967). Acquisition and extinction of the conditioned eyelid response in the squirrel monkey as functions of the CS-UCS interval. *Psychol. Rept.* **20**, 1235-1243.

Pennypacker, H. S., King, F. A., Achenbach, K. E., and Roberts, L. (1966). An apparatus and procedure for conditioning the eye-blink reflex in the squirrel monkey. *J. Exptl. Analy. Behavior* **9**, No. 5, 601-604.

Peters, J. C. (1966). An epizootic of monkey pox at Rotterdam Zoo. *Intern. Zoo Yearbook* **6**, 274-275.

Peters, J. H., and Gordon, G. R. (1968). Histaminase activities in the plasma of subhuman primates and man. *Nature* **217**, 274-275.

Peters, J. H., Gordon, G. R., and Ferguson, S. A. (1967). Studies on histamine release and degradation in rhesus and squirrel monkeys. *Life Sci.* **6**, 1163-1168.

Peters, J. H., Gordon, G. R., and Ferguson, S. A. (1968). Pharmacologic response to and metabolism of chloral hydrate in squirrel and rhesus monkeys. *Federation Proc.* **27**, 404.

Ploog, D. W. (1964) Verhaltensforschung als Grundlagenwissenschaft fur die Psychiatrie. *Ver. Psychiat.* **10**, 1-23.

Ploog, D. W. (1966). Biological basis for instinct and behavior: Studies on the development of social behavior in squirrel monkeys. *Recent Advan. Biol. Psychiat.* Vol. 8, Chapter 16, pp. 199-223. Plenum Press, New York.

Ploog, D. W., and MacLean, P. D. (1961). A study of functions of the mammillary bodies. *Excerpta Med. Intern. Congr. Ser.* **38**, 69.

Ploog, D. W., and MacLean, P. D. (1963). On functions of the mamillary bodies in the squirrel monkey. *Exptl. Neurol.* **7**, 76-85.

Porter, J. A., Jr., Johnson, C. M., and DeSousa, L. (1966). Prevalence of malaria in Panamanian primates. *J. Parasitol.* **52**, No. 4, 669-670.

Portman, O. W. (1965). Comparative evaluation of three species of New World monkeys for studies of dietary factors, tissue lipids and atherogenesis. *J. Nutri.* **87**, No. 4, 429-438.

Portman, O. W., Alexander, M. and Maruffo, C. A. (1967). Nutritional control of arterial lipid compositon in squirrel monkeys: Major ester classes and types of phospholipids. *J. Nutri.* **91**, No. 1, 35-46.

Prejzner-Morawska, A. (1965). Ganglia of the lumbar portion of the sympathetic trunk in platyrrhine monkeys. *Folia Morphol.* **24**, No. 4, 402-406.

Pritchard, R. W., and Bullock, B. C. (1965). Spontaneous myocardial necrosis in a squirrel monkey. *Federation Proc.* **24**, No. 2, 1.

Quenod, M., Casey, K. L., and MacLean, P. D. (1963). Microelectrode study of sensory projections of posterior limbic cortex of squirrel monkey. *Federation Proc.* **22**, (Part 1), 577.

Reeves, A. G., Sudakov, K., and MacLean, P. D. (1968). Exploratory unit analysis of exteroceptive inputs to the insular cortex in awake, sitting, squirrel monkeys. *Federation Proc.* **27**, 388.

Renjifo, S., Sanmartin, C., and de Zulueta, J. (1952). A survey of the blood parasites of vertebrates in Eastern Colombia. *Acta Trop.* **9**, 151-169.

Revzin, A. M. (1968). Effects of chronic endrin administration on brain electrical activity in the squirrel monkey. *Federation Proc.* **27**, 597.

Rewell, R. E. (1954). Uterine fibromyomas and bilateral ovarian granulosa cell tumors in senile squirrel monkey, *Saimiri sciurea*. *J. Pathol. Bacteriol.* **68**, 291-293.

Richter, C. P. (1968). Inherent twenty-four hour and lunar clocks of a primate—the squirrel monkey. *Commun. Behav. Biol.* **1**, No. 5 (Part A), 305-332.

Roddenberry, H., and Allen, L. (1967). Observations on the abdominal lymphaticovenous communications of the squirrel monkey (*Saimiri sciureus*). *Anat. Record* **159**, No. 2, 147-158.

Rodhain, J. (1937). Notes sur *Trypanosoma minasense* (Chagas). Evolution du Trypanosome du *Saimiri* chez divers arthropodes. *Compt. Rend. Soc. Biol.* **126**, 69-72.

Rodhain, J. (1941). Notes sur *Trypanosoma minasense* Chagas. Identite specifique du trypanosome du *Saimiri: Chrysothrix sciureus*. *Acta Biol. Belg.* **1**, 187-192.

Rosabal, F. (1967). Cytoarchitecture of the frontal lobe of the squirrel monkey. *J. Comp. Neurol.* **130**, 87-108.

Rose, J. E., Brugge, J. F., Anderson, D. J., and Hind, J. E. (1967). Phase-locked response to low-frequency tones in single auditory nerve fibers on the squirrel monkey. *J. Neurophysiol.* **30**, 769-793.

Rumbaugh, D. M. (1963). Squirrel monkey maintenance at San Diego State College. *Lab. Primate Newsletter* **2**, No. 3, 2-4.

Rumbaugh, D. M., and Ternes, J. W. (1964). Two trial problem measurement of established learning set in the squirrel monkey. *Psychol. Rept.* **14**, 460.

Sadun, E. H., von Lichtenberg, F., and Bruce, J. I. (1966). Susceptibility and comparative pathology of ten species of primates exposed to infection with *Schistosoma mansoni*. *Am. J. Trop. Med. Hyg.* **15**, No. 5, 705-718.

St. Clair, R. W., MacNintch, J. E., Middleton, C. C., Clarkson, T. B., and Lofland, H. B. (1967). Changes in serum cholesterol levels of squirrel monkeys during importation and acclimation. *Lab. Invest.* **16**, 828-832.

St. Clair, R. W., Middleton, C. C., Clarkson, T. B., and Lofland, H. B. (1966). Serum lipids, lipoproteins and atherosclerosis in New World primates. *Federation Proc.* **25**, 388.

Sarich, V. M., and Wilson, A. C. (1966). Quantitative immunochemistry and the evolution of primate albumins: micro-complement fixation. *Science* **154**, 1563-1566.

Schmidek, H. H., Ervin, F. R., and Sweet, W. H. (1968). Alterations in the pain threshold produced by mesencephalic, thalamic, and limbic stimulation in the awake squirrel monkey (*Saimiri sciureus*). *Federation Proc.* **27**, 518.

Schmidt, U., and Seitz, E. (1967). Waschen mit Harn zum Zweck der thermoregulation bei totenkopfaffen (*Saimiri sciureus* L.). *Anthropol. Anz.* **30**, 162-165.

Seal, U. S., and Doe, R. P. (1965). Vertebrate distribution of corticosteroid-binding globulin and some endocrine effects on concentration. *Steroids*, **5**, No. 6, 827-841.

Seal, U. S., and Doe, R. P. (1967). The role of corticosteroid-binding globulin in mammalian pregnancy. *Excerpta Med. Intern. Congr. Ser.* **132**, 697-706.

Seaman, A. J., and Malinow, M. R. (1968). Blood clotting in nonhuman primates. *Lab. Animal Care* **18**, No. 1, 80-84.

Segal, E. F. (1964). Sequential effects in a multiple schedule involving double alternation of a pair of two link chains. *J. Exptl. Anal. Behavior* **7**, 167 (abstr.).

Segal, E. F. (1966). Contingent and noncontingent responding in squirrel monkeys as a joint function of quality of, distant from, and schedule of food reinforcement. *Psychon. Sci.* **4**, 5-6.

Sehmsdorf, J., and Moore, R. Y. (1968). Projections of the inferior colliculus in the squirrel monkey and marmoset. *Anat. Record* **160**, 426.

Selkurt, E. E., Walthen, R. L. (1967). Renal concentrating mechanism of the squirrel monkey. *Amer. J. Physiol.* **213**, 191-197.

Selkurt, E. E., Walthen, R. L., and Santos-Martinez, J. (1967). Creatinine excretion in the squirrel monkey *(Saimiri sciureus)*. *Federation Proc.* **26**, 266.

Shantha, T. R., Iijima, K., and Bourne, G. H. (1967). Histochemical studies on the cerebellum of squirrel monkey *(Saimiri sciureus)*. *Acta Histochem.* **27**, 129-162.

Shantha, T. R., Manocha, S. L., and Bourne, G. H. (1967). Enzyme histochemistry of the mesenteric and dorsal root ganglion cells of cat and squirrel monkey. *Histochemie* **10**, 234-245.

Shanthaveerappa, T. R., and Bourne, G. H. (1965). Histochemical studies on the distribution of oxidative and dephosphorylating enzymes and esterases in the olfactory bulb glomeruli of squirrel monkey. *Anat. Record* **151**, 475.

Shanthaveerappa, T. R., and Bourne, G. H. (1965). Histochemical studies on distribution of dephosphorylating and oxidative enzymes and esterases in olfactory bulb of the squirrel monkey. *J. Natl. Cancer Inst.* **35**, No. 1, 153-165.

Shanthaveerappa, T. R., and Bourne, G. H. (1965). Histochemical studies on the olfactory glomeruli of squirrel monkey. *Histochemie* **5**, 125-129.

Shanthaveerappa, T. R., and Bourne, G. H. (1965). The thiamine pyrophosphatase technique as an indicator of the morphology of the Golgi apparatus in the neurons. *Z. Zellforsch. Mikroskop. Anat.* **68**, 699-710.

Shanthaveerappa, T. R., and Bourne, G. H. (1966). Pacinian corpuscle on the olfactory bulb of the squirrel monkey. *Nature*, **209**, 1260.

Shanthaveerappa, T. R., Waitzman, M. B., and Bourne, G. H. (1966). Studies on the distribution of phosphorylase in the eyes of the rabbit and the squirrel monkey. *Histochemie* **7**, 80-95.

Sharpe, L. G., and Otis, L. S. (1966). Notes on the maintenance of squirrel monkeys out-of-doors. *Lab. Primate Newsletter* **5** No. 1,5-7.

Sharpe, L. G., Otis, L. S., and Schusterman, R. J. (1967). Disruption of size discrimination in squirrel monkeys *(Saimiri sciureus)* by LSD-25. *Psychon. Sci.* **7**, No. 3, 103-104.

Smith, J. L., Reynolds, D. H., Rane, L., and Justice, J., Jr. (1964). The fundus oculi in the squirrel, owl, and marmoset monkey. A study with fluorescein angiography. *Am. J. Opthalmol.* [3] **57**, 431-435.

Sparks, D. L., and Travis, R. P. (1967). A head-mounted manipulator for chronic single unit recording from the squirrel monkey. *Physiol. Behavior* **2**, 449-453.

Stahl, W. R., and Gummerson, J. Y. (1967). Systematic allometry in five species of adult primates. *Growth* **31**, 21-34.

Stephan, H. (1965). Der Bulbus olfactorius accessorius bei insektivoren und Primaten. *Acta Anat.* **62**, 215-253.

Steward, H. L. (1966). Pulmonary cancer and adenomatosis in captive wild mammals and birds from the Philadelphia Zoo. *J. Natl. Cancer Inst.* **36**, 117-138.

Stretch, R., and Skinner, N. (1967). Schedule-control of behavior in squirrel monkeys: Effects of methylphenidate. *Psychon. Sci.* **8**, 385-386.

Stunkard, H. W. (1965). New intermediate hosts in the life cycle of *Prosthenorchis elegans* (Diesing, 1951), an acanthocephalan parasite of primates. *J. Parasitol.* **51**, No. 4, 645-649.

Sussman, R. W. (1966). Gaits of a *Saimiri* on inclined surfaces. *Amer. J. Phys. Anthropol.* **25**, 205-206.

Syner, F. N., and Goodman, M. (1966). Differences in the lactic dehydrogenases of primate brains. *Nature* **209**, 426-428.

Tashjian, A. H., Jr., Levine, L. and Wilhelmi, A. E. (1965). Immunochemical relatedness of porcine, bovine, ovine and primate pituitary growth hormones. *Endocrinology* **77**, No. 3, 563-573.

Taylor, J. L. (1968). A breeding note on *Saimiri sciureus*. *Lab. Primate Newsletter* **7**, 1-2.

Thom, T. E. (1965). A roentgenographic cephalometric study of craniofacial variability in the squirrel monkey (*Saimiri sciureus*), MSD Thesis, University of Washington, Seattle, Washington.

Travis, R. P., and Sparks, D. L. (1968). Unitary responses and discrimination learning in the squirrel monkey: The globus pallidus. *Physiol. Behavior* **3**, 187-196.

Travis, R. P., Sparks, D. L., and Hooten, T. F. (1968). Single unit responses related to sequences of food motivated behavior. *Brain Res.* **7**, 455-458.

Ushijima, R. N., Shiniger, R. S., and Gardner, C. E. (1966). Susceptibility of cultured renal cells from different species of subhuman primates to simian virus 40. *Proc. Soc. Exptl. Biol. Med.* **122**, 673-675.

Uyeno, E. T. (1967). Lysergic acid diethylamide and dominance behavior of the squirrel monkey. *Arch. Intern. Pharmacodyn.* **169**, 66-69.

Verhaart, W. J. C. (1966). The pyramidal tract of *Tupaia*, compared to that in other primates. *J. Comp. Neurol.* **126**, 43-50.

Warren, K. S., and Jane, J. A. (1967). Comparative susceptibility to *Schistosoma mansoni* of the squirrel monkey, the slow loris and the tree shrew. *Trans. Roy. Soc. Trop. Med. Hyg.* **61**, 534-537.

Watson, R. G., and Mims, G. R. (1965). Antiglobulins in normal serum. III. Demonstration of antiglobulins in the normal sera of dogs, guinea pigs, sheep, swine, squirrel monkeys and turkeys. *J. Immunol.* **94**, 184-190.

Webster, W. A. (1968). *Molineus vexillarus* Dunn 1961 from South American primates. *Canad. J. Zool.* **46**, 287.

Wells, H. (1967). Convulsant level of Metrazol in the squirrel monkey. *Lab. Primate Newsletter* **6**, No. 1, 13.

Wells, H. and Deffenbacher, K. (1966). Concept learning with one relevant dimension in the squirrel monkey. *Psychon. Sci.* **6**, No. 5, 237-238.

Wells, H., and Deffenbacher, K. (1967). Conjunctive and disjunctive concept learning in humans and squirrel monkeys. *Can. J. Psychol.* **21**, 301-308.

Wiener, A. S., Moor-Jankowski, J., and Gordon, E. B. (1964). Blood groups of apes and monkeys. V. Studies on the human blood group factors A, B, H and Le in Old and New World monkeys. *Am. J. Phys. Anthropol.* **22**, No. 2, 175-187.

Wiener, A. S., Moor-Jankowski, J., and Gordon, E. B. (1966). Blood groups of apes and monkeys. VI. Further studies on the human blood group factors A, B, H and Le in monkeys. *Folia Primat.* **4**, 81-102.

Wiener, A. S., Moor-Jankowski, J., Gordon, E. B., and Davis, J. (1965). The blood factors I and i in Primates including Man, and in lower species. *Am. J. Phys. Anthropol.* **23**, No. 4, 389-396.

Wilson, J. D. (1968). Biosynthetic origin of serum cholesterol in the squirrel monkey: Evidence for a contribution by the intestinal wall. *J. Clin. Invest.* **47**, 175-187.

Wilson, J. G., and Gavan, J. A. (1967). Congenital malformations in nonhuman primates: spontaneous and experimentally induced. *Anat. Record* **158**, No. 1, 99-109.

Winborn, W. B. (1965). Light and electron microscopy of the islets of langerhans of the *Saimiri* monkey pancreas. *Anat. Record* **147**, No. 1, 65-94.

Winter, P. (1966). Verstandigung durch Laute bei Totenkopffaffen. *Umschau*, **20**, 653-658.

Winter, P., and Ploog, D. (1967). Social organization and communication of squirrel monkeys in captivity. *In* "Progress in Primatology" (D. Starck, R. Schneider, and H. J. Kuhn, eds.) pp. 263-271. Fischer, Stuttgart.

Wislocki, G. B. (1929). On the placentation of primates, with a consideration of the phylogeny of the placenta. *Contrib. Embryol.* **20** (III), Nos. 109-117, 51-80.

Wiswell, O. B., and Gibbs, W. E. (1964). Comparative response of ovarian and adrenal transplants (to gonadotropins) in the squirrel monkey, *Saimiri sciureus. Anat. Record* **148**, No. 2, 351.

Wiswell, O. B., and Gibbs, W. E. (1965). Infant maturation and maternal tolerance in the *Saimiri sciureus.* (Motion picture, 15 minutes.) *Excerpta Med. Intern. Congr. Ser.* **99**, E52-E53.

Wolin, L. R., and Massopust, L. C., Jr. (1965). Evoked potentials of the superior colliculus to colored photic stimulation. *Anat. Record* **151**, 482.

Woodburne, L. S. (1963). Notes on *Saimiri sciurea* as an experimental animal. *Lab. Primate Newsletter* **2**, No. 1, 4-7.

Woodburne, L. S., and Rieke, G. K. (1966). Response to symbols by squirrel monkeys. *Psychon. Sci.* **5**, 429-430.

Wynn, R. M. (1964). Comparative morphogenesis and vascular relationships of the villous hemochorial placenta. *Am. J. Obstet. Gynecolo.* **90**, No. 6, 758-768.

Yokota, T., and MacLean, P. D. (1966). Interaction of fornix and fifth nerve at thalamic level in squirrel monkey. *Federation Proc.* **25**, No. 2, 395.

Yokota, T., and MacLean, P. D. (1968). Fornix and fifth-nerve interaction on thalmic units in awake, sitting squirrel monkeys. *J. Neurophysiol.* **31**, 358-370.

Yokota, T., and MacLean, P. D. (1968). Inhibitory effect of hippocampal seizures on unit responses evoked by fifth nerve stimulation in squirrel monkey. *Electroenceph. Clin. Neurophysiol.* **24**, 190.

Yokota, T., Reeves, A. G., and MacLean, P. D. (1967). Intracellular olfactory response of hippocampal neurons in awake, sitting squirrel monkeys. *Science* **157**, 1072-1074.

Young, F., and Middleton, C. C. (1964). Fatty acid composition of various tissues in squirrel monkeys (*Saimiri sciureus*) with spontaneous atherosclerosis. *Federation Proc.* **23**, No. 2, Part 1, 101.

Zaias, N. (1964). The regeneration of the primate nail studies of the squirrel monkey, *Saimiri. J. Invest. Dermatol.* **44**, No. 2, 107-117.

Zimmerman, I. D. (1968). A triple representation of the body surface in the sensorimotor cortex of the squirrel monkey. *Exptl. Neurol.* **20**, 415-431.

Author Index

Numbers in italics indicate the pages on which the complete references are listed.

T

U

V

W

Subject Index

A

Abortion, 25, 163–167, 177, 182, 191
Acanthocephalan infections, 39–40, 46–47, 61, 411, 417, *see also* Thorny-headed worm
Acariasis, 56
Acclimatization, 27, 394–398
  by dealers, 27
  to seminatural environment, 96–97
  stress of, 394
Activity cycle, 74, 110–113
Adoption of bonnet infants, 228
Aggression, 138–141, 247
  vocalizations of, 240–243
Alarm calls, 239, *see also* Vocalizations, Signals
Amobarbital sodium, 403
Amoeba, *see Entamoeba*
Amphetamine, 389, *see also* d-Amphetamine
d-Amphetamine, 372, 373, 376–379
Amitriptyline, 373
Anatomy, 351–352, 358–359
  cortex, 321–326
  inner ear, 358–359
  organ weights and lengths, 351
Ancylostomatidae, *see* Hookworms
Anesthetics and anesthesia, 174, 183, 190, 326–329, 383, 388, 402–404, *see also* specific drugs
Anestrus, 152–157, *see also* Reproduction, Estrus cycle
Antibiotic therapy, 409, 412–414
Arthropod infestations, 55–58, 60, 61
Arboreality, 109–110
  play and, 110
Artificial insemination, 153–154, *see also* Semen collection, Ovulation
Arousal
  control of, 339–340
  "kick," 119, 122
  learning and, 294
Atriotaenia megastoma, 46
Atropine, 355, 380–383
Audycoptes spp., 56

Audiograms, 308
Audition
  brain structure and, 308, 326
  thresholds, 308
Aunt–infant relations, 75, 123, 125–127, 214, 226–229

B

Back rubbing, 80, 108
Bacterial infections, 39–41, 58, 409, 411
Ballistic missile flights, 348–349
Barbary ape, 157
Behavior, 1, 370–379
  effect of chlorpromazine on, 370–371
  of thiopropazate on, 370–371
"Behavioral arrest," 339
Biochemical studies, 388–389, 418
  (+)-amphetamine, 389
  catecholamine levels, 388
    effect of chlorpromazine on, 388
    of ether on, 388
    of fluothane on, 388
    of haloperidol on, 388
    of reserpine on, 388
    of stress on, 388
  γ-chlordane, 388
Bipedalism, 108, 212–213, 219
Birth
  season, 97–101, 148, 154, *see also* Reproduction
  time of day, 209
  weight, 178, 183, 197
Blood cell values, 408, 419
  pregnancy outcome and, 163–167
Blood collection, 405, 418
Blood pressure, 383–388, *see also* Cardiovascular studies
  atropine, 382
  carbachol, 382, 383
  dibenzyline, 385, 387, 388
  epinephrine, 383–388
  histamine, 383, 384, 388
  mecamylamine, 384, 386
  methacholine, 383–385

444